Engine Management and Fuel Injection Systems Pin Tables & Wiring Diagrams TechBook

Volume 2: Mercedes Benz - Volvo

Charles White

(3578-312)

© Haynes Publishing 2000

ISBN 1 85960 578 8

British Library Cataloguing in Publication Data
A catalogue record for this book is available from the British Library

We take great pride in the accuracy of information given in this book, but vehicle manufacturers make alterations and design changes during the production run of a particular vehicle of which they do not inform us. No liability can be accepted by the compilers or publishers for loss, damage or injury caused by any errors in, or omissions from, the information given.

Printed by **J H Haynes & Co Ltd, Sparkford, Nr Yeovil, Somerset BA22 7JJ, England**

Haynes Publishing
Sparkford, Nr Yeovil, Somerset BA22 7JJ, England

Haynes North America, Inc
861 Lawrence Drive, Newbury Park, California 91320, USA

Editions Haynes S.A.
Tour Aurore - La Défense 2, 18 Place des Reflets,
92975 PARIS LA DEFENSE Cedex, France

Haynes Publishing Nordiska AB
Box 1504, 751 45 UPPSALA, Sweden

Systems covered

Bosch KE Jetronic
Bosch KE 1.2 Motronic
Bosch KE 3.1 Jetronic
Bosch KE 3.5 Jetronic
Bosch KE 5.2 Jetronic
Bosch LE Jetronic
Bosch LE 2 Jetronic
Bosch LE 3 Jetronic
Bosch LE 3.1 Jetronic
Bosch LH 2.2 Jetronic
Bosch LH 2.4 Jetronic
Bosch LH 3.2 Jetronic
Bosch LH 4.1 Jetronic
Bosch Mono-Jetronic
Bosch Mono-Jetronic A 2.2
Bosch Mono-Motronic 1.2.1
Bosch Mono-Motronic 1.2.3
Bosch Mono-Motronic 1.3
Bosch Mono-Motronic MA 1.7
Bosch Mono-Motronic MA 3.0
Bosch Mono-Motronic MA 3.1
Bosch Motronic M 1.0
Bosch Motronic M 1.1
Bosch Motronic M 1.2
Bosch Motronic M 1.3
Bosch Motronic M 1.5
Bosch Motronic M 1.5.2
Bosch Motronic M 1.5.4
Bosch Motronic M 1.7
Bosch Motronic M 1.8
Bosch Motronic M 2.3
Bosch Motronic M 2.4
Bosch Motronic M 2.5
Bosch Motronic M 2.7
Bosch Motronic M 2.8
Bosch Motronic M 2.8.1
Bosch Motronic M 2.8.3
Bosch Motronic M 2.9
Bosch Motronic M 2.10.2
Bosch Motronic M 2.10.3
Bosch Motronic M 2.10.4
Bosch Motronic M 3.1
Bosch Motronic M 3.2
Bosch Motronic M 3.3
Bosch Motronic M 3.3.1
Bosch Motronic M 3.8.2
Bosch Motronic ML 4.1
Bosch Motronic M 4.3
Bosch Motronic M 5.1
Bosch Motronic M 5.1.1
Bosch Motronic M 5.2
Bosch Motronic M 7.0
Bosch Motronic MP 9.0
Chrysler MPFi
Daihatsu MPi

Fenix 1B
Fenix 3B MPi
Fenix 3BF SPi
Fenix 4
Fenix 5.1
Fenix 5.2
Ford EEC IV
Ford EEC V
Ford MECS
GM-Multec CFI
GM-Multec MPi
Honda PGMFI
Hyundai ECI-multi MPi
Isuzu I-Tec
Kia EGi
Lucas 9CU
Lucas 10CU SPi
Lucas 11CU
Lucas 14CU
Lucas 14CUX
Lucas 15CU
Magneti-Marelli 1AP40
Magneti-Marelli 1AV
Magneti-Marelli 8P
Magneti-Marelli G5 (MPi)
Magneti-Marelli G5 (SPi)
Magneti-Marelli G6 (SPi)
Magneti-Marelli SPi (Renault)
Mazda EGi MPi
Mazda EGi SPi
Mercedes HFM
Mercedes PMS
Nissan ECCS MPi
Nissan ECCS SPi
Proton ECI Multi SEFi
Renix MPi
Renix SPi
Rover MEMS MPi
Rover MEMS SPi
SAAB Trionic
Sagem/Lucas SL96
Siemens MS 40
Siemens MS 41
Simos 2
Simos 4S
Simtec 56, 56.1, 56.5
Subaru MPFi
Suzuki EPi-MPi
Suzuki EPi-SPi
Toyota TCCS
VAG Digifant
VAG MPi
Weber-Marelli 8F
Weber-Marelli IAW-MPi
Weber-Marelli IAW-SPi

Note: *Some of these systems are only covered in Volume 1*

Contents

GENERAL INFORMATION

SYSTEM SPECIFICS (BY MANUFACTURER)

REFERENCE

Introduction

This book provides essential data and wiring diagrams for the technician engaged in diagnosing and fixing faults in engine management and fuel injection systems on modern automobiles. The Pin-Table & Wiring Diagram Techbook is a companion volume to the Haynes *Engine Management & Fuel Injection Techbook* and the Haynes *Fault Code Techbook*. For a complete understanding of Engine Management, the content of all three books should be studied.

Because the Wiring Diagram Techbook contains ECM pintable data and wiring diagrams, it must be assumed that the technician is conversant with the values and illustrations given. Each chapter is devoted to a particular vehicle manufacturer, and data on the majority of fuel systems fitted to the vehicles constructed by that company makes up the chapter content.

The vehicle manufacturer (vm) may not specifically endorse the values given in this Techbook. Mainly this is because values have been gleaned from a variety of sources within the industry and reflect the well defined test methods taught in independent training schools and used by many modern vehicle technical specialists. However, in some instances and where available, vehicle manufacturer data has also been used.

Mostly the pin table data contains values obtained with the aid of the ubiquitous Digital Multi-Meter (DMM). However, an oscilloscope may be necessary to examine the more complex signals originating from the components in some of the more sophisticated systems.

Refer to the Haynes Engine Management Techbook for a portrayal of system operation and a description of test procedures required when working with the modern EMS. Refer also to the Haynes *Fault Code Techbook* for descriptions of Fault Codes and associated tests. In the following paragraphs we describe a few basic principles for working with the data in this book.

Design of pin tables

The pin tables are divided into four columns.

The first column contains the ECM pin number and by comparing this number to the multiplug diagram, the position of the pin may be ascertained. Some ECM pins are unoccupied in the multiplug for the vehicle used as model. However, some of these unoccupied pins may be attached to components when the ECM is connected to another vehicle. In addition, where the vehicle may be equipped with different levels of equipment i.e. ABS, AT or A/C, some of the unoccupied pins may come into use.

The second column describes the component or signal to which the pin is connected. A note of the component terminal connection (i.e. CTS signal : t2) is also detailed.

In order to allow instant recognition of the various connections to certain components, the following conventions have been used to annotate the component terminal numbers in the wiring diagrams and pin tables:

ATS & CTS 2-pin sensors

The signal terminal is annotated with 2. The earth or earth return terminal is annotated with 1.

Oxygen Sensor (OS)

The OS heater supply terminal is annotated with 2. The OS heater earth or heater driver connection to the ECM is annotated with 1. The OS signal terminal is annotated with 3. The OS signal earth terminal is annotated with 4. Please note that that the vehicle manufacturer may use any combination of numbers or letters to annotate the small multiplug connected to the OS in any particular application.

All other sensors

Numbering of all other sensors, with 3-pin or more terminals, are annotated in accordance with vehicle manufacturer standard numbering sequence.

Actuators (2-pin) i.e. CFSV, ICOV, TBCV etc

The supply terminal from battery, ignition or relay are annotated with 2. The earth connection or driver connection to the ECM is annotated with 1.

The third column describes the conditions under which the test values may be obtained. Some values may be obtained at the pin by simply turning on the ignition or running the engine. The '/' indicates that the same value is available for one or more separate actions. Where secondary actions are required, such as different positions of the throttle, these conditions will normally be detailed on the next few lines with associated values listed in column four.

The fourth column describes the test values that may be obtained:

a) *All measurement values, whether described as (approx) or not are actually approximate and may differ slightly in different vehicles.*

b) *Nominal Battery Voltage (nbv) is a coined term used to describe the voltage obtained under various operating conditions. See Glossary in Reference for a fuller meaning.*

c) *Signals that are measured at the ECM pins will essentially be voltage values that may be either AC or DC in structure.*

d) *Where the voltage value is switching, a frequency in Hz and a duty cycle in % will also be generated (frequency and duty cycle values are not always available). Sometimes the duty cycle may be given in ms.*

e) *Where the switching is DC volts, the signal will usually assume the form of a square waveform that may be viewed upon an oscilloscope.*

f) *Although the values given, when the signal is switching, are mainly the full switching values (i.e. 0 to nbv), in some instances the values are mean or average (i.e. 2 to 3 V).*

g) *Generally speaking, the longer the time the component is switched 'on' (duty cycle), the lower will be the average or mean voltage displayed upon the voltmeter. For a component switching between 0 and 5 V, this could give a mean voltage of less than one volt where the switch 'on' time is quite long.*

h) *AC voltage values are best viewed upon an oscilloscope and the values given may vary from peak to peak of the positive to negative waveform amplitude to a RMS value that may be measured with an AC voltmeter.*

i) *Where a component is 'driven' to earth by a driver pin in the ECM, the voltage measured at that pin may typically be 0.80 volts. However, a value of up to 1.25 volts is acceptable and this is the value used as a specification for the majority of ECM driver pins in the pin tables.*

j) *A value of 0 volts should be measured at the majority of ECM earth or ECM earth return connections. However, a maximum value of 0.25 volts is acceptable.*

k) *The signs < and > are used to indicate that less than (<) or greater than (>) the value is acceptable.*

Making voltage tests

The measuring of data values from sensors and actuators at the ECM multi-plug (ECM multi-plug connected) is often considered the more accurate form of testing. This is because it is the point through which all incoming and outgoing signals pass.

a) *If the ECM terminals are accessible, then backprobe the ECM pins using the meter probes.*

b) *If the ECM terminals are not accessible, then connect a BOB between the ECM and its multi-plug. This is the preferred method and will avoid damage to the ECM pins.*

c) *Refer to Warning no 3 (in Reference) before disconnecting the ECM multiplug.*

Alternatively, the ECM multi-plug could be disconnected and the multi-plug terminals probed for voltages or the component could be directly probed or backprobed at its own terminal connections. In this instance, attach the negative voltmeter test lead to an earth on the engine, and probe or backprobe the terminal under test with the positive voltmeter test lead. Refer to Warning no 5 (in Reference).

In all diagrams illustrating a multiplug (including the main ECM multiplug), the illustration depicts the terminals of the harness connector. When back-probing the multi-plug (or viewing the connector terminals on the sensor), the terminal positions will be reversed.

The process of probing and backprobing are perfectly safe to carry out on electronic systems so long as certain simple rules are observed (Please refer to the **Warnings** section in Reference). These rules are actually the observation of good electrical practice. Be aware that damage resulting in the replacement of a very expensive Electronic Control Module (ECM) may be the result of not following the rules.

Test equipment

The minimum equipment required to make tests at the ECM pins is a DMM with an electrical impedance of less than 10 megohms. The DMM should include scales to measure voltage, resistance, current, dwell, duty cycle, frequency, rpm and temperature. A millisecond scale and a bargraph would also be very useful.

The professional technician should also be equipped with an oscilloscope, a Break Out Box (BOB) and a FCR that can measure Datastream.

Live Data or Datastream displayed via a FCR are the signal values that the ECM sees at the various components and can be reconciled with the values given in the pin tables. However, in some instances, the values measured through Datastream may be in different units to the values given in the tables. For example the AFS signal may be measured in kg/h and the coolant sensor may be output as a temperature. In this case, look for changes in value over engine rpm or temperature changes.

Terminology

Throughout Europe, the USA and the Far East the various vehicle manufacturer's tend to use their own coined terms to describe a particular component. Of course, all of these terms tend to be different and the problem is exacerbated by translation from the various languages. This often leads to confusion when several different terms may be used to describe the same component. There have been attempts to bring all vehicle manufacturers into line with a common standard - and one does now exist (SAE J1930). It is difficult to judge whether all vehicle manufacturer's will adopt this particular standard and we do not wish to use terms that are unfamiliar and not in current use. So, to avoid confusion, the terms used in all chapters of this book will tend to follow the terms commonly used by the UK automotive industry. One set of terms have therefore been used in all pin tables and in the Master component key. Alternative descriptions are described in the Glossary.

Component codes

To avoid a 'cluttered' look in the various wiring diagrams, component codes have been introduced and these follow the Automotive DIN 40719 standard for group designation. An abbreviated list of the various group designations is as follows:

Group Type

A   Assemblies and control units
B   Transducers and sensors
C   Condenser and capacitors
E   Various devices and equipment
F   Protection device
G   Power supply & Generators
H   Alarms & signalling devices
K   Relays
M   Motors
P   Measuring instruments
R   Resistors & potentiometers
S   Switches
T   Transformers
V   Semiconductors & diodes
X   terminals & connections
Y   Actuators

Although the DIN standard divides components into groups, there is not a standard designation for each component. Where the vehicle manufacturer and other information providers use the DIN standard (DIN is not used universally), the grouping of components will remain constant but the actual component code designations will differ widely.

Ignition ECM pins

Systems covered by this book may be sub-divided into engine management systems and fuel injection systems. The engine management system is usually a self-contained unit that controls both ignition and the fuel system. However, some of the older fuel injection systems were controlled by an ECM in conjunction with a ignition control module or a self-contained electronic ignition. In order to provide the fullest picture we have provided wiring diagrams of vehicles equipped with older fuel injection systems and an associated typical electronic ignition system. Pin table data for ignition systems are beyond the remit for this book and have therefore not been provided.

No data available

Some data is labelled 'No data available' and mainly this refers to connections to other Electronic Control Modules or miscellaneous components that are not strictly part of the engine management system. Such components could include Air conditioning, Anti Lock Brake System, Electronic throttle, immobiliser, A/C etc. etc. Regretfully, providing such data is beyond the scope of the book and it has not been possible to provide data for many of these pins at this time. However, all pin destinations (where known) have been listed so that the technician is able to build the fullest picture of pin destinations.

Lists of vehicles and applications

In each chapter is detailed a list of vehicles and system applications. The vehicle(s) accentuated in bold type are the actual vehicles upon which the ECM pin tables and wiring diagrams are based. Other vehicle with the same system may be similar; but are also likely to contain some differences.

Acknowledgements

We would like to thank all of those at Sparkford and elsewhere that helped us in the production of this manual. In particular we would like to thank Equiptech for permission to use illustrations from the 'CAPS' fuel injection fault diagnosis database and for providing much of the technical information that was used in authoring this book. We also thank the staff at Equiptech and Simon Ashby of Diagnostic Technique for additional technical information.

Chapter 18
Mercedes Benz

Contents

Index of Mercedes Benz vehicles/systems

Model	Engine code	Year	System
190E Cat	102.962	1988 to 1993	Bosch KE3.5 Jetronic
190E 2.3 Cat	102.985	1989 to 1993	Bosch KE3.5 Jetronic
190E 2.5-16	**102.990**	**1988 to 1993**	**Bosch KE3.1 Jetronic**
190E 2.5-16	102.990	1988 to 1993	Bosch KE3.1 Jetronic
190E 2.5-16 Cat	102.990	1988 to 1993	Bosch KE3.1 Jetronic
190E 2.5-16 Evolution	102.991	1989 to 1992	Bosch KE3.1 Jetronic
190E 2.6 Cat	103.942	1987 to 1993	Bosch KE3.5 Jetronic
190E 2.6	**103.942**	**1989 to 1993**	**Bosch KE3.5 Jetronic**
200E cat	102.963	1988 to 1993	Bosch KE3.5 Jetronic
200TE Cat	102.963	1988 to 1993	Bosch KE3.5 Jetronic
230CE Cat	102.982	1988 to 1993	Bosch KE3.5 Jetronic
230CE 2.3	102.982	1987 to 1989	Bosch KE3.1 Jetronic
230E Cat	102.982	1988 to 1993	Bosch KE3.5 Jetronic
260E	103.940	1989 to 1993	Bosch KE3.5 Jetronic
260E Cat	103.940	1989 to 1993	Bosch KE3.5 Jetronic
260E 2.6 Cat	103.943	1985 to 1992	Bosch KE3.1 Jetronic
230GE	102.980	1989 to 1991	Bosch KE3.5 Jetronic
230TE Cat	102.982	1988 to 1993	Bosch KE3.5 Jetronic
260SE 2.6 Cat	103.941	1985 to 1991	Bosch KE3.1 Jetronic
260SE 2.6	103.941	1985 to 1991	Bosch KE3.1 Jetronic
260E 4-Matic	103.943	1988 to 1992	Bosch KE3.5 Jetronic
260E 4-Matic Cat	103.943	1988 to 1992	Bosch KE3.5 Jetronic
260SE	103.941	1988 to 1992	Bosch KE3.5 Jetronic
260SE Cat	103.941	1989 to 1992	Bosch KE3.5 Jetronic
300CE	103.983	1987 to 1993	Bosch KE3.5 Jetronic
300CE Cat	103.983	1987 to 1993	Bosch KE3.5 Jetronic
300CE-24 Cat	104.980	1989 to 1993	Bosch KE5.2 Jetronic
300E	103.983	1987 to 1993	Bosch KE3.5 Jetronic
300E	103.985	1988 to 1993	Bosch KE3.5 Jetronic
300E Cat	103.983	1987 to 1993	Bosch KE3.5 Jetronic
300E Cat	103.985	1988 to 1993	Bosch KE3.5 Jetronic

Index of Mercedes Benz vehicles/systems (continued)

Model	Engine code	Year	System
300E-24 Cat	**104.980**	**1989 to 1993**	**Bosch KE5.2 Jetronic**
300E/TE 6cyl	103.980	1985 to 1991	Bosch KE3.1 Jetronic
300E/TE 4x4 Cat	103.983/5	1985 to 1993	Bosch KE3.1 Jetronic
300E/TE 6cyl	103.983/5	1985 to 1993	Bosch KE3.1 Jetronic
300GE 3.0 6cyl Cat	103.987	1989 to 1995	Bosch KE3.1 Jetronic
300SE	103.981	1986 to 1992	Bosch KE3.5 Jetronic
300SE Cat	103.981	1986 to 1992	Bosch KE3.5 Jetronic
300SEL	103.981	1986 to 1992	Bosch KE3.5 Jetronic
300SEL Cat	103.981	1986 to 1992	Bosch KE3.5 Jetronic
300SE/SEL 3.0 6cyl Cat	103/981	1985 to 1991	Bosch KE3.1 Jetronic
300SE/SEL 3.0 6cyl	103/981	1985 to 1991	Bosch KE3.1 Jetronic
300SL	103.984	1989 to 1995	Bosch KE5.2 Jetronic
300SL-24	104.981	1989 to 1995	Bosch KE5.2 Jetronic
300SL-24 Cat	104.981	1989 to 1995	Bosch KE5.2 Jetronic
300SL Cat	103.984	1989 to 1995	Bosch KE5.2 Jetronic
300TE	103.983	1987 to 1993	Bosch KE3.5 Jetronic
300TE 4-Matic	103.985	1988 to 1993	Bosch KE3.5 Jetronic
300TE 4-Matic Cat	103.985	1988 to 1993	Bosch KE3.5 Jetronic
300TE Cat	103.983	1987 to 1993	Bosch KE3.5 Jetronic
300TE-24 Cat	104.980	1989 to 1993	Bosch KE5.2 Jetronic
400S	119.971	1991 on	Bosch LH 4.1 Jetronic
400SE	119.971	1991 on	Bosch LH 4.1 Jetronic
400SEL	119.971	1991 on	Bosch LH 4.1 Jetronic
420SE/SEL 4.2 8cyl Cat	116.965	1989 to 1991	Bosch KE3.1 Jetronic
420SE/SEL 4.2 8cyl	116.965	1989 to 1991	Bosch KE3.1 Jetronic
500E	119.974	1992 on	Bosch LH 4.1 Jetronic
500SL	119.972	1992 on	Bosch LH 4.1 Jetronic
500SE	119.970	1991 on	Bosch LH 4.1 Jetronic
500SEC	119.970	1992 on	Bosch LH 4.1 Jetronic
500SEL	119.970	1991 on	Bosch LH 4.1 Jetronic
500SE/SEL 5.0 8cyl Cat	117.965	1989 to 1991	Bosch KE3.1 Jetronic
500SE/SEL 5.0 8cyl	117.965	1989 to 1991	Bosch KE3.1 Jetronic
560SE 5.5 8cyl Cat	117.968	1989 to 1991	Bosch KE3.1 Jetronic
560SE 5.5 8cyl	117.968	1989 to 1991	Bosch KE3.1 Jetronic
600SEL	120.980	1991 to 1996	Bosch LH 4.1 Jetronic
C180	111.920	1993 to 1998	Mercedes Benz PMS
C200	**111.941**	**1994 to 1998**	**Mercedes Benz PMS**
C220	**111.961**	**1993 to 1997**	**Mercedes Benz HFM**
C230	111.974	1995 to 1999	Mercedes Benz HFM
C230 Kompressor	111.975	1995 to 1999	Mercedes Benz HFM
C280	104.941	1993 to 1998	Mercedes Benz HFM
E200	111.942	1995 to 1999	Mercedes Benz HFM
E220	111.960	1992 to 1997	Mercedes Benz HFM
E280 Cat	104.942	1992 to 1996	Mercedes Benz HFM
E300	103.985	1992 to 1995	Bosch KE3.5 Jetronic
E320	104.992	1992 to 1997	Mercedes Benz HFM
E420	**119.975**	**1992 to 1995**	**Bosch LH 4.1 Jetronic**
E500	119.974	1992 to 1995	Bosch LH 4.1 Jetronic
S280	104.944	1993 to 1998	Mercedes Benz HFM
SL280	104.94	1993 to 1999	Mercedes Benz HFM
S320	104.994	1993 to 1998	Mercedes Benz HFM
SL320	104.991	1993 to 1999	Mercedes Benz HFM
S420	119.971	1993 to 1998	Bosch LH 4.1 Jetronic
S500	119.970	1993 to 1998	Bosch LH 4.1 Jetronic
SL500	119.972	1993 to 1998	Bosch LH 4.1 Jetronic
S600 Cat	120.980	1991 to 1996	Bosch LH 4.1 Jetronic
S600	120.980	1996 to 1998	Bosch LH 4.1 Jetronic
SL600	120.981	1993 to 1999	Bosch LH 4.1 Jetronic

Note: *The vehicles accentuated in bold type are the actual vehicles upon which the ECM pin tables and wiring diagrams are based. Other vehicles with the same system may be similar; but are also likely to contain some differences.*

Pin Table – Bosch KE3.1 Jetronic

Pin	Item	Test Condition	Measurements
1	supply from main relay : t87	ignition on/engine running	nbv
2	earth	ignition on/engine running	0.25 V (max)
3	ISCV driver : t1	ignition on	nbv
		engine running, idle speed:	
		cold	6.0 to 6.5 V
		hot	7.0 to 9.0 V
		duty cycle	30 to 60%
4	instrument panel connector		data not available
5	TS, full load contact : t3	ignition on/engine running:	
		throttle closed/part open	5 V (approx)
		throttle fully open	0 V
6	cruise control		data not available
7	sensor return (CTS : t1)	ignition on/engine running	0.25 V (max)
8	OS signal : t3	ignition on, OS multiplug disconnected	0.4 to 0.5 V
		engine running, hot	200 to 1000 mV (switching)
		throttle fully-open	0.5 to 1.0 V
		deceleration (fuel cut-off)	0 to 0.5 V
		switching frequency	1 sec intervals (approx)
9	fuel pump relay driver : t2	ignition on	nbv
		engine cranking/running	1.25 V (max)
10	differential pressure regulator	idle speed, cold	55 to 75 mA (approx)
		idle speed, hot	0 to 1 mA (approx)
		deceleration from 3000 rpm	−40 mA (approx)
11	ATS signal : t2	ignition on/engine running	20° C: 3.00 to 3.50 V
			50° C: 2.00 to 2.30 V
12	differential pressure regulator	idle speed, cold	55 to 75 mA (approx)
		idle speed, hot	0 to 1 mA (approx)
		deceleration from 3000 rpm	−40 mA (approx)
13	TS, idle contact : t1	Ignition on/engine running:	
		throttle closed	0 V
		throttle part/fully open	5 V (approx)
14-16	–		
17	AFS signal : t2	ignition on, sensor plate closed	0.20 to 0.30 V
		voltage range	0.1 to 4.5 V (approx)
		open/close sensor plate	voltage increase/decrease
18	AFS supply : t1	ignition on/engine running	5.0 V ± 0.1
19	air conditioning		data not available
20	earth	ignition on/engine running	0.25 V (max)
21	CTS signal : t2	ignition on/engine running	20° C: 3.00 to 3.50 V
			80° C: 0.50 to 1.0 V
22	–		
23	SD connector		data not available
24	fuel pump cut off switch	ignition on/engine running	nbv
		< 3000 rpm and TS (idle contact closed)	0.25 V (max)
25	ignition amplifier speed signal : tTD	engine cranking/running	0.16 to 0.21 V

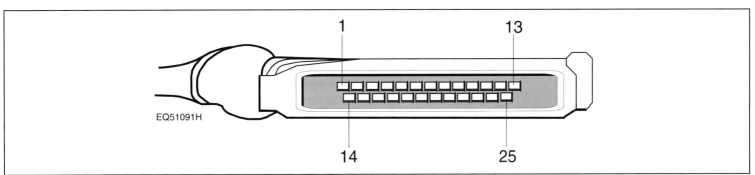

EQ51091H

25 pin ECM multi-plug, Bosch KE3.1 Jetronic

Pin Table – Bosch KE3.5 Jetronic

Pin	Item	Test Condition	Measurement
1	supply from main relay : t87	ignition on/engine running	nbv
2	earth	ignition on/engine running	0.25 V (max)
3	ISCV driver : t1	ignition on	nbv
		engine running, idle speed:	
		cold	6.0 to 6.5 V
		hot	7.0 to 9.0 V
		duty cycle	30 to 60%
4	instrument panel connector		data not available
5	TS, full load contact : t3	ignition on/engine running:	
		throttle closed/part open	5 V (approx)
		throttle fully open	0 V
6	cruise control		data not available
7	sensor return (CTS : t1)	ignition on/engine running	0.25 V (max)
8	OS signal : t3	ignition on OS, multiplug disconnected	0.4 to 0.5 V
		engine running, hot	200 to 1000 mV (switching)
		throttle fully-open	0.5 to 1.0 V
		deceleration (fuel cut-off)	0 to 0.5 V
		switching frequency	1 sec intervals (approx)
9	fuel pump relay driver : t2	ignition on	nbv
		engine cranking/running	1.25 V (max)
10	differential pressure regulator	idle speed, cold	55 to 75 mA (approx)
		idle speed, hot	0 to 1 mA (approx)
		deceleration from 3000 rpm	–40 mA (approx)
11	ATS signal : t2	ignition on/engine running	20° C: 3.00 to 3.50 V
			50° C: 2.00 to 2.30 V
12	differential pressure regulator	idle speed, cold	55 to 75 mA (approx)
		idle speed, hot	0 to 1 mA (approx)
		deceleration from 3000 rpm	–40 mA (approx)
13	TS, idle contact : t1	Ignition on/engine running:	
		throttle closed	0 V
		throttle part/fully open	5.0 V (approx)
14-16	–		
17	AFS signal : t2	ignition on, sensor plate closed	0.20 to 0.30 V
		voltage range	0.1 to 4.5 V (approx)
		open/close sensor plate	voltage increase/decrease
18	AFS supply : t1	ignition on/engine running	5.0 V ± 0.1
19	air conditioning		data not available
20	earth	ignition on/engine running	0.25 V (max)
21	CTS signal : t2	ignition on/engine running	20° C: 3.00 to 3.50 V
			80° C: 0.50 to 1.0 V
22	–		
23	SD connector		data not available
24	fuel pump cut off switch	ignition on/engine running	nbv
		< 3000 rpm and TS (idle contact closed)	0.25 V (max)
25	ignition amplifier speed signal : tTD	engine cranking/running	0.16 to 0.21 V

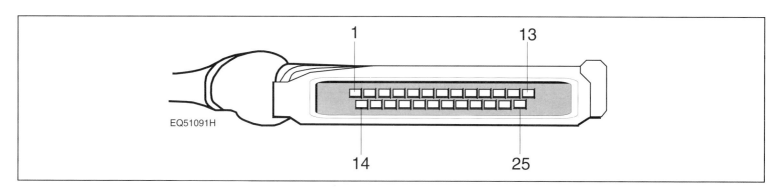

25 pin ECM multi-plug, Bosch KE3.5 Jetronic

Pin Table – Bosch KE5.2 Jetronic

Pin	Connection	Test condition	Measurement
1	supply from battery : t30	ignition off/on/engine running	nbv
2	CFSV driver : t1	ignition on	nbv
		engine running, above idle, operating temperature:	
		CFSV inactive	nbv
		CFSV active	0 to 12 V (switching)
		duty cycle	0 to 99%
3	–		
4	ISCV driver : t1	ignition on	nbv
		engine running, idle speed:	
		cold	6.0 to 6.5 V
		hot	7.0 to 9.0 V
		duty cycle	30 to 60%
5	ATS return : t1	ignition on/engine running	0.25 V (max)
6	earth	ignition on/engine running	0.25 V (max)
7-9	–		
10	fuel pump cut off micro switch	ignition on/engine running:	
		throttle closed	switch activated
		throttle open	switch not activated
11	cranking signal : t50	engine cranking	nbv
12	–		
13	OS signal : t3	ignition on, OS multiplug disconnected	0.4 to 0.5 V
		engine running, hot	200 to 1000 mV (switching)
		throttle fully-open	0.5 to 1.0 V
		deceleration (fuel cut-off)	0 to 0.5 V
		switching frequency	1 sec intervals (approx)
14	ATS signal : t2	ignition on/engine running	20° C: 3.00 to 3.50 V
			50° C: 2.00 to 2.30 V
15	–		
16	CTS return : t1	ignition on/engine running	0.25 V (max)
17	–		
18	fuel pump supply module : t8		data not available
19	earth	ignition on/engine running	0.25 V (max)
20	cold start valve (CSV) driver : t1	engine cranking:	
		engine cold	1.25 V (max)
		engine hot	nbv
21-22	–		
23	ISVC supply : t2	ignition on/engine running	12.0 V ± 0.1
24-25	–		
26	amplifier control signal : tA7	engine cranking/running	0 to 5.0 V (switching)
27	amplifier control signal : tA4	engine cranking/running	0 to 5.0 V (switching)
28-29	–		
30	SD connector		data not available
31	fuel pump supply module : t18		data not available
31	AFS return ; t 3	ignition on/engine running	0.25 V (max)
32	–		
33	equalise connector		data not available
34	AFS supply : t1	ignition on/engine running	5.0 V ± 0.1
35	CTS signal : t2	ignition on/engine running	20° C: 2.00 to 2.50 V
			80° C: 1.00 to 1.30 V
36	–		
37	differential pressure regulator	ignition off	20 mA
		engine running, cold:	
		after start enrichment	20° C: 1-3 mA (0-8 secs)
		warm-up base value	20° C: 0-1 mA (12-120 secs)
		engine running, hot:	
		idle speed	80° C: mA oscillation
		part-load correction	mA oscillation
		full-load enrichment, 2000 rpm	2-4 mA
		acceleration	> 15 mA
		deceleration from 3000 rpm	–40 mA (approx)

Pin Table – Bosch KE5.2 Jetronic (continued)

Pin	Connection	Test condition	Measurement
38-39	–		
40	vacuum solenoid valve driver : t1	ignition on/engine running:	
		valve inactive	nbv
		valve active	1.25 V (max)
41	supply from main relay : t87	ignition on/engine running	nbv
42	fuel pump supply module : t17		data not available
43-44	–		
45	fuel pump supply module : t9		data not available
46	TS, full-load contact : t3	ignition on/engine running:	
		throttle closed/part open	0 V
		throttle fully open	12.0 V (approx).
47	TS, idle contact : t2	ignition on/engine running:	
		throttle closed	12.0 V (approx).
		throttle open	0 V
48	–		
49	equalise connector		data not available
50-51	–		
52	AFS signal : t2	ignition on, sensor plate closed	0.20 to 0.30 V
		voltage range	0.1 to 4.5 V (approx)
		open/close sensor plate	voltage increase/decrease
53-54	–		
55	differential pressure regulator	ignition off	20 mA
		engine running, cold:	
		after start enrichment	20° C: 1-3 mA (0-8 secs)
		warm-up base value	20° C: 0-1 mA (12-120 secs)
		engine running, hot:	
		idle speed	80° C: mA oscillation
		part-load correction	mA oscillation
		full-load enrichment, 2000 rpm	2-4 mA
		acceleration	> 15 mA
		deceleration from 3000 rpm	–40 mA (approx)

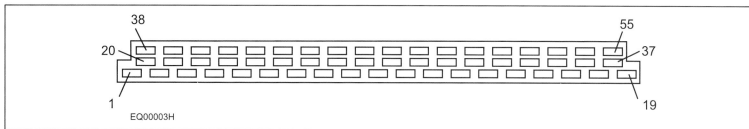

EQ00003H

55 pin ECM multi-plug, Bosch KE5.2 Jetronic

Pin Table – Bosch LH 4.1 Jetronic

Connector A

Pin	Connection	Test condition	Measurement
A1-A10	–		
A11	cruise control		data not available
A12			
A13	SD connector		data not available
A14-A17	–		
A23	earth	ignition on/engine running	0.25 V (max)
A24	supply from ECM supply module : tA7	ignition on/engine running	nbv
A25	fuel pump relay driver: t85	ignition on	nbv
		engine cranking/running	1.25 V (max)

Pin	Connection	Test condition	Measurement
A26	ECM supply module : tA12		data not available
A27	–		
A28	ECM supply module : tA31		data not available
A29	–		
A30	cruise control		data not available
A31-A33	–		
A34	cranking signal : t50	engine cranking	nbv
A35	earth	ignition on/engine running	0.25 V (max)
A36	earth	ignition on/engine running	0.25 V (max)
A37	earth	ignition on/engine running	0.25 V (max)
A38	–		

Connector B

Pin	Connection	Test condition	Measurement
B1	injector driver (cyl 2) : t1	ignition on	nbv
		engine running, cold	> 3.5 ms
		engine running, hot	3.5 ms
		snap acceleration	20 ms (approx)
		deceleration	0 ms (approx)
B2	injector driver (cyl 3) : t1	ignition on	nbv
		engine running, cold	> 3.5 ms
		engine running, hot	3.5 ms
		snap acceleration	20 ms (approx)
		deceleration	0 ms (approx)
B3	injector driver (cyl 7) : t1	ignition on	nbv
		engine running, cold	> 3.5 ms
		engine running, hot	3.5 ms
		snap acceleration	20 ms (approx)
		deceleration	0 ms (approx)
B4	injector driver (cyl 5) : t1	ignition on	nbv
		engine running, cold	> 3.5 ms
		engine running, hot	3.5 ms
		snap acceleration	20 ms (approx)
		deceleration	0 ms (approx)
B5	amplifier control signal : tA4	engine cranking/running	0 to 5.0 V (switching)
B6	amplifier control signal : tA8	engine cranking/running	0 to 5.0 V (switching)
B7	CO pot signal : t2	ignition on/engine running	2.45 V ± 0.5
B8	ATS signal : t2	ignition on/engine running	20° C: 3.00 to 3.50 V
			50° C: 2.00 to 2.30 V
B9	OS heater supply : t2	ignition on/engine running	12.0 V
B10-B12	–		
B13	shield earth	ignition on/engine running	0.25 V (max)
B14	OS signal : t3	ignition on, OS multiplug disconnected	0.4 to 0.5 V
		engine running, hot	200 to 1000 mV (switching)
		throttle fully-open	0.5 to 1.0 V
		deceleration (fuel cut-off)	0 to 0.5 V
		switching frequency	1 sec intervals (approx)
B15	earth	ignition on/engine running	0.25 V (max)
B16	sensor return (CO pot : t1, ATS : t1,CTS : t1, Eq connector)	ignition on/engine running	0.25 V (max)
B17	MAF sensor supply : t5	ignition on/engine running	12 V
B18	CTS signal : t3	ignition on/engine running	20° C: 2.00 to 2.50 V
			80° C: 1.00 to 1.30 V
B19	secondary air solenoid valve relay driver: t85	ignition on	nbv
		secondary air inactive	nbv
		secondary air active	1.25 V (max)
B20	transmission kick down solenoid valve driver : t1	ignition on	nbv
		engine running:	
		valve inactive	nbv
		valve active	1.25 V (max)

Pin Table – Bosch LH 4.1 Jetronic (continued)

Connector B (continued)

Pin	Connection	Test condition	Measurement
B21	–		
B22	camshaft solenoid valve driver : t1	ignition on	nbv
		engine running:	
		valve inactive	nbv
		valve active	1.25 V (max)
B23	MAF hot wire burn-off: t4	coolant above 65° C, rpm above 2500, switch off engine	hot wire glows for 1.0 second
B24	injector driver (cyl 8) : t1	ignition on	nbv
		engine running, cold	> 3.5 ms
		engine running, hot	3.5 ms
		snap acceleration	20 ms (approx)
		deceleration	0 ms (approx)
B25	injector driver (cyl 6) : t1	ignition on	nbv
		engine running, cold	> 3.5 ms
		engine running, hot	3.5 ms
		snap acceleration	20 ms (approx)
		deceleration	0 ms (approx)
B26	injector driver (cyl 4) : t1	ignition on	nbv
		engine running, cold	>3.5 ms
		engine running, hot	3.5 ms
		snap acceleration	20 ms (approx)
		deceleration	0 ms (approx)
B27	injector driver (cyl 1) : t1	ignition on	nbv
		engine running, cold	> 3.5 ms
		engine running, hot	3.5 ms
		snap acceleration	20 ms (approx)
		deceleration	0 ms (approx)
B28-B29	–		
B30	equalise connector : t2		data not available
B31	CTS signal : t2	ignition on/engine running	20° C: 2.00 to 2.50 V
			80° C: 1.00 to 1.30 V
B32-B33	–		
B34	MAF sensor return : t2	ignition on/engine running	0.25 V (max)
B35	–		
B36	SD connector		data not available
B37	MAF sensor signal : t3	ignition on:	
		idle	0.7 V
		3000 rpm	1.25 V
		snap accelerate	3.00 to 3.50 V (approx)
B38	CFSV driver : t1	ignition on	nbv
		engine running, above idle, operating temperature:	
		CFSV inactive	nbv
		CFSV active	0 to 12 V (switching)
		duty cycle	0 to 99%
B39	EGR solenoid valve driver : t1	ignition on	nbv
		engine running:	
		EGR inactive	nbv
		EGR active	1.25 V (max)
B40	–		
B41	camshaft solenoid valve driver : t1	ignition on	nbv
		engine running:	
		valve inactive	nbv
		valve active	1.25 V (max)

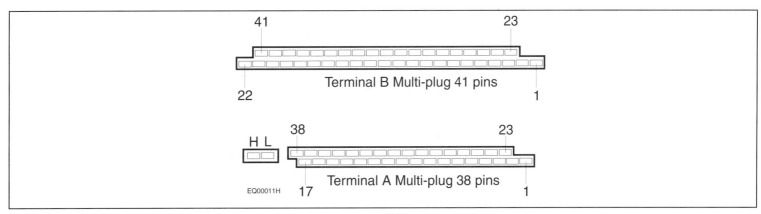

38+41pin ECM multi-plug, Bosch LH 4.1 Jetronic

Pin Table – Mercedes Benz HFM

Connector A

Pin	Connection	Test condition	Measurement
A1-A4	–		
A5	AT		data not available
A6	coding connector	ignition on	0.9 to 4.7 V
A7	–		
A8	ABS	vehicle in motion	3 V (min)
A9-A11	–		
A15-A17	–		
A18	instrument panel connector		data not available
A19	SD connector		data not available
A20	AT		data not available
A20	earth (MT only)	ignition on/engine running	0.25 V (max)
A21	cranking signal : t50 (AT only)	engine cranking	nbv
A22	cruise control		data not available
A23-A26	–		
A27	supply from main relay : t87m	ignition on/engine running	nbv
A28	–		
A29	ECM supply to fuel pump relay driver coil : t86	ignition on	nbv briefly, then 0 V
		engine cranking/running	nbv
A30	OS heater supply : t2	ignition on	0 V
		engine running, first start	0 V
		engine running, after 2 minutes	nbv
A31	–		
A32	earth	ignition on/engine running	0.25 V (max)
A33	earth	ignition on/engine running	0.25 V (max)
A34	OS return : t4	engine running, hot	0.25 V (max)
A35	OS signal : t3	ignition on, OS multiplug disconnected	0.4 to 0.5 V
		engine running, hot	200 to 1000 mV (switching)
		throttle fully-open	0.5 to 1.0 V
		deceleration (fuel cut-off)	0 to 0.5 V
		switching frequency	1 sec intervals (approx)
A36-A38	–		
A39	supply from main relay : t87	ignition on/engine running	nbv
A40	supply from battery : t30	ignition off/on/engine running	nbv
A41-A42	–		
A43	CFSV driver : t1	ignition on	nbv
		engine running, above idle, operating temperature:	
		CFSV inactive	nbv
		CFSV active	0 to 12 V (switching)
		duty cycle	0 to 99%
A44	–		

Pin Table – Mercedes Benz HFM (continued)

Connector B

Pin	Connection	Test condition	Measurement
B1	camshaft solenoid valve driver : t1	ignition on	nbv
		engine running:	
		valve inactive	nbv
		valve active	1.25 V (max)
B2	injector driver (cyl 4) : t1	ignition on	nbv
		engine running, cold	> 3.5 ms
		engine running, hot	3.5 ms
		snap acceleration	20 ms (approx)
		deceleration	0 ms (approx)
B3	–		
B4	stepper motor (TCA : t4)	idle speed, active	0 to 5.0 V (switching)
B5	MAF sensor signal : t1	ignition on:	
		idle	0.7 to 1.1 V
		3000 rpm	1.25 V
		snap accelerate	3.00 to 3.50 V (approx)
B6	sensor return (TCA : t7)	ignition on/engine running	0.25 V (max)
B7	TVPS signal (TCA : t2)	ignition on	3.5 to 3.7 V
		idle speed	3.0 to 4.3 V
B8	camshaft sensor (inductive) signal : t2	idle speed	> 0.2 V AC (RMS)
B9	ignition coil driver (cyls 1 & 4) : t1	ignition on	nbv
		engine running:	
		dynamic volt drop	2.0 V (max)
		primary switching	200 V (min)
B10-B11	–		
B12	injector driver (cylinder 3) : t1	ignition on	nbv
		engine running, cold	> 3.5 ms
		engine running, hot	3.5 ms
		snap acceleration	20 ms (approx)
		deceleration	0 ms (approx)
B13-B17	–		
B18	sensor supply (TCA : t3)	ignition on/engine running	5.0 V ± 0.1
B19	camshaft sensor (inductive) return : t1	ignition on/engine running	0.25 V (max)
B20	–		
B21	ignition coil driver (cyl 2 & 3): t1	ignition on	nbv
		engine running:	
		dynamic volt drop	2.0 V (max)
		primary switching	200 V (min)
B22	earth	ignition on/engine running	0.25 V (max)
B23	injector driver (cyl 1) : t1	ignition on	nbv
		engine running, cold	> 3.5 ms
		engine running, hot	3.5 ms
		snap acceleration	20 ms (approx)
		deceleration	0 ms (approx)
B24	injector driver (cyl 2) : t1	ignition on	nbv
		engine running, cold	> 3.5 ms
		engine running, hot	3.5 ms
		snap acceleration	20 ms (approx)
		deceleration	0 ms (approx)
B25	–		
B26	stepper motor (TCA : t8)	idle speed, active	0 to 5.0 V (switching)
B27	MAF sensor return : t5	ignition on/engine running	0.25 V (max)
B28	sensor return (CTS : t1, ATS : t1)	ignition on/engine running	0.25 V (max)
B29	CAS return : t1	engine running	0.25 V (max)
B30	CAS signal : t2	engine cranking	> 0.4 V AC (RMS)
		idle	> 1.0 V AC (RMS)
B31-B33	–		

Pin	Connection	Test condition	Measurement
B34	idle switch (TCA : t6)	Ignition on/engine running:	
		throttle closed	0 V
		throttle part/fully open	nbv
B35	–		
B36	CTS signal : t2	ignition on/engine running	20° C: 3.00 to 3.50 V
			80° C: 1.00 to 1.30 V
B37	ATS signal : t2	ignition on/engine running	20° C: 2.40 to 2.80 V
B38	–		
B39	TPS signal (TCA : t1)	ignition on/engine running:	
		throttle closed	4.0 V (approx)
		open	1.0 V (approx)
B40	KS return : t1	engine running, KS active	0.25 V (max)
B41	KS signal : t1	engine running, KS active	1.0 to 2.0 V AC (peak to peak)
B42-B44	–		

44 pin ECM multi-plug, Mercedes Benz, HFM

Pin Table – Mercedes Benz PMS

Connector A

Pin	Connection	Test condition	Measurement
A1	earth	ignition on/engine running	0.25 V (max)
A2	supply from ignition switch : t15	ignition on/engine running	nbv
A3	AT		data not available
A4-A5	–		
A6	OS signal : t3	ignition on, OS multiplug disconnected	0.4 to 0.5 V
		engine running, hot	200 to 1000 mV (switching)
		throttle fully-open	1.0 V constant
		deceleration (fuel cut-off)	0 V constant
		switching frequency	1 sec intervals (approx)
A7	earth	ignition on/engine running	0.25 V (max)
A8	fuel pump relay driver : t86	ignition on	nbv
		engine cranking/running	1.25 V (max)
A9	earth	ignition on/engine running	0.25 V (max)
A10	supply from battery : t30	ignition off/on/engine running	nbv
A11	–		
A12	air conditioning		data not available
A13	SD connector		data not available
A14	–		
A15	SD connector		data not available
A16	OS heater driver : t1	ignition on	0 V
		engine running:	
		hot	0 to 12 V (switching)
		duty cycle	0 to 99%
A17	CFSV driver : t1	ignition on	0 V
		engine running:	
		idle speed	nbv
		above idle, operating temperature,	
		CFSV active	0 to 12 V (switching)
		duty cycle	0 to 99%

Pin Table – Mercedes Benz PMS (continued)

Connector B

Pin	Connection	Test condition	Measurement
B1-B3	–		
B4	injector driver (cyls 1 and 4) : t1	ignition on	nbv
		engine running, cold	> 3.5 ms
		engine running, hot	2.1 ms
		snap acceleration	20 ms (approx)
		deceleration	0 ms (approx)
B5	stepper motor (TCA : t1)	idle speed, active	0 to 5.0 V (switching)
B6	sensor supply (TCA : t4)	ignition on/engine running	5.0 V ± 0.1
B7	CTS signal : t2	ignition on/engine running	20° C: 2.75 to 3.25 V
			80° C: 0.75 to 1.25 V
B8	TVPS signal (TCA : t8)	ignition on	3.6 V
		engine running	3.0 to 4.2 V
B9	sensor return (TCA : t7, CTS : t1, ATS : t1)	ignition on/engine running	0.25 V (max)
B10	ignition coil driver (cyls 1 and 4) : t1	ignition on	nbv
		engine running:	
		dynamic volt drop	2.0 V (max)
		primary switching	200 V (min)
B11	ignition coil driver (cyls 2 and 3) : t1	ignition on	nbv
		engine running:	
		dynamic volt drop	2.0 V (max)
		primary switching	200 V (min)
B12	immobiliser		data not available
B13	injector driver (cyls 2 and 3) : t1	ignition on	nbv
		engine running, cold	> 3.5 ms
		engine running, hot	2.1 ms
		snap acceleration	20 ms (approx)
		deceleration	0 ms (approx)
B14	stepper motor (TCA : t2)	idle speed, active	0 to 5.0 V (switching)
B15	TPS signal (TCA : t3)	ignition on/engine running:	
		throttle closed	4.2 V (approx)
		open	0 V
B16	ATS signal : t2	ignition on/engine running	20° C: 2.25 to 2.75 V
B17	idle switch signal : t1	ignition on/idle speed	
		throttle closed	0 V
		throttle open	5.0 V

Connector C

Pin	Connection	Test condition	Measurement
C1	CAS signal : t2	engine cranking	> 0.7 V AC (peak to peak)
		idle	> 4.5 V AC (peak to peak)
		cruise	> 8.0 V AC (peak to peak)
C2	CAS return : t1	engine running	0.25 V (max)

Eq52092

Connector C

Connector B

Connector A

36 pin ECM multi-plug, Mercedes Benz PMS

Wiring Diagrams

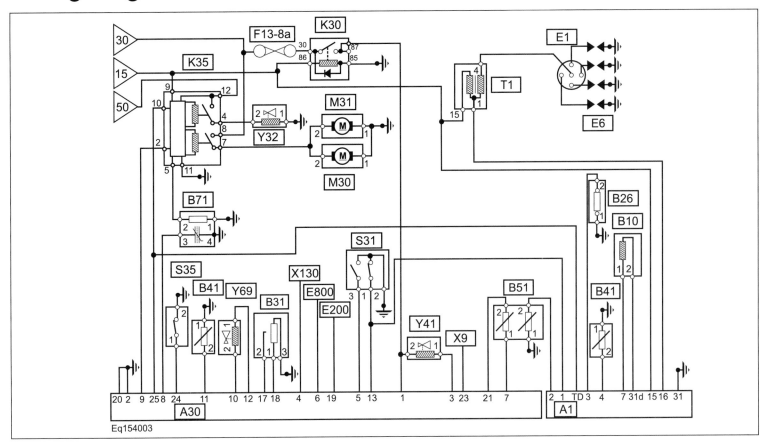

System wiring diagram, Bosch KE3.1 Jetronic

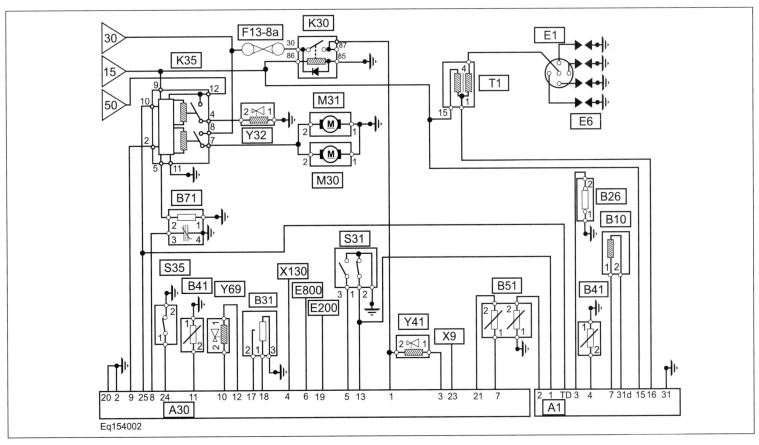

System wiring diagram, Bosch KE3.5 Jetronic

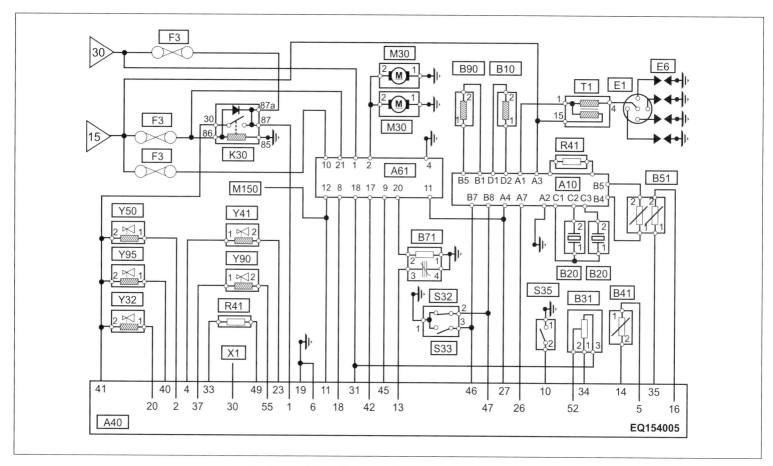

System wiring diagram, Bosch KE5.2 Jetronic

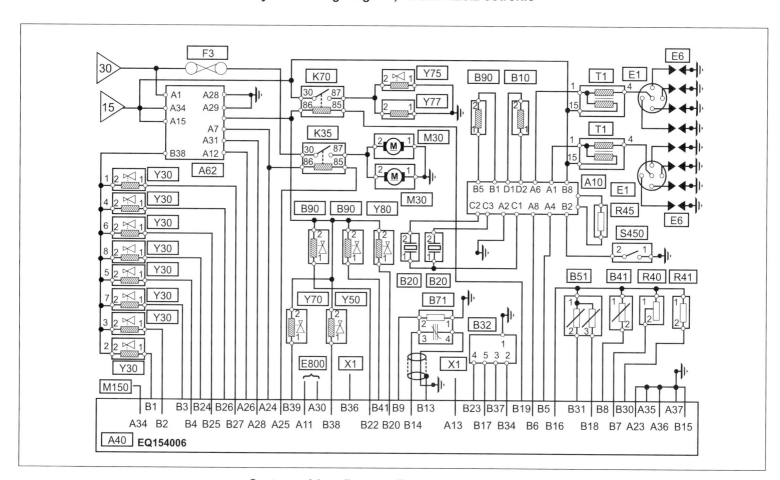

System wiring diagram, Bosch LH 4.1 Jetronic

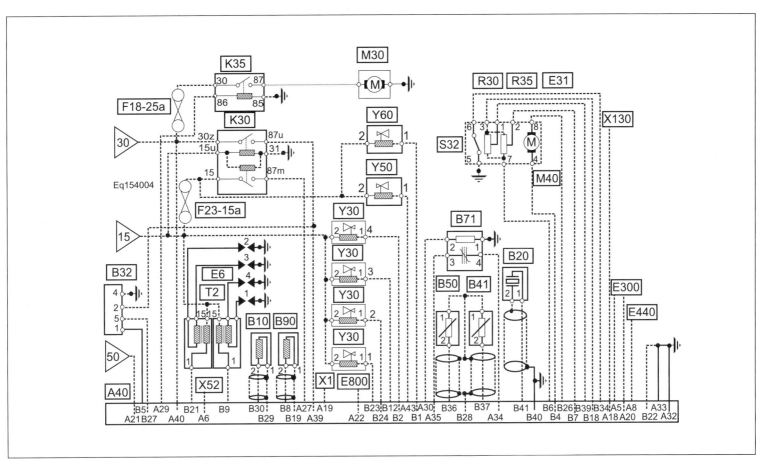

System wiring diagram, Mercedes Benz HFM

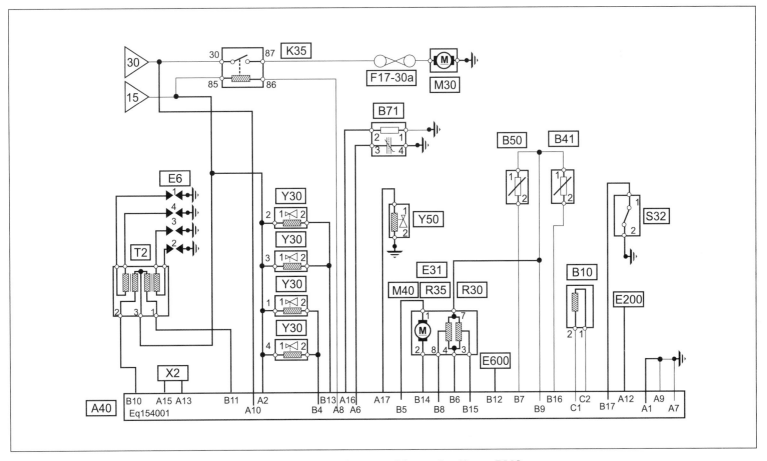

System wiring diagram, Mercedes Benz PMS

Notes

Notes

Chapter 19
Mitsubishi

Contents

Index of Mitsubishi vehicles/systems

Model	Engine code	Year	System
Carisma 1.6 SOHC 16v	4G92	1996 to 1997	Mitsubishi ECI-Multi MPi
Carisma 1.8 DOHC 16v	4G93	1996 to 1997	Mitsubishi ECI-Multi MPi
Carisma 1.8 SOHC 16v	4G93	1996 to 1997	Mitsubishi ECI-Multi MPi
Colt1.3 SOHC 12v	4G13	1996 to 1997	Mitsubishi ECI-Multi MPi
Colt1.3i cat SOHC 12V	4G13	1992 to 1996	Mitsubishi ECI-Multi MPi
Colt 1600 GTi DOHC	4G61	1988 to 1990	Mitsubishi ECI-Multi MPi
Colt 1.6 SOHC 16V	4G92	1996 to 1997	Mitsubishi ECI-Multi MPi
Colt 1.6i SOHC 16V	4G92	1992 to 1996	Mitsubishi ECI-Multi MPi
Colt 1.6i 4x4 cat SOHC 16V	4G92	1992 to 1996	Mitsubishi ECI-Multi MPi
Colt 1.8 GTi cat DOHC 16V	4G93	1992 to 1995	Mitsubishi ECI-Multi MPi
Colt 1800 GTi DOHC 16V	4G67	1990 to 1993	Mitsubishi ECI-Multi MPi
Cordia 1800 Turbo	4G62T	1985 to 1989	Mitsubishi ECI-Multi MPi
Galant 1800 cat SOHC 16V	4G93	1993 to 1997	Mitsubishi ECI-Multi MPi
Galant Turbo	4G63T	1985 to 1988	Mitsubishi ECI-Multi MPi
Galant 2000 GLSi SOHC	4G63	1988 to 1993	Mitsubishi ECI-Multi MPi
Galant 2000 GTi 16V DOHC	4G63	1988 to 1993	Mitsubishi ECI-Multi MPi
Galant 2000 4WD DOHC	4G63	1989 to 1994	Mitsubishi ECI-Multi MPi
Galant 2000 4WS cat DOHC	4G63	1989 to 1994	Mitsubishi ECI-Multi MPi
Galant 2.0i cat SOHC 16V	4G63	1993 to 1997	Mitsubishi ECI-Multi MPi
Galant 2.0i V6 DOHC 24V	6A12	1993 to 1997	Mitsubishi ECI-Multi MPi
Galant Sapporo 2400	4G64	1987 to 1989	Mitsubishi ECI-Multi MPi
Galant 2.5i V6 DOHC 24V	6G73	1993 to 1995	Mitsubishi ECI-Multi MPi
L300 SOHC 16V	4G63	1994 to 1997	Mitsubishi ECI-Multi MPi
Lancer 1600 GTi 16V DOHC	4G61	1988 to 1990	Mitsubishi ECI-Multi MPi
Lancer 1.6i SOHC 16V	4G92	1992 to 1996	Mitsubishi ECI-Multi MPi
Lancer 1.6i 4x4 cat SOHC 16V	4G92	1992 to 1996	Mitsubishi ECI-Multi MPi
Lancer 1.8 GTi cat DOHC 16V	4G93	1992 to 1995	Mitsubishi ECI-Multi MPi
Lancer 1800 GTi DOHC 16V	4G67	1990 to 1993	Mitsubishi ECI-Multi MPi
Lancer 1800 4WD cat	4G37-8	1989 to 1993	Mitsubishi ECI-Multi MPi
Shogun 2.5 4 SOHC	4G54	1983 to 1994	Mitsubishi ECI-Multi MPi
Shogun 3.0 V6 12v	6G72	1991 to 1994	Mitsubishi ECI-Multi MPi
Shogun 3.0 V6 24v	**6G72**	**1994 to 1998**	**Mitsubishi ECI-Multi MPi**
Shogun 3.5i V6 DOHC 24V	6G74	1994 to 1997	Mitsubishi ECI-Multi MPi
Sigma Estate 12V	6G72	1993 to 1996	Mitsubishi ECI-Multi MPi
Sigma Wagon cat 12V	6G72	1993 to 1996	Mitsubishi ECI-Multi MPi
Sigma 3.0i 24V cat	6G72	1991 to 1996	Mitsubishi ECI-Multi MPi
Space Wagon 1.8i SOHC 16V	4G93	1991 to 1997	Mitsubishi ECI-Multi MPi
Space Wagon 2.0i DOHC 16V	4G63	1992 to 1997	Mitsubishi ECI-Multi MPi
Starion Turbo	4G63T	1986 to 1989	Mitsubishi ECI-Multi MPi
Starion 2.6 Turbo cat	G54B1	1989 to 1991	Mitsubishi ECI-Multi MPi
3000 GT 24v	6G72	1992 to 1997	Mitsubishi ECI-Multi MPi

Note: *The vehicles accentuated in bold type are the actual vehicles upon which the ECM pin tables and wiring diagrams are based. Other vehicles with the same system may be similar; but are also likely to contain some differences.*

Pin Table – Mitsubishi ECI-Multi MPi

Pin	Item	Test Condition	Measurements
1	injector driver (cylinder 1) : t1	ignition on	nbv
		engine running:	
		cold	> 3.5 ms
		hot, idle	3.5 ms
		3000 rpm	3.4 ms
		snap acceleration	20 ms (approx)
		deceleration (fuel cut off)	1 ms (approx)
2	injector driver (cylinder 2) : t1	ignition on	nbv
		engine running:	
		cold	> 3.5 ms
		hot, idle	3.5 ms
		3000 rpm	3.4 ms
		snap acceleration	20 ms (approx)
		deceleration (fuel cut off)	1 ms (approx)
3	injector driver (cylinder 3) : t1	ignition on	nbv
		engine running:	
		cold	> 3.5 ms
		hot, idle	3.5 ms
		3000 rpm	3.4 ms
		snap acceleration	20 ms (approx)
		deceleration	1 ms (approx)
4	stepper motor : t1	idle speed, active	0 to 5.0 V (switching)
5	stepper motor : t4	idle speed, active	0 to 5.0 V (switching)
6-7	–		
8	fuel pump relay driver : t85a	ignition on	nbv
		engine cranking/running	1.25 V (max)
9	CFSV driver : t1	ignition on	nbv
		engine running, above idle, operating temperature	
		CFSV inactive	nbv
		CFSV active	0 to 12 V (switching)
		duty cycle	0 to 99%
10	amplifier control signal	engine cranking/running	0 to 5.0 V (switching)
11	amplifier control signal	engine cranking/running	0 to 5.0 V (switching)
12	supply from main relay : t86a	ignition on/engine running	nbv
13	earth	ignition on/engine running	0.25 V (max)
14	injector driver (cylinder 4) : t1	ignition on	nbv
		engine running:	
		cold	> 3.5 ms
		hot, idle	3.5 ms
		3000 rpm	3.4 ms
		snap acceleration	20 ms (approx)
		deceleration	1 ms (approx)
15	injector driver (cylinder 5) : t1	ignition on	nbv
		engine running:	
		cold	> 3.5 ms
		hot, idle	3.5 ms
		3000 rpm	3.4 ms
		snap acceleration	20 ms (approx)
		deceleration	1 ms (approx)
16	injector driver (cylinder 6) : t1	ignition on	nbv
		engine running:	
		cold	> 3.5 ms
		hot, idle	3.5 ms
		3000 rpm	3.4 ms
		snap acceleration	20 ms (approx)
		deceleration	1 ms (approx)
17	stepper motor : t3	idle speed, active	0 to 5.0 V (switching)
18	stepper motor : t6	idle speed, active	0 to 5.0 V (switching)

Pin	Item	Test Condition	Measurements
19	AFS signal : t7	ignition on/engine running:	
		throttle closed, 750 rpm, idle	20 to 33 Hz
		throttle open, 2000 rpm	60 to 80 Hz
20-21	–		
22	air conditioning		data not available
23	amplifier control signal	engine cranking/running	0 to 5.0 V (switching)
24	–		
25	supply from main relay : t86b	ignition on/engine running	nbv
26	earth	ignition on/engine running	0.25 V (max)
27-30	–		
31	RPM check connector		data not available
32-33	–		
34	service connector		data not available
35	–		
36	SD warning lamp : t1	ignition on, lamp on	1.25 V (max)
		engine running:	
		no faults present	nbv
		faults present, lamp on	1.25 V (max)
37	PSPS signal : t2	idle speed:	
		front wheels turned	nbv
		front wheels straight	0.25 V (max)
38	main relay driver : t85	ignition on	nbv
		engine cranking/running	1.25 V (max)
39-41	–		
42	SD connector		data not available
43	SD connector		data not available
44	ABS		data not available
45	air conditioning		data not available
46-50	–		
51	cranking signal : t50	engine cranking	nbv
52	ATS signal (AFS : t6)	ignition on/engine running	20° C: 2.3 to 2.9 V
			40° C: 1.50 to 2.1 V
53	–		
54	EGR solenoid valve driver : t1	ignition on	nbv
		engine running:	
		EGR inactive	nbv
		EGR active	1.25 V (max)
55	–		
56	OS signal : t3	ignition on, OS multiplug disconnected	0.4 to 0.5 V
		engine running, hot	200 to 1000 mV (switching)
		throttle fully-open	0.5 to 1.0 V
		deceleration (fuel cut-off)	0 to 0.5 V
		switching frequency	1 sec intervals (approx)
57-59	–		
60	ignition switch supply: t15	ignition on/engine running	nbv
61	sensor supply (AFS : t1, TPS : t4)	ignition on/engine running	5.0 V ± 0.1
62	supply from ignition switch : t15	ignition on/engine running	nbv
63	CTS signal : t2	ignition on/engine running	20° C: 2.00 to 2.50 V
			80° C: 1.00 to 1.30 V
64	TPS signal : t3	ignition on/engine running:	
		throttle closed	0.5 V
		throttle fully open	4.2 V (approx)
65	barometric pressure signal (AFS : t2)	ignition on/engine running:	
		sea level	3.7 to 4.3 V
		altitude, 1220m above sea level	3.2 to 3.8 V
66	VSS signal : t3	vehicle in motion	0 to 12 V (switching)
67	idle switch (TPS : t2)	ignition on/engine running:	
		throttle closed	0 V
		open	4.2 V (approx)
68	camshaft sensor signal : t2	engine cranking/running	0 to 5 V (switching)
69	CAS (HE) signal : t2	engine cranking/running	0 to 5 V (switching)

Pin Table – Mitsubishi ECI-Multi MPi

Pin	Item	Test Condition	Measurements
70	AFS supply : t3	ignition on/engine running	5.0 V ± 0.1
71	earth	ignition on/engine running	0.25 V (max)
72	sensor return (CTS : t1, TPS : t1, AFS : t5)	ignition on/engine running	0.25 V (max)

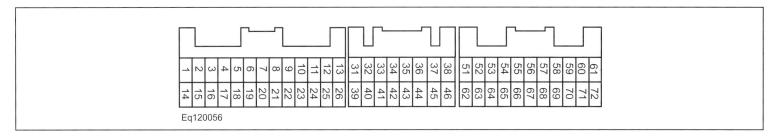

Eq120056

72 pin ECM multi-plug, Mitsubishi ECI-Multi MPi

Wiring Diagram

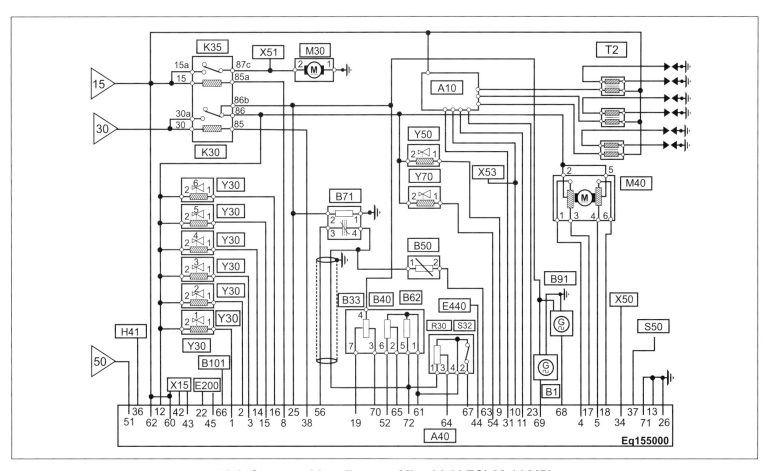

19.2 System wiring diagram, Mitsubishi ECI-Multi MPi

Chapter 20
Nissan

Contents

Index of Nissan vehicles/systems

Model	Engine code	Year	System
Almera 1.4 DOHC 16v	GA14DE	1996 to 1997	ECCS MPi (4-cyl)
Almera 1.6 DOHC 16v	GA16DE	1996 to 1997	ECCS MPi (4-cyl)
Almera 2.0 Gti	SR20DE	1996 to 1997	ECCS MPi (4-cyl)
Maxima	VG30E	1989 to 1994	ECCS MPi (4-cyl)
Maxima cat	VG30E	1989 to 1994	ECCS MPi (4-cyl)
Maxima (J30)	VG30E	1989 to 1994	ECCS MPi (6cyl)
Maxima (J30) R-cat	**VG30E**	**1989 to 1994**	**ECCS MPi (6cyl)**
Micra 1.0 DOHC	CG10DE	1994 to 1997	ECCS MPi (4-cyl)
Micra 1.3 DOHC	**CG13DE**	**1994 to 1997**	**ECCS MPi (4-cyl)**
Patrol 4.2I OHV	TB42E	1992 to 1997	ECCS MPi (4-cyl)
Patrol GR (Y60) R-cat	TB42E	1992 to 1998	ECCS MPi (6-cyl)
Primera 1.6 DOHC	GA16DE	1996 to 1998	ECCS MPi (4-cyl)
Primera 1.6I DOHC 16v	GA16DE	1994 to 1996	ECCS SPi
Primera 1.6I DOHC 16v	GA16DE	1996 to 1997	ECCS MPi (4-cyl)
Primera 2.0 cat DOHC 16v	**SR20Di (P10)**	**1990 to 1995**	**ECCS SPi**
Primera 2.0 DOHC R-Cat	SR20DE	1991 to 1996	ECCS MPi (4-cyl)
Primera 2.0 DOHC R-Cat	SR20DE	1996 to 1998	ECCS MPi (4-cyl)
Primera 2.0 DOHC 4x4	SR20DE	1990 to 1993	ECCS MPi (4-cyl)
Primera 2.0e cat	SR20DE	1991 to 1995	ECCS MPi (4-cyl)
Primera 2.0e GT	SR20DE	1991 to 1995	ECCS MPi (4-cyl)
Primera 2.0e R-Cat	**SR20DE**	**1990 to 1993**	**ECCS MPi (4-cyl)**
Primera 2.0e ZX DOHC 16v	SR20DE	1991 to 1995	ECCS MPi (4-cyl)
Primera Estate 2.0 cat DOHC 16v	SR20Di (W10)	1990 to 1996	ECCS SPi
Primera 2.0 GT DOHC 16v	SR20DE	1994 to 1996	ECCS SPi
Primera 2.0I GT DOHC 16v	SR20DE	1996 to 1997	ECCS MPi (4-cyl)
Primera 2.0I DOHC 16v	SR20DE	1994 to 1996	ECCS SPi
Primera 2.0I DOHC 16v	SR20DE	1996 to 1997	ECCS MPi (4-cyl)
QX2.0 (A30) R-cat)	VQ20DE	1994 to 1999	ECCS MPi (6cyl)
QX 2.0 DOHC 24v V6	VQ20DE	1994 to 1997	ECCS MPi (4-cyl)
QX3.0	VQ30DE	1994 to 1999	ECCS MPi (6cyl)
QX 3.0 DOHC 24v V6	VQ30DE	1994 to 1997	ECCS MPi (4-cyl)
Serena 1.6I DOHC 16V	GA16DE	1993 to 1997	ECCS MPi (4-cyl)
Serena 2.0I DOHC 16v	SR20DE	1993 to 1997	ECCS MPi (4-cyl)
Sunny 1.6I cat SOHC 12v	GA16I (B12,N13)	1989 to 1991	ECCS SPi
Sunny 2.0 GTi cat DOHC 16v	SR20DE	1991 to 1994	ECCS MPi (4-cyl)
Sunny GTi-R DOHC 16v	SR20DET	1991 to 1994	ECCS MPi (4-cyl)
Terrano/Wagon (WD21) R-cat	VG30E	1987 to 1998	ECCS MPi (6cyl)
24WD Wagon 3.0I cat	VG30E	1990 to 1994	ECCS MPi (4-cyl)
300 ZX (Z31)	VG30E	1984 to 1990	ECCS MPi (6cyl)
300 ZX turbo (Z31)	VG30ET	1987 to 1990	ECCS MPi (6cyl)
300 ZX turbo (Z31) R-cat	VG30ET	1987 to 1990	ECCS MPi (6cyl)
300 ZX turbo (Z32) R-cat	VG30DETT	1990 to 1994	ECCS MPi (6cyl)

Note: *The vehicles accentuated in bold type are the actual vehicles upon which the ECM pin tables and wiring diagrams are based. Other vehicles with the same system may be similar; but are also likely to contain some differences.*

Pin Table – Nissan ECCS MPi (4-cyl)

Pin	Item	Test Condition	Measurements
1	amplifier control signal	engine running, idle	0.2 to 0.4 V
		2000 rpm	0.6 to 0.8 V
2	tachometer		data not available
3	ignition coil (via resistor)	ignition on	nbv
		engine running	200 V (min)
4	main ECCS relay driver	ignition off	nbv
		ignition on/engine running	0 to 1 V
		approximately 2 seconds after switching off	nbv
5	–		
6	earth	ignition on/engine running	0.25 V (max)
7	SD connector		data not available
8	–		
9	radiator fan relay driver	ignition on/engine running:	
		fan active	0.6 to 0.8 V
		fan inactive	nbv
10	–		
11	A/C relay driver	ignition on/engine running:	
		A/C switch and blower switch on	0 V
		A/C switch off	nbv
12	–		
13	earth	ignition on/engine running	0.25 V (max)
14	SD connector		data not available
15	SD connector		data not available
16	MAF sensor signal	ignition on	0.8 V
		idle speed	1.4 to 1.9 V
		snap acceleration	3.0 to 4.0 V
17	–		
18	CTS signal : t2	ignition on/engine running	20° C: 3.0 V (approx)
			80° C: 1.0 V (approx)
19	OS signal : t3	ignition on, OS multiplug disconnected	0.4 to 0.5 V
		engine running, hot	200 to 1000 mV (switching)
		throttle fully-open	0.5 to 1.0 V
		deceleration (fuel cut-off)	0 to 0.5 V
		switching frequency	1 sec intervals (approx)
20	TPS signal	ignition on/engine running:	
		throttle closed	0.6 to 0.7 V
		throttle fully open	4.0 V (approx)
21	sensor return (TPS : t1, CTS : t1)	ignition on/running	0.25 V (max)
22	CAS (ref signal) : t3	engine running (do not run engine at high speed under no load)	0 to 5 V (switching)
23	SD connector		
24-26	–		
27	ABS-ECM		data not available
28	–		
29	CTS return : t1	ignition on/engine running	0.25 V (max)
30	CAS (ref. signal) : t3	engine running (do not run engine at high speed under no load)	0 to 5 V (switching)
31	–		
32	VSS (reed switch)	vehicle in motion	0 to 12 V (switching)
33	load signal (lights, demister)		data not available
34	ignition switch : t30	engine cranking	nbv
35	neutral switch	ignition off	0 V
		ignition on, switch active	6.0 V
36	ignition switch : t15	ignition off	0 V
		ignition on/engine running	nbv
37	TPS supply	ignition on/engine running	5.0 V (approx)
38	supply from main relay : t87	ignition on/engine running	nbv
39	earth	ignition on/engine running	0.25 V (max)

Pin	Item	Test Condition	Measurements
40	–		
41	air conditioning switch	engine running:	
		A/C switch and blower on	0 V
		A/C switch off	nbv
42	–		
43	PSPS signal : t2	engine running:	
		front wheels pointing straight ahead	0 V
		front wheels turned	5 V
44-45	–		
46	supply from battery : t30	ignition on/off/engine running	nbv
47	supply from main relay : t87	ignition on/engine running	nbv
48	earth	ignition on/engine running	0.25 V (max)
49 to			
100	–		
101	injector driver (cyl 1) : t1	ignition off/on	nbv
		engine running, cold	4 ms
		engine running, hot	2.5 to 3.0 ms
		snap acceleration	15 ms
102	–		
103	injector driver (cyl 3) : t1	ignition off/on	nbv
		engine running, cold	4 ms
		engine running, hot	2.5 to 3.0 ms
		snap acceleration	15 ms
104	fuel pump relay driver	ignition on	nbv
		engine cranking/running	0.7 to 0.9 V
105	OS heater : t1	ignition on	nbv
		engine running:	
		OS heater non-active	nbv
		OS heater active	0 V
106	–		
107	earth	ignition on/engine running	0.25 V (max)
108	earth	ignition on/engine running	0.25 V (max)
109	–		
110	injector driver (cyl 2) : t1	ignition off/on	nbv
		engine running, cold	4 ms
		engine running, hot	2.5 to 3.0 ms
		snap acceleration	15 ms
111	ISCV driver : t1	ignition on	nbv
		engine running, idle speed:	
		cold	6.0 to 6.5 V
		hot	7.0 to 9.0 V
		duty cycle	30 to 60%
112	injector driver (cyl 4) : t1	ignition off/on	nbv
		engine running, cold	4 ms
		engine running, hot	2.5 to 3.0 ms
		snap acceleration	15 ms
113	ISCV driver	ignition on	nbv
		engine running, idle speed:	
		cold	6.0 to 6.5 V
		hot	7.0 to 9.0 V
		duty cycle	30 to 60%
114-115	–		
116	earth	ignition on/engine running	0.25 V (max)

eq6209

116 pin ECM multi-plug, ECCS MPi (4-cyl)

Pin Table – Nissan ECCS MPi (6-cyl)

Pin	Item	Test Condition	Measurements
1	amplifier control signal	engine cranking/running	0.4 to 0.6 V (switching)
		4000 rpm	1.9 to 2.1 V
2	ignition coil (via resistor)	ignition on	nbv
		engine running: dynamic volt drop	2.0 V (max)
		primary switching	200 V (min)
3	–		
4	stepper motor : t1	idle speed, active	0 to 12.0 V (switching)
5	stepper motor : t5	idle speed, active	0 to 12.0 V (switching)
6	radiator fan relay driver (high speed) : t85	ignition on:	
		fan inactive	nbv
		fan active	0.7 to 0.8 V
7	tachometer		data not available
8	ICOV driver : t1	ignition on	nbv
		engine running, idle speed	nbv
		engine running, > 4000 rpm	0.7 to 0.8 V
9	A/C relay driver : t1	ignition on/engine running	nbv
		relay inactive	nbv
		relay active	1.25 V (max)
10	earth	ignition on/engine running	0.25 V (max)
11-13	–		
14	stepper motor : t3	idle speed, active	0 to 12.0 V (switching)
15	stepper motor : t6	idle speed, active	0 to 12.0 V (switching)
16	main relay driver : t85	ignition off/on/engine running	1.25 V (max)
17	–		
18	fuel pump relay driver : t85	ignition on	
		engine cranking/running	1.25 V (max)
19	radiator fan relay driver (low speed) : t85	fan inactive	nbv
		fan active	0.7 to 0.8 V
20	earth	ignition on/engine running	0.25 V (max)
21-22	–		
23	KS signal : t1	engine running, KS active	3.0 to 4.0 V AC (peak to peak)
24	–		
25	heated rear window	ignition on/engine running:	
		heater off	nbv
		heater on	1.25 V (max)
26	MAF sensor return : tD	ignition on/engine running	0.25 V (max)
27	MAF sensor signal : tB	idle	1.0 to 1.3 V
		3000 rpm	1.8 to 2.0 V
		snap accelerate	3.00 to 3.50 V (approx)
28	CTS signal : t2	ignition on/engine running	20° C: 2.00 to 2.50 V
			80° C: 1.00 to 1.30 V
29	–		
30	sensor return (CTS : t1, TPS : t1)	ignition on/engine running	0.25 V (max)
31-33	–		
34	PSPS signal : t2	idle speed:	
		front wheels turned	nbv
		front wheels straight	0.25 V (max)
35	AT		data not available
36	AT		data not available
37	MAF sensor signal : tA	idle speed	1.0 to 1.3 V
		3000 rpm	1.8 to 2.0 V
		snap accelerate	3.00 to 3.50 V (approx)
38	TPS signal : t3	ignition on/engine running:	
		throttle closed	0.5 V
		throttle fully open	4.2 V
39-40	–		
41	OCAS reference signal : tD	engine running	0.2 to 0.4 V
42	OCAS signal : tB	engine running	2.5 to 2.7 V
43	cranking signal : t50	engine cranking	nbv

Pin	Item	Test Condition	Measurements
44	neutral switch	ignition off	0 V
		ignition on	12.0 V
45	supply from ignition switch : t15	ignition on/engine running	nbv
46	air conditioning		data not available
47	–		
48	TPS supply	ignition on/engine running	5.0 V ± 0.1
49	supply from battery : t30	ignition off/on/engine running	nbv
50	earth	ignition on/engine running	0.25 V (max)
51	OCAS reference signal : tD	engine running	0.2 to 0.4 V
52	OCAS signal : tB	engine running	2.5 to 2.7 V
53	VSS signal : t3	drive wheels rotating	0 to 12 V (switching)
54	idle switch signal : tA	ignition on/idle speed:	
		throttle closed	0 V
		throttle open	nbv
55	–		
57	idle switch return : tB	ignition on/engine running	0.25 V (max)
58	–		
60	earth	ignition on/engine running	0.25 V (max)
101	injector driver (cylinder 1) : t1	ignition on	nbv
		engine running, cold	> 3.5 ms
		engine running, hot	3.5 ms
		snap acceleration	20 ms (approx)
		deceleration	0 ms (approx)
102	EGR solenoid valve : t1	engine running :> 3400 rpm	0.7 to 0.8 V
		< 3400 rpm	nbv
103	injector driver (cylinder 3) : t1	ignition on	nbv
		engine running, cold	> 3.5 ms
		engine running, hot	3.5 ms
		snap acceleration	20 ms (approx)
		deceleration	0 ms (approx)
104	fuel pump control voltage	ignition on/engine running	
		first 30 seconds after start	4.0 to 4.5 V
		< 4000 rpm	2.0 to 4.5 V
105	injector driver (cylinder 5) : t1	ignition on	nbv
		engine running, cold	> 3.5 ms
		engine running, hot	3.5 ms
		snap acceleration	20 ms (approx)
		deceleration	0 ms (approx)
106	–		
107	earth	ignition on/engine running	0.25 V (max)
108	earth	ignition on/engine running	0.25 V (max)
109	reverse polarity protection relay : t87	ignition on/engine running	nbv
110	injector driver (cylinder 2) : t1	ignition on	nbv
		engine running, cold	> 3.5 ms
		engine running, hot	3.5 ms
		snap acceleration	20 ms (approx)
		deceleration	0 ms (approx)
111	–		
112	injector driver (cylinder 4) : t1	ignition on	nbv
		engine running, cold	> 3.5 ms
		engine running, hot	3.5 ms
		snap acceleration	20 ms (approx)
		deceleration	0 ms (approx)
113	–		
114	injector driver (cylinder 6) : t1	ignition on	nbv
		engine running, cold	>3.5 ms
		engine running, hot	3.5 ms
		snap acceleration	20 ms (approx)
		deceleration	0 ms (approx)
115	–		
116	earth	ignition on/engine running	0.25 V (max)

116 pin ECM multi-plug, ECCS MPi (6-cyl)

Pin Table – Nissan ECCS SPi

Pin	Item	Test Condition	Measurements
1	amplifier control signal : t1	engine running	0 to 5.0 V (switching)
		idle speed	0.3 to 0.5 V
		4000 rpm	1.5 V (approx)
2	–		
3	ignition coil : t1 (via resistor)	amplifier disconnected, ignition on	nbv
		engine running	200 V (min)
4	main relay driver : t85	ignition off	
		ignition on/engine running	1.25 V (max)
5	–		
6	earth	ignition on/engine running	0.25 V (max)
7	SD connector		data not available
8	ATS (AFS: t1)	ignition on/engine running	5.0 to 7.0 V
9	EGR/CFSV driver : t1	engine running, hot:	
		idle speed	nbv
		2000 rpm, EGR active	1.0 V (max)
10	–		
11	A/C relay driver : t85	ignition on/engine running:	
		A/C switch and blower switch on	0.5 to 1.0 V
		A/C switch off	nbv
12	–		
13	earth	ignition on/engine running	0.25 V (max)
14	SD connector		data not available
15	SD connector		data not available
16	AFS signal : t4	ignition on	0.9 V
		engine running, idle speed	1.4 to 1.9 V
		snap accelerate	3.6 V (approx)
17	AFS signal return	ignition on/engine running	0.25 V (max)
18	CTS signal : t2	ignition on/engine running	20° C: 3.0 V (approx)
			100° C: 1.0 V (approx)
19	OS signal : t3	ignition on (OS multiplug disconnected)	0.4 to 0.5 V
		engine running, hot	200 to 1000 mV (switching)
		throttle fully-open	0.5 to 1.0 V
		deceleration (fuel cut-off)	0 to 0.5 V
		switching frequency	1 sec intervals (approx)
20	TPS signal : t3	ignition on/engine running:	
		throttle closed	0.52 to 0.62 V
		throttle fully open	4.0 V (approx)
21	sensor return (CTS : t1,TPS : t2)	ignition on/engine running	0.25 V (max)
22	OCAS signal : t3	engine running	0 to 5 V (switching)
23	SD connector		data not available
24	SD warning lamp	ignition on, lamp on	1.25 V (max)
		engine running:	
		no ECM faults present	nbv
		ECM faults present	1.25 V (max)
25-26	–		
27	tachometer		data not available
28	–		
29	sensor return (CTS : t1, TPS : t2)	ignition on/engine running	0.25 V (max)
30	OCAS signal (TDC) : t3	engine running	0 to 5 V (switching)

Pin	Item	Test Condition	Measurements
31	OCAS signal (RPM) : t4	engine running	0 to 5 V (switching)
32	VSS signal : t2	vehicle in motion	0 to 12 V (switching)
33	–		
34	ignition switch : t50	engine cranking	nbv
35	inhibitor switch, AT	ignition on/engine running:	
		AT in P or N	0 V
		AT not in P or N	nbv
35	neutral switch, MT	ignition on/engine running:	
		gear lever in neutral	0 V
		gear lever not in neutral	nbv
36	supply from ignition switch : t15	ignition on/engine running	nbv
37	TPS supply : t1	ignition on/engine running	5.0 V ± 0.1
38	supply from main relay : t87	ignition on/engine running	nbv
39	earth	ignition on/engine running	0.25 V (max)
40	OCAS signal (RPM) : t4	engine running	0 to 5 V (switching)
41	A/C pressure switch	engine running, A/C	
		and blower switches on	0 V (approx)
		engine running, A/C switch off	8.0 V (approx)
42	KS signal : t1	engine running, KS active	2.0 to 3.0 V AC (peak to peak)
43	PSPS signal : t2	wheels straight	8.0 V (approx)
		wheels turned	0.25 V (max)
44-45	–		
46	supply form battery : t30	ignition off/on/engine running	nbv
47	supply from main relay : t87	ignition on/engine running	nbv
48	earth	ignition on/engine running	0.25 V (max)
101	injector driver : t1	engine running, idle speed	1.0 ms
		deceleration (fuel cut off)	0 ms (approx)
102	radiator fan relay no1 driver : t85	engine running:	
		fan off	nbv
		fan on	1.25 V (max)
103	–		
104	fuel pump relay driver : t85	ignition on	nbv briefly, then 0 V
		engine cranking/running	1.25 V (max)
105	radiator fan relay no 2 driver : t85	engine running:	
		fan off	nbv
		fan on	1.25 V (max)
106	throttle body heater relay driver : t85	engine running:	
		temp below 65° C	1.25 V (max)
		temp above 65° C	nbv
107	earth	ignition on/engine running	0.25 V (max)
108	earth	ignition on/engine running	0.25 V (max)
109	supply from battery : t30	ignition off/ on/engine running	nbv
110	injector driver : t1	engine running, idle speed	1.0 ms
		deceleration (fuel cut off)	0 ms (approx)
111-113	–		
114	ISCV driver : t1	ignition on	nbv
		engine running, idle speed:	
		cold	6.0 to 6.5 V
		hot	7.0 to 9.0 V
		duty cycle	30 to 60%
115	AT lock up solenoid valve		data not available
116	earth	ignition on/engine running	0.25 V (max)

64 pin ECM multi-plug, ECCS SPi

Wiring Diagrams

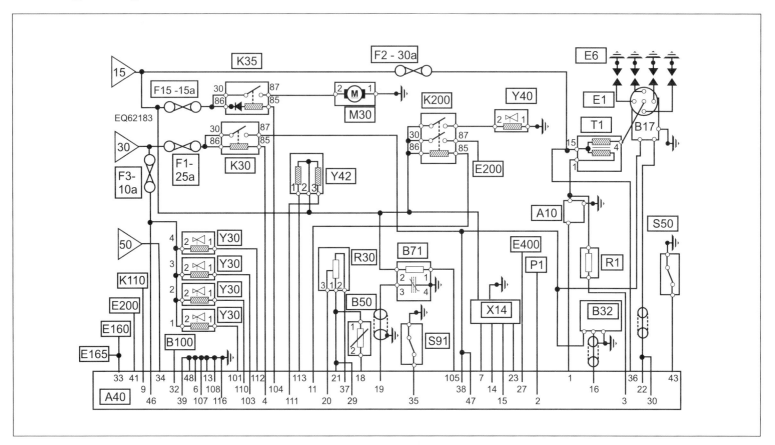

System wiring diagram, ECCS MPi (4-cyl)

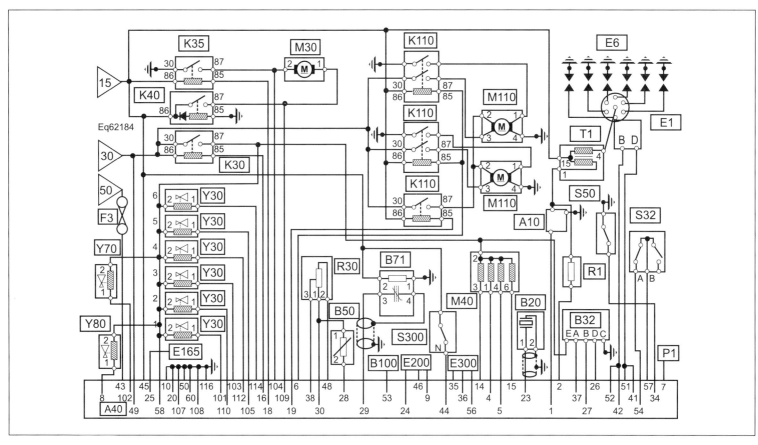

System wiring diagram, ECCS MPi (6-cyl)

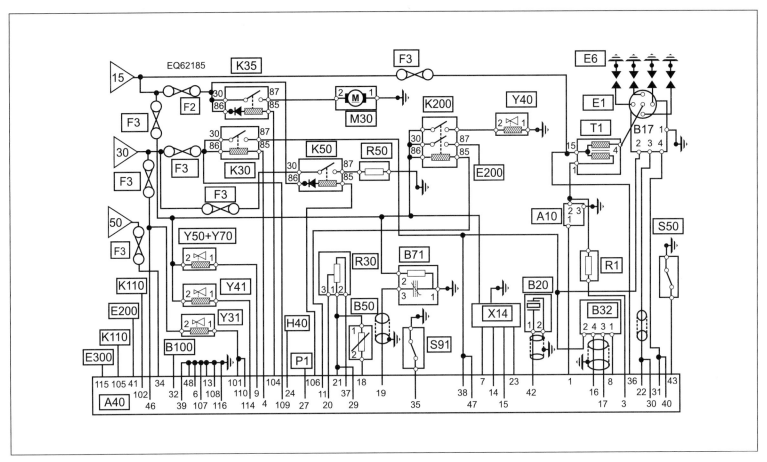

System wiring diagram, ECCS SPi

Notes

Chapter 21
Peugeot

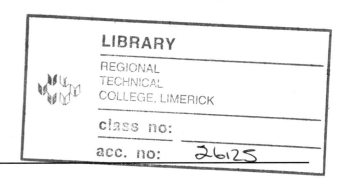
Contents

Index of Peugeot vehicles/systems

Model	Engine code	Year	System
106 1.0 cat	TU9ML/Z (CDY)	1993 to 1996	Mono-Motronic MA3.0
106 1.0 cat	TU9ML/Z (CDZ)	1993 to 1996	Mono-Motronic MA3.0
106 1.1	TU1M/L3/L (HDY)	1996 to 1998	Mono-Motronic MA3.1
106 1.1	TU1M/L3/L (HDZ)	1996 to 1998	Mono-Motronic MA3.1
106 1.1i cat	TU1M/Z (HDZ)	1991 to 1992	Mono-Jetronic A2.2
106 1.1i cat	TU1ML/Z (HDY)	1991 to 1992	Mono-Jetronic A2.2
106 1.1i cat	TU1M/Z (HDZ)	1993 to 1996	Magneti-Marelli G5/G6 SPi
106 1.4i cat	TU3M/Z (KDY)	1991 to 1993	Mono-Jetronic A2.2
106 1.4i cat	**TU3MCL/Z (KDX)**	**1993 to 1996**	**Mono-Motronic MA3.0**
106 1.4i DIS cat	**TU3FJ2 (KFZ)**	**1991 to 1996**	**Bosch Motronic MP3.1**
106 1.4i DIS	TU3FJ2 (K6B)	1991 to 1992	Bosch Motronic 3.1
106 1.6	TU5JP/L3 (NFZ)	1996 to 1997	Bosch Motronic M5.2
106 1.6i 16V	NFX (TU5JP/L3)	1996 to 1998	Magneti-Marelli 1AP40
106 XT/ XSi 1.6	**TU5JPL/Z (NFZ)**	**1994 to 1996**	**Bosch Motronic M5.1/5.1.1**
205 1.1i cat	TU1/M (HDZ)	1989 to 1996	Mono-Jetronic A2.2
205 1.1i cat	TU1M/Z (HDZ)	1992 to 1996	Magneti-Marelli G5/G6 SPi
205 1.4 HC cat	TUML/Z (KDY)	1991 to 1994	Mono-Jetronic A2.2
205 1.4i LC cat	**TU3M (KDZ)**	**1988 to 1991**	**Mono-Jetronic A2.2**
205 1.4i	TU3FM/L (KDY2)	1994 to 1996	Mono-Motronic MA3.0
205 1.6i cat	**XU5M2Z (BDY)**	**1990 to 1991**	**Magneti-Marelli G5/G6 SPi**

Index of Peugeot vehicles/systems (continued)

Model	Engine code	Year	System
205 1.6i cat	**XU5M3Z (BDY)**	**1992 to 1996**	**Magneti-Marelli G5/G6 SPi**
205 1.9 8v 83kW	XU9JAZ (DKZ)	1989 to 1994	Bosch Motronic 1.3
306 1.1i	TU1ML/Z (HDY)	1993 to 1996	Mono-Motronic MA3.0
306 1.1i	TU1ML/Z (HDZ)	1993 to 1996	Mono-Motronic MA3.0
306 1.4	KFX (TU3JP/L3)	1996 to 1998	Magneti-Marelli 1AP40
306 1.4i cat	TU3MCL/Z (KDX)	1993 to 1995	Mono-Motronic MA3.0
306 1.6i	TU5JP/L3	1997 to 1999	Bosch Motronic M5.2
306 2.0i 16v	XU10J4R/L3	1997 to 1999	Bosch Motronic M5.2
306 2.0i cat	XU10J2C (RFX)	1994 to 1996	Magneti-Marelli 8P
306 XL/XR/XS/XT 1.6i cat	TU5JPL/Z (NFZ)	1993 to 1996	Bosch Motronic M5.1/5.1.1
306 XT 1.8i cat	XU7JP/Z (LFZ)	1993 to 1996	Bosch Motronic M5.1/5.1.1
309 1.1i cat	TU1M (HDZ)	1991 to 1994	Mono-Jetronic A2.2
309 1.4i cat	TO3M (KDY)	1991 to 1994	Mono-Jetronic A2.2
309 1.4i cat	TU3M (KDZ)	1988 to 1991	Mono-Jetronic A2.2
309 1.6i cat	XU5M2Z (BDY)	1991 to 1992	Magneti-Marelli G5/G6 SPi
309 1.6i cat	XU5M3Z (BDY)	1992 to 1994	Magneti-Marelli G5/G6 SPi
309 1.6i cat	XU5MZ (BDZ)	1989 to 1991	Magneti-Marelli G5/G6 SPi
309 1.9 16v	XU9J4K (D6C)	1990 to 1993	Bosch Motronic 1.3
309 1.9 16v cat	XU9J4Z (DFW)	1990 to 1992	Bosch Motronic 1.3
309 1.9 16v	**XU9J4 (D6C)**	**1990 to 1991**	**Bosch Motronic 4.1**
309 1.9 8v 83kW	XU9JAZ (DKZ)	1989 to 1993	Bosch Motronic 1.3
309 1.9 SPi cat	XU9M/Z (DDZ)	1988 to 1993	Fenix 1B
405 1.4i cat	TU3MCL/Z (KDX)	1992 to 1994	Mono-Motronic MA3.0
405 1.6i cat	XU5M2Z (BDY)	1989 to 1991	Magneti-Marelli G5/G6 SPi
405 1.6i cat	XU5M3L/Z (BDY)	1992 to 1993	Magneti-Marelli G5/G6 SPi
405 1.6i cat	XU5M3Z (BDY)	1991 to 1992	Magneti-Marelli G5/G6 SPi
405 1.6i cat	XU5MZ (BDZ)	1989 to 1991	Magneti-Marelli G5/G6 SPi
405 1.9 16v	XU9J4K (D6C)	1990 to 1993	Bosch Motronic 1.3
405 1.9 16v	**XU9J4Z (DFW)**	**1990 to 1993**	**Bosch Motronic 1.3**
405 1.9 8v 83kW	XU9JAZ (DKZ)	1989 to 1993	Bosch Motronic 1.3
405 1.9 SPi cat	**XU9M/Z (DDZ)**	**1989 to 1992**	**Fenix 1B**
405 1.9i DIS	XU9J2 (D6D)	1991 to 1992	Bosch Motronic MP3.1
405 1.9i with distributor	XU9J2 (D6D)	1990 to 1991	Bosch Motronic MP3.1
405 2.0i & 4X4 cat	**XU10J2C/Z (RFX)**	**1992 to 1996**	**Magneti-Marelli 8P**
405 mi16 1905cc	XU9J4 (D6C)	1988 to 1991	Bosch Motronic 4.1
405 Quasar/GL/GR/GX 1.8 cat	XU7JPL/Z (LFZ)	1992 to 1996	Bosch Motronic M5.1/5.1.1
406 1.8 16v	XU7JP4L	1995 to 1996	Bosch Motronic M5.1/5.1.1
406 2.0 16v	**XU10J4R (RFV)**	**1996 to 1997**	**Bosch Motronic M5.2**
406 2.0 16v	XU10J4RL	1995 to 1996	Bosch Motronic M5.1/5.1.1
406 V6 cat	**XFZ (ES9J4)**	**1997 to 1998**	**Bosch Motronic M7.0**
605 2.0 Turbo cat	**RGY (XU10J2TE/Z)**	**1993 to 1995**	**Bosch Motronic 3.2 (turbo)**
605 2.0i 16v	XU10J4RL/Z/L3 (RFV)	1995 to 1996	Bosch Motronic M5.1/5.1.1
605 2.0i DIS cat	XU10J2Z (RFZ)	1991 to 1995	Bosch Motronic MP3.1
605 2.0i with distributor cat	XU10J2Z (RFZ)	1990 to 1991	Bosch Motronic MP3.1
605 3.0i 24V DOHC cat	**ZPJ4L/Z (SKZ)**	**1990 to 1994**	**Fenix 4**
605 3.0i 24v V6	ZPJ4L/Z (UKZ)	1995 to 1997	Fenix 4
605 3.0i cat	**ZPJL/Z (SFZ)**	**1990 to 1995**	**Fenix 3B**
605 V6	ZPJ/L/Z (UFX)	1995 to 1997	Fenix 3B
806 2.0 Turbo cat	RGX (XU10J2CtEZ/L)	1995 to 1997	Bosch Motronic 3.2 (turbo)
Boxer 2.0i cat	XU10J2.U (RFW)	1994 to 1996	Magneti-Marelli 8P
Partner 106 1.1	**TU1M/L3/L (HDZ)**	**1996 to 1998**	**Mono-Motronic MA3.1**
Partner 106 1.4	**KFX (TU3JP/L3)**	**1996 to 1998**	**Magneti-Marelli 1AP40**

Note: *The vehicles accentuated in bold type are the actual vehicles upon which the ECM pin tables and wiring diagrams are based. Other vehicles with the same system may be similar; but are also likely to contain some differences.*

Pin Table – Bosch Mono-Jetronic A2.2

Pin	Item	Test Condition	Measurements
1	ignition coil speed signal :	engine cranking/running	0 to nbv (switching)
2	CTS signal : t2	ignition on/engine running	20° C: 2.5 to 3.0 V
			80° C: 0.3 to 0.6 V
3	idle switch (stepper motor : t3)	ignition on/engine running:	
		idle switch closed	0.25 V (max)
		idle switch open	nbv
4	supply from battery : t30	ignition off/on/engine running	nbv
5	earth	ignition on/engine running	0.25 V (max)
6	earth	ignition on/engine running	0.25 V (max)
7	TPS signal : t2	ignition on/engine running:	
		throttle closed	1.0 V
		throttle fully open	4.5 V (approx.)
8	TPS supply : t5	ignition on/engine running	5.0 V ± 0.1
9	supply from main relay : t5	ignition on/engine running	nbv
10 -11	–		
12	CFSV driver : t1	ignition off/on	nbv
		engine running:	
		CFSV non-active	nbv
		CFSV active	0 to 12 V (switching)
		duty cycle	0 to 99%
13	injector driver : t3	engine running:	
		cranking, cold	> 3.0 ms
		running, cold	3.0 to 4.0 ms
		running, hot	1.5 to 2.5 ms
		snap acceleration	10 to 15 ms
		deceleration	0 ms
14	ATS signal : t1	ignition on/engine running	20°C: 2.5 to 3.0 V
			80°C: 0.3 to 0.6 V
15-16	–		
17	fuel pump relay driver : t2	ignition on	nbv
		engine cranking/running	1.25 V (max)
18	TPS signal : t4	ignition on/engine running:	
		throttle closed	0 V
		throttle fully open	4.0 V (approx.)
19	–		
20	OS signal : t3	engine running, hot	200 to 1000 mV (switching)
		throttle fully-open	0.5 to 1.0 V
		deceleration (fuel cut-off)	0 V to 0.5 V
		switching frequency	1 sec intervals (approx.)
21	–		
22	SD connector/SD warning lamp	ignition on/engine running:	
		no faults present	nbv
		faults present	1.25 V (max)
23	stepper motor : t2	idle speed, active	0 to 5.0 V (switching)
24	stepper motor : t1	idle speed, active	0 to 5.0 V (switching)
25	earth	ignition on/engine running	0.25 V (max)

EQ51091H

25 pin ECM multiplug, Bosch Mono-Jetronic A2.2

Pin Table – Bosch Mono-Motronic MA3.0

Pin	Connection	Test condition	Measurements
1	DIS ignition coil driver (cyls 1 & 4) : t1	engine cranking/running	200 V (min)
		dynamic volt drop	2.0 V (max)
2	earth	ignition on/engine running	0.25 V (max)
3	fuel pump relay driver : t10	ignition on	nbv
		engine cranking/running	1.25 V (max)
4	–		
5	CFSV driver : t1	engine running, above idle, operating temperature:	
		CFSV inactive	nbv
		CFSV active	0 to 12 V (switching)
		duty cycle	0 to 99%
6	tachometer		data not available
7	TPS signal : t2	ignition on/engine running:	
		throttle closed	1.0 V
		open	5.0 V (approx.)
8	–		
9	VSS signal : t3	vehicle in motion	0 to 12 V (switching)
10	OS return : t4	ignition on/engine running	0.25 V (max)
11	CAS signal : t2	engine cranking:	> 2.0 V AC (peak to peak)
		idle:	> 11.0 V AC (peak to peak)
		cruise:	> 14.0 V AC (peak to peak)
12	TPS supply : t5	ignition on/engine running	5.0 V ± 0.1
13	SD connector		data not available
14	earth	ignition on/engine running	0.25 V (max)
15	stepper motor : t2	idle speed, active	0 to 5.0 V (switching)
16	SD connector		data not available
17	injector driver : t4	ignition on	nbv
		engine running, idle speed, hot	1.5 ms (min)
		deceleration (cut-off)	0 ms
18	supply from battery : t30	ignition off/on/engine running	nbv
19	earth	ignition on/engine running	0.25 V (max)
20	DIS ignition coil driver (cyls 2 & 3) : t2	engine cranking/running	200 V (min)
		dynamic volt drop	2.0 V (max)
21	–		
22	SD warning lamp	engine running:	
		lamp off, no fault	nbv
		lamp on, fault present	1.25 V (max)
23-24	–		
25	CTS signal : t2	ignition on/engine running	20° C: 2.5 to 3.0 V
			80° C: 0.3 to 0.6 V
26	sensor return (TPS : t1, CTS : t1, ATS : t1)	ignition on/engine running	0.25 V (max)
27	ATS signal : t2	ignition on/engine running	20° C: 2.5 to 3.0 V
			80° C 0.3 to 0.6 V
28	OS signal : t3	ignition on, OS multiplug disconnected	0.4 to 0.5 V
		engine running, hot	200 to 1000 mV (switching)
		throttle fully-open	0.5 to 1.0 V
		deceleration (fuel cut-off)	0 to 0.5 V
		switching frequency	1 sec intervals (approx.)
29	TPS signal : t4	ignition on/engine running:	
		throttle closed	0 V
		throttle fully open	4.2 V (approx.)
30	CAS return : t1	engine running	0.25 V (max)
31	stepper motor : t3	ignition on/idle speed:	
		idle switch closed	0.25 V (max)
		idle switch open	nbv
32	A/C compressor : t2		data not available
33	stepper motor : t1	idle speed, active	0 to 5 V (switching)
34	–		

Pin	Connection	Test condition	Measurements
35	A/C compressor		data not available
36	–		
37	supply from main relay : t4	ignition on/engine running	nbv
38-55	–		

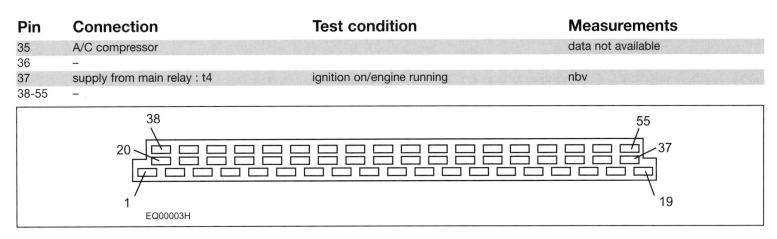

55 pin ECM multiplug, Bosch Mono-Motronic MA3.0

Pin Table – Bosch Mono-Motronic MA3.1

Pin	Connection	Test condition	Measurements
1	DIS ignition coil driver (cyls 1 and 4) : t1	engine cranking/running	200 V (min)
		dynamic volt drop	2.0 V (max)
2	earth	ignition on/engine running	0.25 V (max)
3	fuel pump relay driver (via inertia switch) : t10	ignition on	nbv
		engine cranking/running	1.25 V (max)
4	–		
5	CFSV driver : t1	ignition on	nbv
		engine running, above idle, operating temperature:	
		CFSV inactive	nbv
		CFSV active	0 to 12 V (switching)
		duty cycle	0 to 99%
6	tachometer		data not available
7	TPS signal : t2	ignition on/engine running:	
		throttle closed	2.0 V
		throttle fully open	5.0 V
8	–		
9	VSS signal	vehicle in motion	0 to 12 V (switching)
10	OS return : t4	engine running	0.25 V (max)
11	CAS signal : t2	engine cranking:	> 2.0 V AC (peak to peak)
		Idle:	> 11.0 V AC (peak to peak)
		cruise:	> 14.0 V AC (peak to peak)
12	TPS supply : t5	ignition on/engine running	5.0 V ± 0.1
13	SD connector		data not available
14	earth shield	ignition on/engine running	0.25 V (max)
15	stepper motor : t6	idle speed, active	0 to 5.0 V (switching)
16	SD connector		data not available
17	injector driver : t4	ignition on	nbv
		engine running:	
		idle speed, hot	1.5 ms
		3000 rpm	1.6 ms
		deceleration (cut-off)	0 ms
18	supply from battery : t30	ignition off/on/engine running	nbv
19	earth	ignition on/engine running	0.25 V (max)
20	DIS ignition coil driver (cyls 2 and 3) : t2	engine cranking/running	200 V (min)
		dynamic volt drop	2.0 V (max)
21	–		
22	SD warning lamp	engine running:	
		lamp off, no fault :	nbv
		lamp on, fault present:	1.25 V (max)
23	–		

Pin Table – Bosch Mono-Motronic MA3.1 (continued)

Pin	Connection	Test condition	Measurements
24	HES signal (TVPS) : t2	engine cranking/running	0 to 5.0 V (switching)
25	CTS signal : t2	ignition on/engine running	20° C: 2.5 V (approx.)
			80° C: 0.7 V (approx.)
26	sensor return (TPS : t1, CTS : t1, ATS : t1)	ignition on/engine running	0.25 V (max)
27	ATS signal : t2	ignition on/engine running	20° C: 2.5 V (approx.)
			80° C: 0.7 V (approx.)
28	OS signal : t3	ignition on, OS multiplug disconnected	0.4 to 0.5 V
		engine running, hot	200 to 1000 mV (switching)
		throttle fully-open	0.5 to 1.0 V
		deceleration (fuel cut-off)	0 to 0.5 V
		switching frequency	1 sec intervals (approx.)
29	TPS signal : t4	ignition on/engine running:	
		throttle closed	0 V
		throttle fully open	4.2 V
30	CAS return : t1	ignition on/engine running	0.25 V (max)
31	idle switch : t5	ignition on/engine running:	
		idle switch closed	0.25 V (max)
		idle switch open	nbv
32	A/C		data not available
33	stepper motor : t1	idle speed, active	0 to 5.0 V (switching)
34	–		
35	A/C		data not available
36	manifold heater relay driver : t2	ignition on	nbv
		engine running, cold	1.25 V (max)
		engine running, hot	nbv
37	supply from main relay : t5	ignition on/engine running	nbv
38 -55	–		

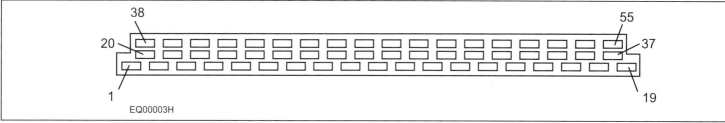

55 pin ECM multiplug, Bosch Mono-Motronic MA3.1

Pin Table – Bosch Motronic 1.3

Pin	Connection	Test condition	Measurements
1	amplifier control signal : t5&t6, ECM : t20	engine cranking/running	0 to nbv (switching)
2	–		
3	fuel pump relay driver : t2	ignition on	nbv
		engine cranking/running	1.25 V (max)
4	ISCV driver : t1	engine running:	
		cold	6.0 to 6.5 V
		hot	7.0 to 9.0 V
5	CFSV driver t1 (cat models only)	ignition on	nbv
		engine running, above idle, operating temperature:	
		CFSV inactive	nbv
		CFSV active	0 to 12 V (switching)
		duty cycle	0 to 99%
6	–		

Pin	Connection	Test condition	Measurements
7	AFS signal : t2	ignition on	0.20 to 0.30 V
		Idle	0.75 to 1.50 V
		2000 rpm	2.00 to 2.50 V
		3000 rpm	2.00 to 3.50 V
		snap accelerate	3.00 to 4.50 V
8	–		
9	–		
10	OS return : t4 (cat models only)	engine running	0.25 V (max)
11	Knock sensor	engine cranking/running	15 kHz, 1.0 V AC
12	AFS supply : t3	engine cranking/running	5.0 V ± 0.1
13	SD connector		data not available
14	earth	ignition on/engine running	0.25 V (max)
15	SD warning lamp	ignition on/engine running:	
		no faults present	nbv
		faults present, lamp on	1.25 V (max)
16	injector driver (cyls 1 & 2) : t1	engine cranking, cold	11.0 to 12.0 ms
		engine running, cold	3.0 to 3.5 ms
		engine running, hot	2.5 to 3.0 ms
		snap acceleration	> 6.0 ms
17	injector driver (cyls 3 & 4) : t1	engine cranking, cold	11.0 to 12.0 ms
		engine running, cold	3.0 to 3.5 ms
		engine running, hot	2.5 to 3.0 ms
		snap acceleration	> 6.0 ms
18	supply from battery : t30	ignition on/off/running	nbv
19	earth	ignition on/engine running	0.25 V (max)
20	amplifier control signal : t5&t6, ECM : t1	engine cranking/running	0 to nbv (switching)
21	–		
22	–		
23	AC magnetic clutch relay		data not available
24	earth	ignition on/engine running	0.25 V (max)
25	–		
26	AFS return : t4	ignition on/engine running	0.25 V (max)
27	supply from Ignition switch : t15	ignition on/engine running	nbv
28	OS signal : t3	ignition on, OS multiplug disconnected	0.4 to 0.5 V
		engine running	200 to 1000 mV (switching)
		throttle fully open	0.5 to 1.0 V
		fuel cut off	0 to 0.5 V
		switching frequency	15 sec intervals (approx.)
29	–		
30	sensor return (CTS : t1, TS : t2, KS : t1)	ignition on/engine running	0.25 V (max)
31-35	–		
36	main relay driver : t2	ignition off	nbv
		ignition on/engine running	1.25 V (max)
37	supply from main relay : t5	ignition on/engine running	nbv
38-39	–		
40	coolant fan relay		data not available
41	coolant fan relay		data not available
42	–		
43	CO pot signal (AFS : t1), non-cat only	ignition on/engine running	2.45 V ± 0.5
44	ATS signal (AFS : t5)	ignition on/engine running	20° C: 3.30 to 3.75 V
			80° C: 1.25 to 1.50 V
45	CTS signal : t2	engine cranking/running	20° C: 3.50 to 3.75 V
			80° C: 1.0 to 1.30 V
46	–		
47	CAS signal : t3	engine cranking:	> 4.0 V AC (peak to peak)
		idle:	> 8.0 V AC (peak to peak)
		cruise:	> 14.0 V AC (peak to peak)
48	CAS return : t2	engine cranking/running	0.25 V (max)
49-51	–		

Pin Table – Bosch Motronic 1.3 (continued)

Pin	Connection	Test condition	Measurements
52	TS, idle contact : t1	ignition on/engine running:	
		throttle closed	0 V
		throttle part/fully open	5.0 V ± 0.1
53	TS, full load contact : t3	throttle closed/part open	5.0 V ± 0.1
		throttle fully open	0 V
54	–		
55	SD connector		data not available

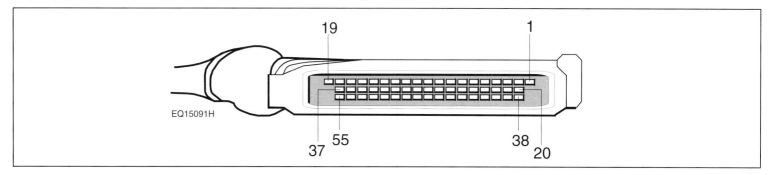

EQ15091H

55 pin ECM multiplug, Bosch Motronic 1.3

Pin Table – Bosch Motronic MP3.1

Pin	Connection	Test condition	Measurements
1	amplifier control signal (coil 1) : t2	engine cranking/running	0 to nbv (switching)
2	amplifier control signal (coil 2) : t7	engine cranking/running	0 to nbv (switching)
3	TPS signal : t3	ignition on/engine running:	
		throttle closed	0.5 to 0.6 V
		throttle fully open	4.8 V (approx)
4	SD warning lamp/SD connector : t2	ignition on, lamp check	1.25 V (max)
		engine running:	
		no major faults	nbv
		major faults, lamp on	1.25 V (max)
5	earth	ignition on/engine running	0.25 V (max)
6	sensor return (ATS : t1, CTS : t1, TPS : t2)	ignition on/engine running	0.25 V (max)
7	–		
8	OS signal return : t4	engine running	0.25 V (max)
9	sensor supply (TPS : t1)	ignition on/engine running	5.0 V ± 0.1
10-11	–		
12	SD connector : t1		data not available
13	CTS signal : t2	ignition on/engine running	20° C: 3.00 to 3.50 V
			80° C: 1.00 to 1.30 V
14	injectors driver : t1	ignition on	nbv
		engine cranking, cold	> 3.5 ms
		engine running, cold	> 3.5 ms
		engine cranking, hot	> 2.4 ms
		engine running, hot	2.4 to 2.6 ms
		acceleration	> 6.0 ms
15	–		
16	earth	ignition on/engine running	0.25 V (max)
17	SD warning lamp/SD connector : t2	ignition on, lamp check	1.25 V (max)
		engine running:	
		no major faults	nbv
		major faults, lamp on	1.25 V (max)
18	supply from battery : t30	ignition on/off/engine running	nbv
19	–		

Pin	Connection	Test condition	Measurements
20	fuel pump relay driver : t2	ignition on	nbv
		engine cranking/running	1.25 V (max)
21	tachometer		data not available
22	ATS signal : t2	ignition on/engine running	20° C: 3.50 to 3.75 V
			80° C: 1.00 to 1.30 V
23	CAS return : t1	engine running	0.25 V (max)
24	OS signal : t3	ignition on, OS multiplug disconnected	0.4 to 0.5 V
		engine running, hot	200 to 1000 mV
		throttle fully-open	0.5 to 1.0 V
		deceleration (fuel cut-off)	0 V to 0.5 V
		switching frequency	1 sec intervals (approx.)
25	CAS signal : t2	engine cranking:	> 2.0 AC V (peak to peak)
		idle:	> 11.0 AC V (peak to peak)
		cruise:	> 14.0 AC V (peak to peak)
26-28	–		
29	A/C switch		data not available
30	–		
31	CFSV driver (no 1) : t1	ignition on	nbv
		engine running, above idle, operating temperature:	
		CFSV inactive	nbv
		CFSV active	0 to 12 V (switching)
		duty cycle	0 to 99%
32	A/C compressor supply relay		data not available
33	ISCV signal : t5	ignition on	nbv
		engine running:	
		duty cycle	30 to 40%
34	ISCV signal : t3	ignition on	nbv
		engine running:	
		duty cycle	30 to 40%
35	supply from main relay : t5	ignition on/engine running	nbv

EQ41094H

35 pin ECM multi-plug, Bosch Motronic 3.1

Pin Table – Bosch Motronic 3.2 (turbo)

Pin	Connection	Test condition	Measurements
1	amplifier control signal : t2	engine cranking/running	0 to 5 V (switching)
2	SD warning lamp, SD connector : tB4/C3	ignition on/engine running:	
		no major faults	nbv
		major faults	0.25 V (max)
3	fuel pump relay driver : t10, via inertia switch : t1 (where fitted)	ignition on	nbv
		engine cranking/running	1.25 V (max)
4	ISCV signal : t3	idle speed, active	0 to 5.0 V (switching)
		duty cycle	69%

Pin Table – Bosch Motronic 3.2 (turbo) (continued)

Pin	Connection	Test condition	Measurements
5	CFSV driver : t1	ignition on	nbv
		engine running, above idle, operating temperature:	
		CFSV inactive	nbv
		CFSV active	0 to 12 V (switching)
		duty cycle	0 to 99%
6	Turbo Boost Control Valve driver : t1	engine running:	
		TBCV inactive	nbv
		TBCV active	0 to 12 V (switching)
		duty cycle	0 to 99%
7-8	–		
9	VSS signal : t1	vehicle in motion	0 to 12 V (switching)
10	OS return : t4	ignition on/engine running	0.25 V (max)
11	KS signal : t2	engine running, KS active	1.0 V AC (approx.)
12	TPS supply : t1	ignition on/engine running	5.0 V ± 0.1
13	SD connector : tC2		data not available
14	earth	ignition on/engine running	0.25 V (max)
15	–		
16	injector driver (cylinder 3) : t1	ignition on	nbv
		engine cranking, cold	11.0 to 12.0 ms
		engine running, cold	> 4.5 ms
		engine cranking, hot	> 3.9 ms
		engine running, hot	3.26 ms
		snap acceleration	> 12.0 ms
17	injector driver (cylinder 1) : t1	ignition on	nbv
		engine cranking, cold	11.0 to 12.0 ms
		engine running, cold	> 4.5 ms
		engine cranking, hot	> 3.9 ms
		engine running, hot	3.26 ms
		snap acceleration	> 12.0 ms
18	supply from battery : t30	ignition off/on/engine running	nbv
19	earth	ignition on/engine running	0.25 V (max)
20	amplifier control signal : t7	engine cranking/running	0 to 5 V (switching)
21			
22	ISCV signal : t1	idle speed, active	0 to 5.0 V (switching)
		duty cycle	31%
23	A/C compressor cut-off : t2		data not available
24	earth	ignition on/engine running	0.25 V (max)
25	–		
26	sensor return (ATS : t1, CTS : t1, TPS : t2)	ignition on/engine running	0.25 V (max)
27	supply from ignition switch : t15	ignition on/engine running	nbv
28	OS signal : t3	ignition on, OS multiplug disconnected	0.4 to 0.5 V
		engine running, hot	200 to 1000 mV (switching)
		throttle fully-open	0.5 to 1.0 V
		deceleration (fuel cut-off)	0 to 0.5 V
		switching frequency	1 sec intervals (approx.)
29	–		
30	KS return : t1	engine running, KS active	0.25 V (max)
31	–		
32	instrument panel		data not available
33	–		
34	injector driver (cylinder 2) : t1	ignition on	nbv
		engine cranking, cold	11.0 to 12.0 ms
		engine running, cold	> 4.5 ms
		engine cranking, hot	> 3.9 ms
		engine running, hot	3.26 ms
		snap acceleration	> 12.0 ms

Pin	Connection	Test condition	Measurements
35	injector driver (cylinder 4) : t1	ignition on	nbv
		engine cranking, cold	11.0 to 12.0 ms
		engine running, cold	> 4.5 ms
		engine cranking, hot	> 3.9 ms
		engine running, hot	3.26 ms
		snap acceleration	> 12.0 ms
36	main relay driver : t7	ignition off	nbv
		ignition on/engine running	1.25 V (max)
37	supply from main relay : t13	ignition on/engine running	nbv
38-39	–		
40	A/C		data not available
41	A/C		data not available
42	P/N switch		data not available
43	tachometer		data not available
44	ATS signal : t2	ignition on/engine running	20° C: 3.0 to 3.5 V
			50° C: 2.5 V
45	CTS signal : t2	ignition on/engine running	20° C: 3.0 to 3.5 V
			80° C: 1.0 to 1.3 V
46	–		
47	A/T		data not available
48	CAS signal : t2	engine cranking:	> 2.0 V AC (peak to peak)
		idle:	> 11.0 V AC (peak to peak)
		cruise:	> 14.0 V AC (peak to peak)
49	CAS return : t1	ignition on/engine running	0.25 V (max)
50	immobiliser : t3 (if fitted)		data not available
51-52	–		
53	TPS signal : t3	ignition on/engine running:	
		throttle closed	0.5 V ± 0.1
		throttle fully open	4.5 V (min)
54	earth	ignition on/engine running	0.25 V (max)
55	SD connector : t1		data not available

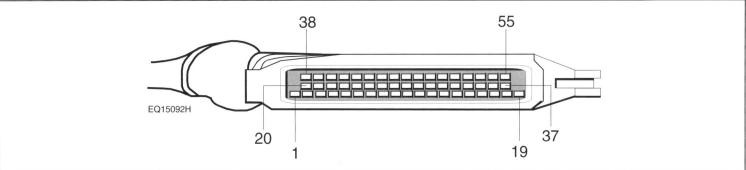

55 pin ECM multiplug, Bosch Motronic 3.2

Pin Table – Bosch Motronic 4.1

Pin	Connection	Test condition	Measurements
1	amplifier control signal : t5&6	engine cranking/running	0 to nbv (switching)
2	TS, idle contact : t2	ignition on/engine running:	
		throttle closed	0 V
		throttle part/fully open	5.0 V ± 0.1
3	TS, full load contact : t3	ignition on/engine running:	
		throttle closed/part open	5.0 V ± 0.1
		throttle fully open	0 V
4	SD connector : t2		data not available
5	earth	ignition on/engine running	0.25 V (max)
6	AFS return : t4	ignition on/engine running	0.25 V (max)

Pin Table – Bosch Motronic 4.1 (continued)

Pin	Connection	Test condition	Measurements
7	AFS signal : t2	ignition on	0.20 to 0.30 V
		idle	0.75 to 1.50 V
		2000 rpm	1.75 to 2.25 V
		3000 rpm	2.00 to 2. 50 V
		snap accelerate	3.00 to 4.50 V
8	–		
9	AFS supply : t3	ignition on/engine running	5.0 V ± 0.1
10-11	–		
12	SD connector : t1		data not available
13	CTS signal : t2	ignition on/engine running	20° C: 3.00 to 3.50 V
			80° C: 1.25 to 1.50 V
14	injectors driver : t1	ignition on	nbv
		engine running, cold	3.0 to 3.5 ms
		engine running, hot	2.0 to 2.5 ms
		snap acceleration	6.0 ms
15	–		
16	earth	ignition on/engine running	0.25 V (max)
17	SD warning lamp/diagnostic connector : t2	ignition on, lamp check	1.25 V (max)
		engine running:	
		no faults present	nbv
		lamp on, faults present	1.25 V (max)
18	supply from battery : t30	ignition off/on/engine running	nbv
19	earth	ignition on/engine running	0.25 V (max)
20	fuel pump relay driver : t2 (t85)	ignition on	nbv
		engine cranking/running	1.25 V (max)
21	–		
22	ATS signal (AFS : t5)	ignition on/engine running	20° C: 3.00 to 3.50 V
23	CAS return : t2	engine running	0.25 V (max)
24	–		
25	CAS signal : t1	engine cranking:	> 4.0 V AC (peak to peak)
		Idle:	> 8.0 V AC (peak to peak)
		cruise:	> 14.0 V AC (peak to peak)
26-28	–		
29	air conditioning		data not available
30	CO pot (AFS : t1)	ignition on/engine running	2.45 V ± 0.5
31	–		
32	air conditioning		
33	ISCV driver : t1	ignition on	nbv
		engine running, idle speed:	
		frequency	100 to 110 Hz
		engine cold:	
		voltage	6.0 to 6.5 V
		duty cycle	56 to 58%
		engine hot:	
		voltage	7.0 to 9.0 V
		duty cycle, no load	40 to 44%
		duty cycle, under load	44 to 50%
34	–		
35	supply from relay : t5 (t87)	ignition on/engine running	nbv

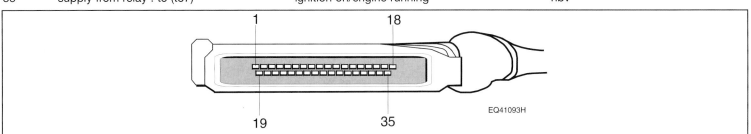

35 pin ECM multi-plug, Bosch Motronic 4.1

Pin Table – Bosch Motronic M5.1/5.1.1

Pin	Connection	Test condition	Measurements
1	DIS coil driver (cyls 1 and 4) : t1	engine cranking/running	200 V (min)
		dynamic volt drop	2.0 V (max)
2	earth	ignition on/engine running	0.25 V (max)
3	fuel pump relay driver : t10	ignition on	nbv
		engine cranking/running	1.25 V (max)
4	–		
5	CFSV driver : t1	ignition off/on	nbv
		engine running, above idle, operating temperature:	
		CFSV inactive	nbv
		CFSV active	0 to 12 V (switching)
		duty cycle	0 to 99%
6	tachometer (if fitted)		data not available
7	MAP signal : t3	ignition on	4.35 V
		engine running:	
		idle speed	1.5 V (approx.)
		WOT	4.35 V
8	–		
9	VSS signal : t3	vehicle in motion	0 to nbv (switching)
10	OS signal return : t4	engine running	0.25 V (max)
11	CAS return : t1	engine cranking/running	0.25 V (max)
12	sensor supply (MAP : t1, TPS : t1)	ignition on/engine running	5.0 V ± 0.5
13	SD connector : t2		data not available
14	earth	ignition on/engine running	0.25 V (max)
15	ISCV driver : t3	ignition on	nbv
		engine running	7.0 to 12.0 V
		duty cycle	30 to 40%
16	SD connector : t1		data not available
17	injectors driver : t1	ignition on/engine running	nbv
		engine cranking, cold	> 3.0 ms
		engine running, cold	3.0 ms
		engine cranking, hot	> 2.4 ms
		engine running, hot	2.0 ms
		snap acceleration	> 6.0 ms
18	supply from battery : t30 (via FI relay)	ignition off/on/engine running	nbv
19	earth	ignition on/engine running	0.25 V (max)
20	DIS coil driver (cyls 2 and 3) : t1	engine cranking/running	200 V (min)
		dynamic volt drop	2.0 V (max)
21	–		
22	SD warning lamp/diagnostic connector : t2	ignition on, lamp check	1.25 V (max)
		engine running:	
		no major faults	nbv
		major faults	1.25 V (max)
23	A/C relay driver : t2 (if fitted)		data not available
24	–		
25	CTS signal : t2	ignition on/engine running	20° C: 3.0 to 3.5 V
			80° C: 1.0 to 1.3 V
26	sensor return (ATS : t1, CTS : t1, MAP : t2, TPS : t2, VSS : t3)	ignition on/engine running	0.25 V (max)
27	ATS signal	ignition on/engine running	20°C: 3.0 to 3.5 V
28	OS signal : t3	ignition on, OS multiplug disconnected	0.4 to 0.5 V
		engine running, hot	200 to 1000 mV (switching)
		throttle fully-open	0.5 to 1.0 V
		deceleration (fuel cut-off)	0 V to 0.5 V
		switching frequency	1 sec intervals (approx.)
29	TPS signal : t3	ignition on/engine running:	
		throttle closed	0.3 V
		throttle fully open	5.0 V (approx.)

Pin Table – Bosch Motronic M5.1/5.1.1 (continued)

Pin	Connection	Test condition	Measurements
30	CAS signal : t2	engine cranking:	> 2.0 V AC (peak to peak)
		idle:	> 11.0 V AC (peak to peak)
		cruise:	> 14.0 V AC (peak to peak)
31	–		
32	A/C		data not available
33	ISCV driver : t1	ignition on/engine running	nbv
		duty cycle	30 to 40%
34	A/C		data not available
35-36	–		
37	supply from main relay : t4	ignition on/engine running	nbv
38-55	–		

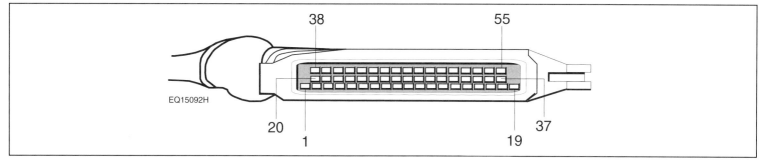

EQ15092H

55 pin ECM multiplug, Bosch Motronic M5.1/5.1.1

Pin Table – Bosch Motronic M5.2

Pin	Connection	Test condition	Measurements
1	ignition coil driver : t1 (cyls 1 & 4)	engine cranking/running	200 V (min)
		dynamic volt drop	2.0 V (max)
2	earth	ignition on/engine running	0.25 V (max)
3	fuel pump relay driver: t10	ignition on	nbv
		engine cranking/running	1.25 V (max)
4	–		
5	CFSV driver : t1	ignition on	nbv
		engine running, above idle, operating temperature:	
		CFSV inactive	nbv
		CFSV active	0 to nbv (switching)
		duty cycle	0 to 99%
6	SD connector : tB3, tachometer : t23 (if fitted)		data not available
7	MAP sensor signal : t1	ignition on	4.35 V (approx.)
		engine running, WOT	4.35 V (approx.)
		idle speed	1.5 V (approx.)
8	KS signal : t1	engine running, KS active	1.0 to 2.0 V AC (peak to peak)
9	VSS signal : t3	vehicle in motion	0 to nbv (switching)
10	OS signal return : t4	engine running	0.25 V (max)
11	CAS return : t2	engine cranking/running	0.25 V (max)
12	sensor supply (MAP : t3, TPS : t2)	ignition on/engine running	5.0 V ± 0.1
13	SD connector : tC2		data not available
14	earth	ignition on/engine running	0.25 V (max)
15	ISSM driver : t4	idle speed, active	0 to nbv (switching)
16	SD connector : tC1		data not available
17	fuel injectors driver : t1	ignition on	nbv
		engine cranking, cold	> 3.0 ms
		engine running, cold	> 3.0 ms
		engine running, hot	2.0 to 3.0 ms
		snap acceleration	> 6.0 ms
		deceleration	0 ms

Pin	Connection	Test condition	Measurements
18	supply from battery : t30	ignition off/on/engine running	nbv
19	earth	ignition on/engine running	0.25 V (max)
20	ignition coil driver : t2 (cyls 2 & 3)	engine cranking/running	200 V (min)
		dynamic volt drop	2.0 V (max)
21	ISSM driver : t3	idle speed, active	0 to nbv (switching)
22	SD warning lamp : t8	ignition on, lamp check	1.25 V (max)
		engine running:	
		no major faults, lamp on	nbv
		major faults	1.25 V (max)
23	A/C ECM : t20		data not available
24	ISSM driver : t2	idle speed, active	0 to nbv (switching)
25	CTS signal : t2	ignition on/engine running	20° C: 3.0 to 3.5 V
			80° C: 1.0 to 1.3 V
26	sensor return (ATS : t1, KS : t2 CTS : t1, MAP : t2, TPS : t1)	ignition on/engine running	0.25 V (max)
27	ATS signal : t2	ignition on/engine running	20° C: 3.0 to 3.5 V
28	OS signal : t3	ignition on, OS multiplug disconnected	0.4 to 0.5 V
		engine running, hot	200 to 1000 mV (switching)
		throttle fully open	0.50 to 1.0 V
		deceleration (fuel cut off)	0 to 0.50 V
		switching frequency	1 sec intervals (approx.)
29	TPS signal : t3	ignition on/engine running:	
		throttle closed	1.5 V (approx.)
		throttle fully open	4.35 V (approx.)
30	CAS signal : t1	engine cranking:	> 2.0 V AC (peak to peak)
		idle:	> 11.0 V AC (peak to peak)
		cruise:	> 14.0 V AC (peak to peak)
31	–		
32	A/C ECM : t21		data not available
33	ISSM driver : t1	idle speed, active	0 to nbv (switching)
34	supply from ignition switch : t15 via relay t2/3	ignition on/engine running	nbv
35	–		
36	main relay driver : t7	ignition off	nbv
		ignition on/engine running	1.25 V (max)
37	supply from main relay : t5	ignition on/engine running	nbv
38-55	–		

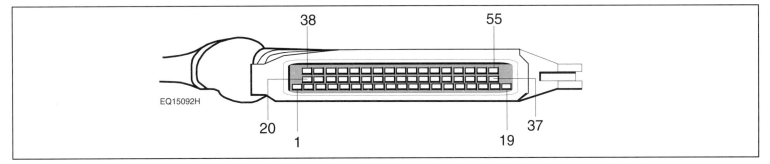

EQ15092H

55 pin ECM multiplug, Bosch Motronic M5.2

Pin Table – Bosch Motronic M7.0

Pin	Connection	Test condition	Measurements
1	ignition coil (cyls 1 & 5) : t1	engine cranking/running	200 V (min)
		dynamic volt drop	2.0 V (max)
2	earth	ignition on/engine running	0.25 V (max)
3	fuel pump relay driver : t10	ignition off	nbv
		ignition on	0 V briefly, then nbv
		engine cranking/running	1.25 V (max)

Pin Table – Bosch Motronic M7.0 (continued)

Pin	Connection	Test condition	Measurements
4	ISCV signal : t3	engine running	7.0 to 12.0 V
		duty cycle	30 to 40%
5	CFSV driver : t1	engine running:	
		CFSV inactive	nbv
		CFSV active	0 to nbv (switching)
6	A/T		data not available
7	MAP sensor : t1	ignition on	4.35 V (approx)
		engine running:	
		WOT	4.35 V (approx)
		idle speed	1.5 V (approx)
8	–		
9	VSS signal : t3	vehicle in motion	0 to nbv (switching)
10	OS signal return : t4	engine running	0.25 V (max)
11	KS signal : t2	engine running, KS active	1.0 to 2.0 V AC (peak to peak)
12	sensor supply (MAP : t3, TPS : t2)	ignition on/engine running	5.0 V ± 0.1
13	SD connector : t2		data not available
14	earth	ignition on/engine running	0.25 V (max)
15	SD warning lamp : t8	engine running:	
		no faults present	nbv
		lamp on, faults present	0.25 V (max)
16	injector driver (cyls 3 & 4) : t1	engine running	3.0 to 3.5 ms
		snap acceleration	> 6.0 ms
17	injector driver (cyls 1 & 5) : t1	engine running	3.0 to 3.5 ms
		snap acceleration	> 6.0 ms
18	supply from battery : t30	ignition off/on/running	nbv
19	earth	ignition on/engine running	0.25 V (max)
20	ignition coil driver (cyl 2 & 6) : t2	ignition on	nbv
		engine cranking/running	200 V (min)
		dynamic volt drop	2.0 V (max)
21	ignition coil driver (cyls 3 & 4) : t3	ignition on	nbv
		engine cranking/running	200 V (min)
		dynamic volt drop	2.0 V (max)
22	ISCV driver : t1	engine running	7.0 to 12.0 V
		duty cycle	30 to 40%
23	A/C : t20		data not available
24	earth	ignition on/engine running	0.25 V (max)
25	–		
26	sensor return (ATS : t1, CTS : t1, MAP : t2, TPS : t1)	ignition on/engine running	0.25 V (max)
27	supply from ignition relay : t6	ignition on/engine running	nbv
28	OS signal : t3	ignition on, OS multiplug disconnected	0.4 to 0.5 V
		engine running	200 to 1000 mV (switching)
		throttle fully open	0.5 to 1.0 V
		deceleration (fuel cut off)	0 to 0.5 V
		switching frequency	1 sec intervals (approx)
29	–		
30	KS return : t1	engine running, KS active	0.25 V (max)
31	suspension control unit		data not available
32	trip computer		data not available
33-34	–		
35	injector driver (cyls 2 and 6) : t2	engine running	3.0 to 3.5 ms
		snap acceleration	> 6.0 ms
36	main relay driver : t7	ignition off	nbv
		ignition on	0 V
		engine cranking/running	1.25 V (max)
37	supply from main relay : t4	engine cranking/running	nbv
38-39	–		
40	A/C		data not available
41	–		

Pin	Connection	Test condition	Measurements
42	A/T		data not available
43	A/T		data not available
44	ATS signal : t2	ignition on/engine running	20° C: 3.0 to 3.5 V
45	CTS signal : t2	ignition on/engine running	20° C: 3.0 to 3.5 V
46	–		
47	P/N selector switch		data not available
48	CAS return : t2	engine cranking/running	0.25 V (max)
49	CAS signal : t1	engine cranking:	> 2.0 V AC (peak to peak)
		idle:	> 11.0 V AC (peak to peak)
		cruise:	> 14.0 V AC (peak to peak)
50	Anti-theft module		data not available
51	OS relay driver : t10	engine running:	
		OS relay inactive	nbv
		OS relay active	1.25 V (max)
52	–		
53	TPS signal : t3	ignition on/engine running:	
		closed	0.3 V
		fully open	5.0 V (approx)
54	PSPS signal : t1		data not available
55	SD connector : t1		data not available

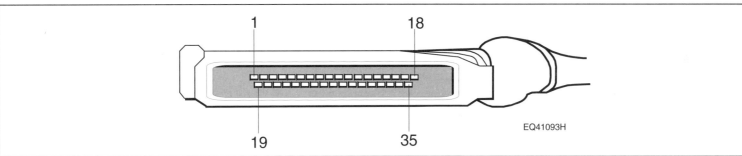

55 pin ECM multiplug, Bosch Motronic M7.0

Pin Table – Fenix 1B

Pin	Connection	Test condition	Measurements
1	earth	ignition on/engine running	0.25 V (max)
2	earth	ignition on/engine running	0.25 V (max)
3	–		
4	supply from battery : t30	ignition off/on/engine running	nbv
5	air conditioning compressor relay: t2		data not available
6	fuel pump relay driver : t2	ignition on	nbv
		engine cranking/running	1.25 V (max)
7	main relay driver : t2	ignition on	nbv briefly, then 1.25 V (max)
		engine running	1.25 V (max)
8	–		
9	TPS signal : tC	ignition on/engine running:	
		throttle closed	0.5 V (approx)
		throttle open	5.0 V (approx)
10	shield return	ignition on/engine running	0.25 V (max)
11	CAS signal : t2	engine cranking	> 4.0 V AC (peak to peak)
		Idle	> 8.0 V AC (peak to peak)
		cruise	> 14.0 V AC (peak to peak)
12	earth	ignition on/engine running	0.25 V (max)
13	–		
14	ATS signal : t2	ignition on/engine running	20° C: 2.0 V (approx)
15	CTS signal : t2	ignition on/engine running	20° C: 2.0 V (approx)
			50° C: 0.5 V (approx)
			80°C: 0.35 V (approx)

Pin Table – Fenix 1B (continued)

Pin	Connection	Test condition	Measurements
16	sensor supply (MAP sensor : tB, TPS : tA)	ignition on/engine running	5.0 V ± 0.1
17	sensor return (MAP sensor : tC, TPS : tB)	ignition on/engine running	0.25 V (max)
18	SD connector		data not available
19	supply from main relay : t5	ignition on/engine running	nbv
20	–		
21	injector driver : t1	engine running, hot	1.7 ms
		snap acceleration	6.0 ms
		deceleration	0 ms
		static voltage supply test: bridge fuel pump relay t87 and t30 with jumper wire	nbv
22	CFSV driver : t1	engine running	
		CFSV inactive	nbv
		CFSV active	0 to 12 V (switching)
		static voltage supply test: bridge fuel pump relay t87 and t30 with jumper wire	nbv
23	ISCV driver : t1	engine running, idle speed	2.0 to 12 V (switching)
		duty cycle	30 to 40%
		static voltage supply test: bridge fuel pump relay t87 and t30 with jumper wire	nbv
24	ISCV driver : t3	engine running, idle speed	2.0 to 12 V (switching)
		duty cycle	30 to 40%
		static voltage supply test: bridge fuel pump relay t87 and t30 with jumper wire	nbv
25-26	–		
27	amplifier control signal : t1B	engine cranking/running	0 to 5.0 V (switching)
28	CAS return : t1	engine cranking/running	0.25 V (max)
29	starter circuit	engine cranking	nbv
30	signal from A/C		data not available
31	–		
32	sensor return (ATS : t1, CTS : t1)	ignition on/engine running	0.25 V (max)
33	MAP sensor signal : tA	ignition on	5.0 V
		engine running, WOT	4.0 V
		250 mbar	3.4 V
		500 mbar	2.0 V
34	A/C		data not available
35	OS signal	engine running, hot	200 to 1000 mV (switching)
		throttle fully open	0.5 to 1.0 V
		deceleration (fuel cut off)	0 V to 0.5 V
		switching frequency	1 sec intervals (approx)

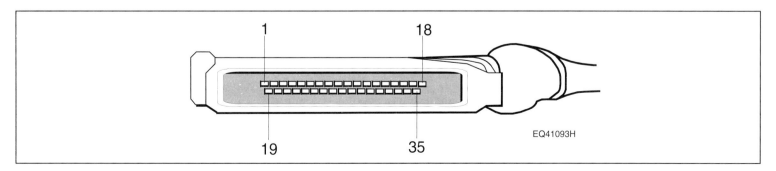

21.11 35 pin ECM multiplug, Fenix 1B

Pin Table – Fenix 3B

Pin	Connection	Test condition	Measurements
1	earth	ignition on/engine running	0.25 V (max)
2	earth	ignition on/engine running	0.25 V (max)
3	VSS amplifier	at 80 km/h (50 mph)	1.5 V
4	supply from battery: t30	ignition off/on/engine running	nbv
5	CFSV signal : t1	engine running:	
		CFSV inactive	nbv
		CFSV active	0 to 12 V (switching)
		duty cycle	0 to 99%
6	fuel pump relay driver : t2	ignition on	nbv
		engine cranking/running	1.25 V (max)
7	KS1 (front) signal : t1	engine running, KS active	1.0 V AC (peak to peak)
8	SD connector, coded anti-theft pad : t3		data not available
9	TPS signal : t2	ignition on/engine running:	
		throttle closed	0.5 ± 0.1 V
		throttle fully open	4.5 V (min)
10	TPS supply : t3	ignition on/engine running	5.0 V ± 0.5
11	CAS signal : t2	engine cranking	> 4.0 V AC (peak to peak)
		idle	> 8.0 V AC (peak to peak)
		cruise	> 14.0 V AC (peak to peak)
12	tachometer		data not available
13	OS relay driver : t2	engine running:	
		OS relay inactive	nbv
		OS relay active	1.25 V (max)
14	ATS signal : t2	ignition on/engine running	20° C: 2.0 V (approx)
15	CTS signal : t2	ignition on/engine running	20°C: 2.0 V (approx)
			50° C:: 0.5 V (approx)
			80°C: 0.35 V (approx)
16	MAP sensor supply : tC	ignition on/engine running	5.0 V ± 0.1
17	sensor return (TPS : t1, MAP : tA)	ignition on/engine running	0.25 V (max)
18	SD connector, coded anti-theft pad : t4, SD warning lamp : t1	ignition on, lamp on	1.25 V (max)
		engine running:	
		no faults present	nbv
		faults present, lamp on	1.25 V (max)
19	supply from main relay : t5	ignition on/engine running	nbv
20	injectors driver : t1	engine running, hot	2.0 to 3.0 ms
		snap acceleration	6.0 ms
		deceleration	0 ms
21	injectors driver : t1	engine running, hot	2.0 to 3.0 ms
		snap acceleration	6.0 ms
		deceleration	0 ms
22	–		
23	ISCV signal : t1	idle speed	2.0 to 12 V (switching)
		engine running:	
		duty cycle	30 to 70%
		static voltage supply test: bridge fuel pump t3 and t5 with jumper wire	nbv
24	ISCV signal : t3	idle speed	2.0 to 12 V (switching)
		engine running	
		duty cycle	30 to 70%
		static voltage supply test: bridge fuel pump t3 and t5 with jumper wire	nbv
25	A/T		data not available
26	trip computer/speedometer		data not available
27	amplifier control signal : t5	engine cranking/running	0 to 5.0 V (switching)
28	CAS return : t1	engine cranking/running	0.25 V (max)
29	cranking signal : t50	engine cranking	nbv

Pin Table – Fenix 3B (continued)

Pin	Connection	Test condition	Measurements
30	supply from ignition switch : t15	ignition on/engine running	nbv
31	KS2 (rear) signal : t1	engine running, KS active	1.0 V AC (peak to peak)
32	sensor return (KS : t2, ATS : t1, CTS : t1)	ignition on/engine running	0.25 V
33	MAP sensor signal : tB	ignition on	5.0 V
		engine running, WOT	5.0 V
		400 Pa	2.5 V
		600 Pa	1.25 V
34	–		
35	OS signal : t3	engine running	200 to 1000 mV (switching)
		throttle fully open	0.5 to 1.0 V
		deceleration (fuel cut off)	0 to 0.5 V
		switching frequency	1 sec intervals (approx)

1   18

19   35
EQ00001H

55 pin ECM multiplug, Fenix 3B

Pin Table – Fenix 4

Pin	Connection	Test condition	Measurements
1-2	–		
3	amplifier control signal : t3	engine cranking/running	0 to 5 V (switching)
4	OS B signal (rear) : t3	ignition on, OS multiplug disconnected	0.4 to 0.5 V
		engine running, hot	200 to 1000 mV (switching)
		throttle fully open	0.5 to 1.0 V
		deceleration (fuel cut off)	0 to 0.5 V
		switching frequency	1 sec intervals (approx)
5	–		
6	air conditioning		data not available
7	earth	ignition on/engine running	0.25 V (max)
8	cranking signal : t50	engine cranking	nbv
9	ATS signal : t2	ignition on/engine running	20°C: 2.0 V (approx)
10	trip computer		data not available
11	TPS signal : t2	ignition on/engine running:	
		throttle closed	0.5 ± 0.1 V
		throttle fully open	4.5 V (approx)
12	camshaft sensor (inductive) signal : t2	idle speed	3.0 V AC (peak to peak)
13	tachometer		data not available
14	earth	ignition on/engine running	0.25 V (max)
15	KS return : t2	ignition on/engine running	0.25 V (max)
16	CAS signal : t1	engine cranking:	> 2.5 V AC (peak to peak)
		idle speed	> 11.0 V AC (peak to peak)
		cruise	> 14.0 V AC (peak to peak)
17	KS B signal (rear) : t1	idle speed, active	5.0 V
		> 4000 rpm	variable
18	supply from battery : t30	ignition off/on/engine running	nbv
19	–		
20	injector driver (cylinder 2) : t1	engine running, hot	4.0 to 5.0 ms
		snap acceleration	> 6.0 ms
21	injector driver (cylinder 5) : t1	engine running, hot	4.0 to 5.0 ms
		snap acceleration	> 6.0 ms
22	VSS amplifier	vehicle in motion	0 to 12.0 V (switching)

Pin	Connection	Test condition	Measurements
23	OS A signal (front) : t3	ignition on, OS multiplug disconnected	0.4 to 0.5 V
		engine running, hot	200 to 1000 mV (switching)
		throttle fully open	0.5 to 1.0 V
		deceleration (fuel cut off)	0 to 0.5 V
		switching frequency	1 sec intervals (approx)
24	–		
25	park/neutral switch		data not available
26	–		
27	CTS signal : t2	ignition on/engine running	20° C: 2.0 V (approx)
			50° C: 0.5 V (approx)
			80° C: 0.35 V (approx)
28	SD connector : t1		data not available
29	SD connector : t2		data not available
30	MAP sensor supply : tB	ignition on/engine running	5.0 V ± 0.1
31	camshaft sensor (inductive) return : t1	ignition on/engine running	0.25 V (max)
32	MAP sensor signal : tC	ignition on	5.0 V
		engine running, WOT	5.0 V
		400 Pa	2.5 V
		600 Pa	1.25 V
33	TPS supply : t3	ignition on/engine running	5.0 V ± 0.1
34	sensor return (ATS : t1, CTS : t1, TPS : t1, MAP sensor : tA)	ignition on/engine running	0.25 V (max)
35	CAS return : t2	ignition on/engine running	0.25 V (max)
36	KS A signal (front) : t1	idle speed, active	5.0 V
		> 4000 rpm	variable
37	supply from main relay : t5	ignition on/engine running	nbv
38	injector driver (cylinder 4) : t1	engine running, hot	4.0 to 5.0 ms
		snap acceleration	> 6.0 ms
39	earth	ignition on/engine running	0.25 V (max)
40	CFSV driver : t1	engine running, hot, above idle:	
		CFSV inactive	nbv
		CFSV active	0 to 12 V (switching)
		duty cycle	0 to 99%
41	SD warning lamp : t1	engine running:	
		no faults present	nbv
		faults present	1.25 V (max)
42	injector driver (cylinder 3) : t1	engine running, hot	4.0 to 5.0 ms
		snap acceleration	> 6.0 ms
43	injector driver (cylinder 1) : t1	engine running, hot	4.0 to 5.0 ms
		snap acceleration	> 6.0 ms
44	injector driver (cylinder 6) : t1	engine running, hot	4.0 to 5.0 ms
		snap acceleration	> 6.0 ms
45	ISCV driver : t3	engine running, idle speed:	
		voltage	2.0 to 12 V (switching)
		duty cycle	30 to 40%
		static voltage supply test: bridge fuel pump t3 and t5 with jumper wire	nbv
46	ISCV driver : t1	engine running, idle speed:	
		voltage	2.0 to 12 V (switching)
		duty cycle	30 to 40%
		static voltage supply test bridge fuel pump t3 and t5 with jumper wire	nbv
47	–		
48	supply from fuel pump relay : t4	engine cranking/running	nbv
49	supply from fuel pump relay : t4	engine cranking/running	nbv
50-51	–		

Pin Table – Fenix 4 (continued)

Pin	Connection	Test condition	Measurements
52	induction changeover valve (short) driver : t1	engine running, under load:	
		idle to 5000 rpm	nbv
		above 5000 rpm	1.25 V (max)
		static voltage supply test bridge fuel pump t3 and t5 with jumper wire	nbv
53	OS heater relay driver : t2	engine running	
		OS heater inactive	nbv
		OS heater active	1.25 V (max)
54	fuel pump relay driver : t2	ignition on	nbv
		engine cranking/running	1.25 V (max)
55	induction changeover valve (long) driver : t1	engine running, under load:	
		idle to 4000 rpm	1.25 V (max)
		above 4000 rpm	nbv
		static voltage supply test bridge fuel pump t3 and t5 with jumper wire	nbv

EQ00001H

55 pin ECM multiplug, Fenix 4

Pin Table – Magneti-Marelli G5/G6 SPi

Pin	Connection	Test condition	Measurements
1	DIS coil driver (cyls 1 & 4) : t1	engine cranking/running	200 V (min)
		dynamic volt drop	2.0 V (max)
2	stepper motor : tC	idle speed, active	0 to nbv (switching)
3	stepper motor : tA	idle speed, active	0 to nbv (switching)
4	SD connector : t2		data not available
5	CAS signal : t2	engine cranking:	> 2.0 V AC (peak to peak)
		idle	> 11.0 V AC (peak to peak)
		3000 rpm	> 14.0 V AC (peak to peak)
6	tachometer		data not available
7	SD warning lamp	ignition on, lamp check	1.25 V (max)
		engine running:	
		no faults present	nbv
		faults present, lamp on	1.25 V (max)
8	–		
9	A/C		data not available
10	MAP sensor signal : t3	ignition on	3.3 to 3.9 V
		engine running, WOT	3.3 to 3.9 V
		idle speed	1.5 V (approx)
11	TPS signal : t3	ignition on/engine running:	
		throttle closed	0.3 to 0.6 V
		throttle fully open	5.0 V (approx)
12	park/neutral switch (AT)		data not available
13	OS signal earth : t4	engine running	0.25 V (max)
14	ATS signal : t2	ignition on/engine running	20° C: 3.30 to 3.75 V
			80° C: 1.25 to 1.50 V
15	MAP sensor supply : t2	ignition on/engine running	5.0 V ± 0.1
16	earth	ignition on/engine running	0.25 V (max)
17	earth	ignition on/engine running	0.25 V (max)

Pin	Connection	Test condition	Measurements
18	injector driver : t1	engine running, cold	> 2.0 ms
		engine running, hot	1.3 to 1.5 ms
		snap acceleration	> 2.0 ms
19	DIS coil driver (cyls 2 & 3) : t1	engine cranking/running	200 V (min)
		dynamic volt drop	2.0 V (max)
20	stepper motor : tB	idle speed, active	0 to nbv (switching)
21	stepper motor : tD	idle speed, active	0 to nbv (switching)
22	CFSV driver : t1	engine running:	
		CFSV inactive	nbv
		CFSV active	0 to 12 V (switching)
		duty cycle	0 to 99%
23	–		
24	CAS return : t1	engine cranking/running	0.25 V (max)
25	FP relay driver : t2	ignition on	nbv
		engine cranking/running	1.25 V (max)
26	A/C cut off relay driver : t2		data not available
27	A/C		data not available
28	diagnostic connector : t1		data not available
29	supply from battery : t30	ignition off/on/engine running	nbv
30	OS signal : t3	ignition on, OS multiplug disconnected	0.4 to 0.5 V
		engine running, hot	200 to 1000 mV (switching)
		throttle fully-open	0.5 to 1.0 V
		deceleration (fuel cut-off)	0 to 0.5 V
		switching frequency	1 sec intervals (approx)
31	sensor return (ATS: t1, CTS: t1, MAP: t1, TPS: t1)	ignition on/engine running	0.25 V (max)
32	–		
33	TPS supply : t2	ignition on/engine running	5.0 V ± 0.1
34	CTS signal : t2	ignition on/engine running	20° C: 3.30 to 3.75 V
			80° C: 1.00 to 1.30 V
35	supply from main relay : t5	ignition on/engine running	nbv

EQ41094H

21.14 35 pin ECM multiplug, Magneti-Marelli G5/G6 SPi

Pin Table – Magneti-Marelli 8P

Pin	Connection	Test condition	Measurements
1	ignition coil driver : t1	ignition on	nbv briefly, then 0 V
		engine cranking/running	200 V (min)
		dynamic volt drop	2.0 V (max)
2	stepper motor : tB	idle speed, active	0 to nbv (switching)
3	stepper motor : tA	idle speed, active	0 to nbv (switching)
4	main relay driver : t10	ignition off	nbv
		ignition on/engine running	1.25 V (max)
5	tachometer		data not available
6	SD warning lamp : t1	ignition on, lamp check	1.25 V (max)
		engine running:	
		faults present	nbv
		no faults present	0.25 V (max)
7-8	–		
9	A/C compressor cut-off relay : t3	ignition on	nbv
10	diagnostic connector : t1		data not available

Pin Table – Magneti-Marelli 8P (continued)

Pin	Connection	Test condition	Measurements
11	CAS return : t1	engine cranking/running	0.25 V
12	OS signal return : t4	engine running	0.25 V (max)
13	CTS signal : t2	ignition on/engine running	20° C: 3.00 to 3.75 V
			80° C: 1.00 to 1.30 V
14	sensor supply (MAP : t2, TPS: t2)	ignition on/engine running	5.0 V ± 0.1
15	SD connector : t2	ignition on	
16	sensor return (TPS : t1, MAP : t1 ATS : t1, KS : t1)	ignition on/engine running	0.25 V (max)
17	earth	ignition on/engine running	0.25 V (max)
18	injector driver : t1	ignition on	nbv briefly, then 0 V
		engine running, cold	2.5 to 3.0 ms
		engine running, hot	2.1 to 2.5 ms
		snap acceleration	> 6.0 ms
19	ignition coil driver : t2	ignition on	nbv briefly, then 0 V
		engine cranking/running	200 V (min)
		dynamic volt drop	2.0 V (max)
20	stepper motor : tC	idle speed, active	0 to nbv (switching)
21	stepper motor : tD	idle speed, active	0 to nbv (switching)
22	CFSV driver : t1	ignition on	nbv briefly, then 0 V
		engine running:	
		CFSV inactive	nbv
		CFSV active	0 to nbv (switching)
		duty cycle	0 to 99%
23	fuel pump relay driver : t7	ignition on	nbv
		engine cranking/running	1.25 V (max)
24	A/C cut off relay driver : t2		data not available
25	–		
26	park neutral switch		data not available
27	VSS signal : t3	vehicle in motion	0 to 12 V (switching)
28	CAS signal : t2	engine cranking:	> 2.0 V AC (peak to peak)
		idle:	> 11.0 V AC (peak to peak)
		cruise:	> 14.0 V AC (peak to peak)
29	OS signal : t3	ignition on, OS multiplug disconnected	0.4 to 0.5 V
		engine running:	200 to 1000 mV (switching)
		throttle fully open	0.5 to 1.0 V
		deceleration (fuel cut off)	0 to 0.5 V
		switching frequency	1 sec intervals (approx)
30	TPS signal : t3	ignition on/engine running:	
		throttle closed	0.3 to 0.6 V
		throttle fully open	5.0 V (approx)
31	ATS signal : t2	ignition on/engine running	20° C: 3.30 to 3.75 V
			80° C: 1.25 to 1.50 V
32	MAP sensor signal : t3	ignition on	3.3 to 3.9 V
		engine running:	
		idle speed	1.5 V (approx)
		WOT	3.3 to 3.9 V
33	KS signal : t3	engine running, KS active	1.0 V AC (peak to peak)
34	earth	ignition on/engine running	0.25 V (max)
35	supply from main relay : t1	ignition on/engine running	nbv

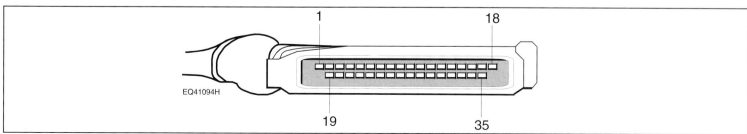

35 pin ECM multiplug, Magneti-Marelli 8P

Pin Table – Magneti-Marelli 1AP40

Pin	Connection	Test condition	Measurements
1	injector driver (cyls 2 and 3) : t1	engine running, cold	3.0 to 3.5 ms
		engine running, hot	2.5 to 3.0 ms
		snap acceleration	> 6.0 ms
		deceleration	0 ms
2	injector driver (cyls 1 and 4) : t1	engine running, cold	3.0 to 3.5 ms
		engine running, hot	2.5 to 3.0 ms
		snap acceleration	> 6.0 ms
		deceleration	0 ms
3	stepper motor : tD	idle speed, active	0 to 5.0 V (switching)
4	OS return : t4	ignition on/engine running	0.25 V (max)
5	–		
6	–		
7	fuel pump relay driver : t7 (via inertia switch : t1)	ignition on	nbv
		engine cranking/running	1.25 V (max)
8	–		
9	SD connector		data not available
10-11	–		
12	SD connector		data not available
13	ignition supply : t15 (via main/pump relay : t12)	ignition on/engine running	nbv
14	–		
15	KS signal : t1	idle speed	5.0 V
		> 4000 rpm	variable voltage
16	sensor supply (TPS : tB, KS : t2)	ignition on/engine running	5.0 V ± 0.1
17	sensor return (MAP : t2, ATS : t1)	ignition on/engine running	0.25 V (max)
18	shield return	ignition on/engine running	0.25 V (max)
19	shield return	ignition on/engine running	0.25 V (max)
20	stepper motor : tC	idle speed, active	0 to 5.0 V (switching)
21	stepper motor : tB	idle speed, active	0 to 5.0 V (switching)
22	OS signal : t3	ignition on, OS multiplug disconnected	0.4 to 0.5 V
		engine running, hot	200 to 1000 mV (switching)
		throttle fully open	0.5 to 1.0 V
		deceleration (fuel cut-off)	0 to 0.5 V
		switching frequency	1 sec intervals (approx.)
23	TPS signal : tC	ignition on/engine running:	
		throttle closed	0.6 to 0.8 V
		throttle fully open	> 4.50 V
24	CFSV driver : t1	ignition on	nbv
		engine running, above idle, operating temperature:	
		CFSV inactive	nbv
		CFSV active	0 to 12 V (switching)
		duty cycle	0 to 99%
25	–		
26	A/C		data not available
27	–		
28	VSS signal : t3	vehicle in motion	0 to 12 V (switching)
29	ATS signal : t2	ignition on/engine running	20° C: 2.5 V (approx.)
			80° C: 0.7 V (approx.)
30	CAS signal : t2	engine cranking:	> 2.0 V AC (peak to peak)
		idle:	> 11.0 V AC (peak to peak)
		cruise:	> 14.0 V AC (peak to peak)
31	SD connector		data not available
32-33	–		
34	MAP sensor supply : t3	ignition on/engine running	5.0 V ± 0.1
35	supply from main relay : t9	ignition on/engine running	nbv
36	earth	ignition on/engine running	0.25 V (max)

Pin Table – Magneti-Marelli 1AP40 (continued)

Pin	Connection	Test condition	Measurements
37	DIS coil driver (cyl 2 and 3) : t2	engine cranking/running	200 V (min)
		dynamic volt drop	2.0 V (max)
38-39	–		
40	stepper motor : tA	idle speed, active	0 to 5.0 V (switching)
41	MAP sensor signal : t1	ignition on	5.0 V
		engine running:	
		WOT	4.5 V
		idle speed	1.25 to 1.30 V
42	tachometer		data not available
43-46	–		
47	CTS signal : t2	ignition on/engine running	20° C: 1.6 to 1.8 V (approx.)
			80° C: 0.4 to 0.6 V (approx.)
48	–		
49	CAS return : t1	ignition on/engine running	0.25 V (max)
50	A/C		data not available
51	–		
52	main relay driver : t10	ignition off	nbv
		ignition on/engine running	1.25 V (max)
53	sensor return (TPS : tA, CTS : t1)	ignition on/engine running	0.25 V (max)
54	earth	ignition on/engine running	0.25 V (max)
55	DIS coil driver (cyls 1 and 4) : t1	engine cranking/running	200 V (min)
		dynamic volt drop	2.0 V (max)

55 pin ECM multiplug, Magneti-Marelli 1AP40

Wiring Diagrams

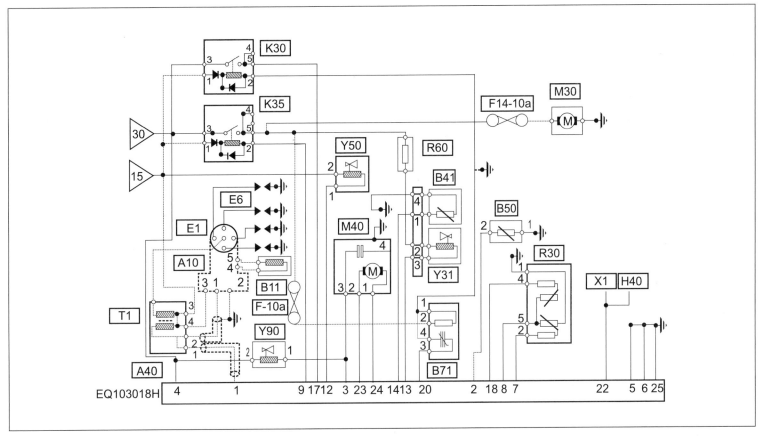

EQ103018H

System wiring diagram, Bosch Mono-Jetronic

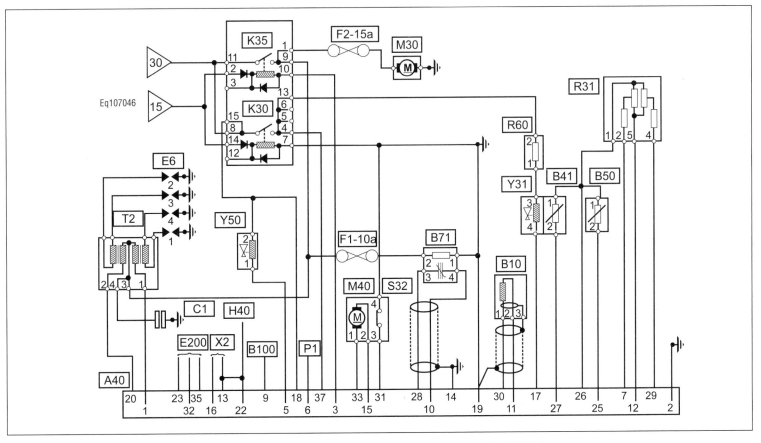

Eq107046

System wiring diagram, Bosch Mono-Motronic MA3.0

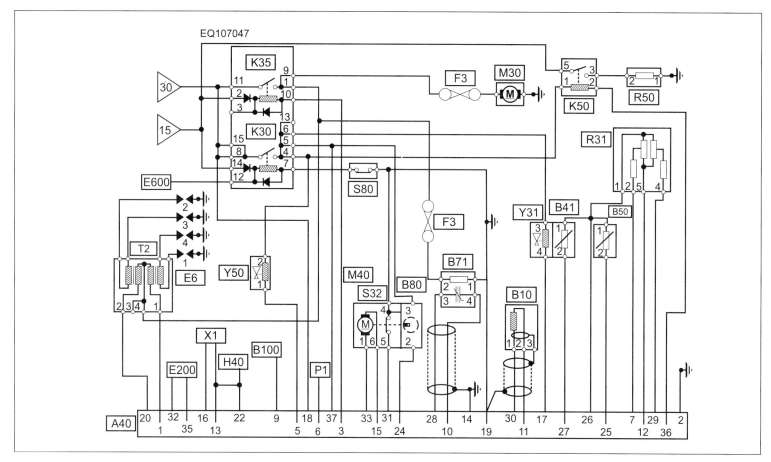

System wiring diagram, Bosch Mono-Motronic MA3.1

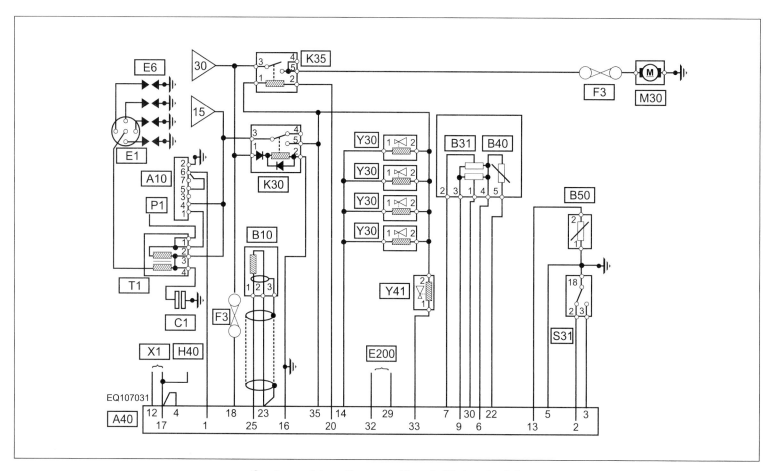

System wiring diagram, Bosch Motronic 4.1

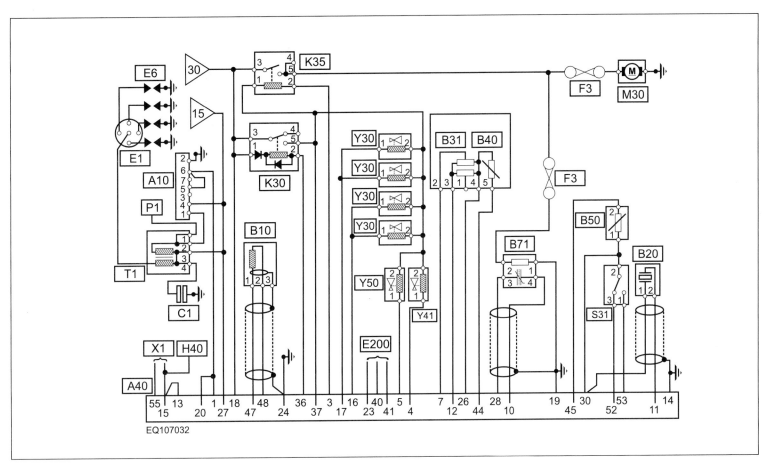

System wiring diagram, Bosch Motronic 1.3

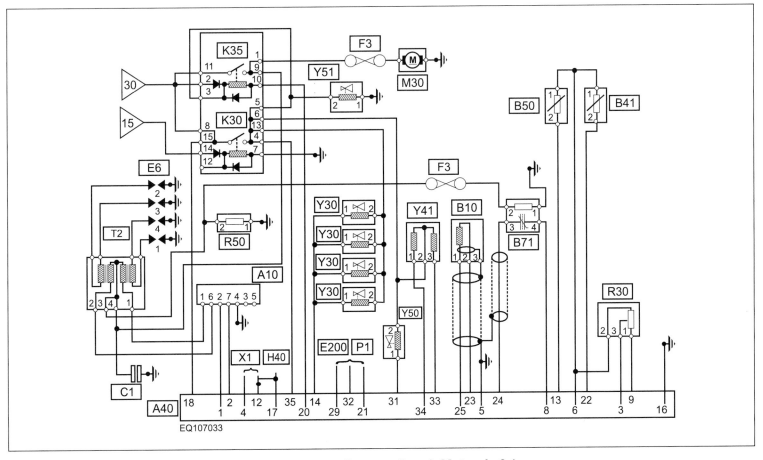

System wiring diagram, Bosch Motronic 3.1

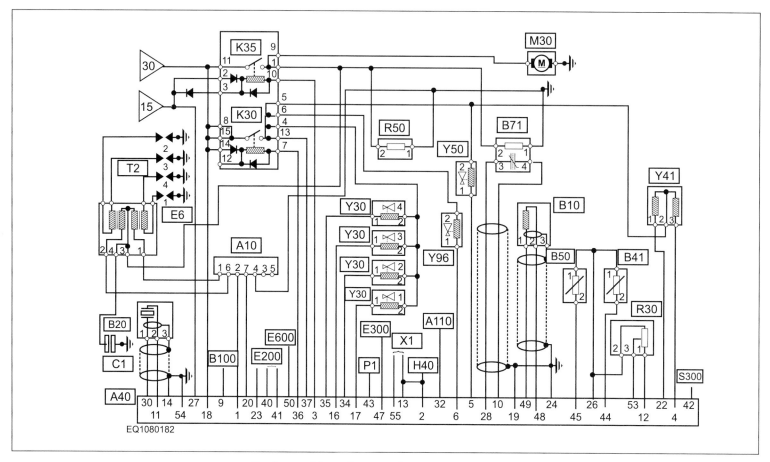

System wiring diagram, Bosch Motronic 3.2

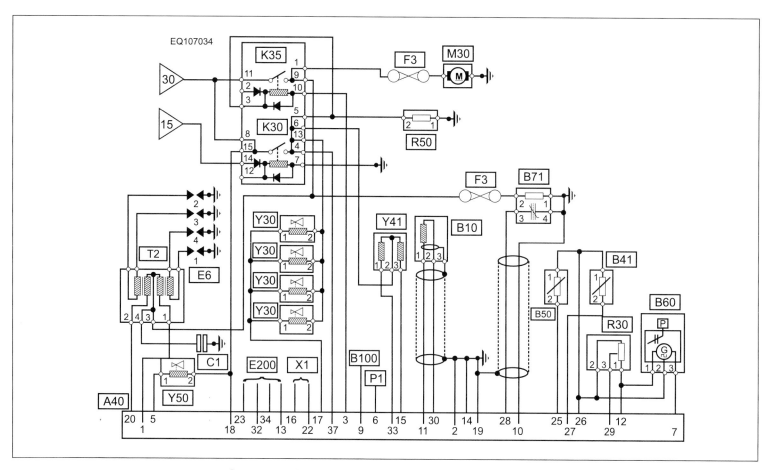

System wiring diagram, Bosch Motronic M5.1/5.1.1

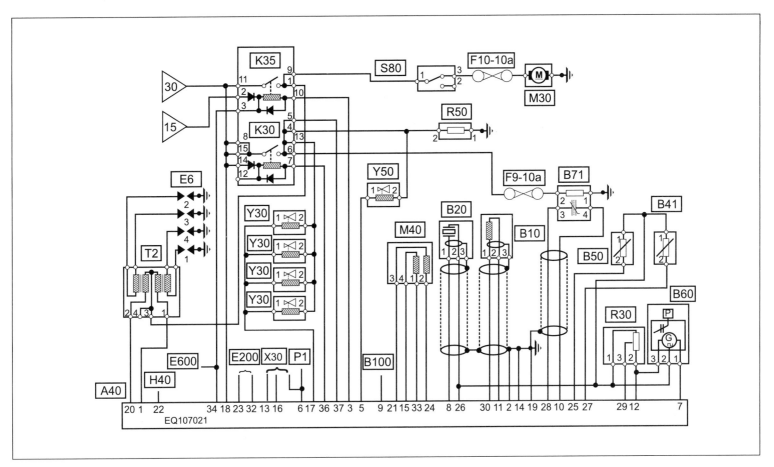

System wiring diagram, Bosch Motronic M5.2

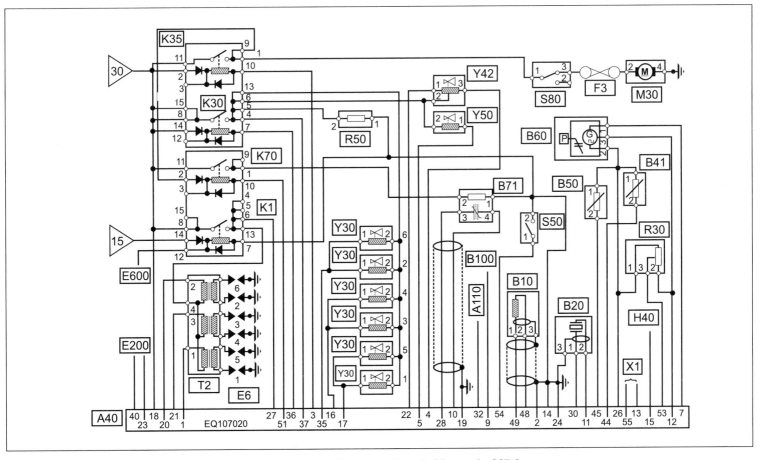

System wiring diagram, Bosch Motronic M7.0

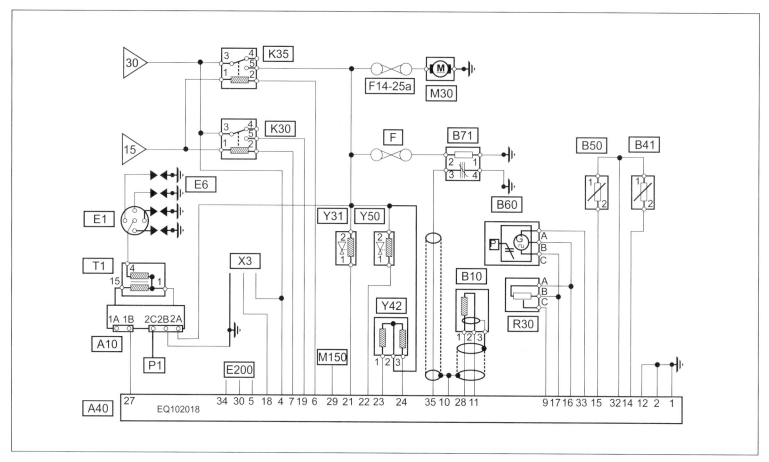

System wiring diagram, Fenix 1B

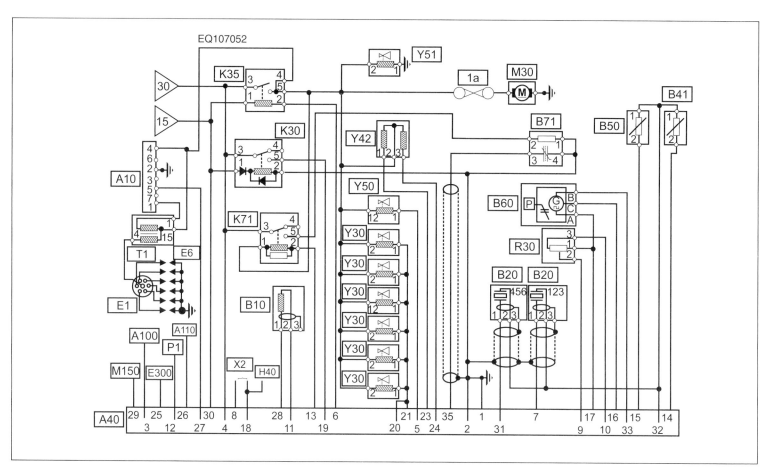

System wiring diagram, Fenix 3B

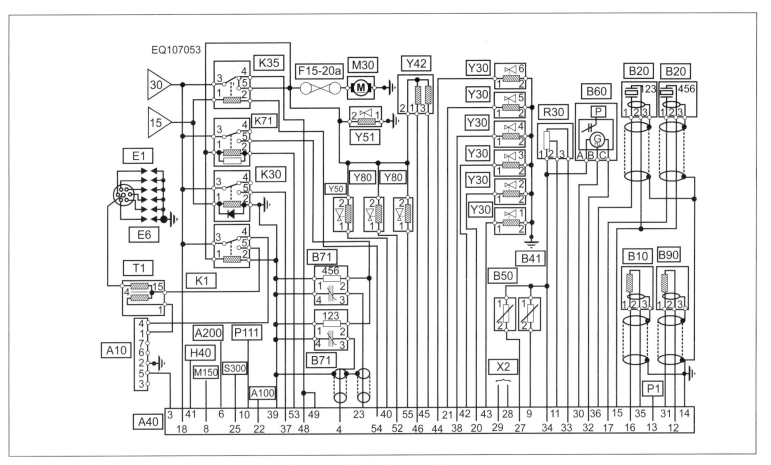

System wiring diagram, Fenix 4

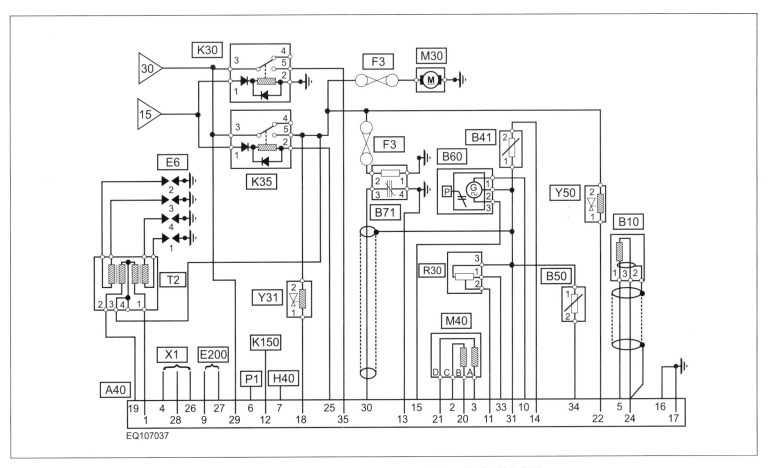

System wiring diagram, Magneti-Marelli G5/G6 SPi

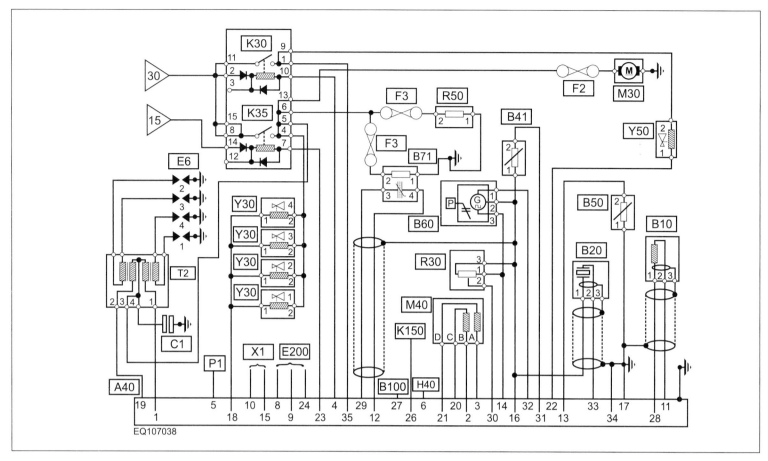

System wiring diagram, Magneti-Marelli 8P

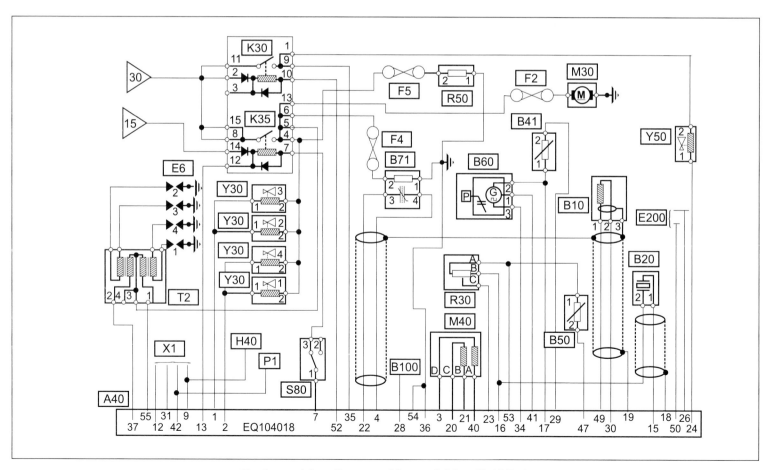

System wiring diagram, Magneti-Marelli 1AP40

Chapter 22
Proton

Contents

Index of Proton vehicles/systems

Model	Engine code	Year	System
Persona 1.5 SOHC 12V	**4G15**	**1993 to 1997**	**ECI Multi SEFi**
Persona 1.5 Compact SOHC 12V	4G15	1993 to 1997	ECI Multi SEFi
1.3 MPi 12V cat SOHC 12V	4G13-2	1992 to 1997	ECI Multi SEFi
1.5 MPi 12V cat SOHC 12V	4G15-2	1992 to 1997	ECI Multi SEFi
Persona 1.3 Compact SOHC 12V	4G13-2	1995 to 1997	ECI Multi SEFi
Persona 1.6 SOHC 16V	4G92	1993 to 1997	ECI Multi SEFi
Persona 1.6 Compact SOHC 16V	4G92	1993 to 1997	ECI Multi SEFi
Persona 1.8 12v SOHC	4G93	1996 to 1997	ECI Multi SEFi
Persona 1.8 16v DOHC	4G93	1996 to 1997	ECI Multi SEFi

Note: *The vehicles accentuated in bold type are the actual vehicles upon which the ECM pin tables and wiring diagrams are based. Other vehicles with the same system may be similar; but are also likely to contain some differences.*

Pin Table – ECI Multi SEFi

Section A

Pin	Item	Test Condition	Measurements
A1	injector driver (cylinder 1) : t1	ignition on	nbv
		engine running:	
		cold	>3.5 ms
		hot idle	3.5 ms
		3000 rpm	3.4 ms
		snap acceleration	20 ms (approx)
		deceleration	1 ms (approx)
A2	injector driver (cylinder 3) : t1	ignition on	nbv
		engine running:	
		cold	>3.5 ms
		hot idle	3.5 ms
		3000 rpm	3.4 ms
		snap acceleration	20 ms (approx)
		deceleration	1 ms (approx)
A3	–		
A4	stepper motor : t5	idle speed, active	0 to 5.0 V (switching)
A5	TVPS signal : t2	ignition on/engine running:	
		valve closed	1.0 V
		open	5.0 V (approx).
A6-A7	–		
A8	fuel pump relay driver: t5	ignition on	nbv
		engine cranking/running	1.25 V (max)
A9	CFSV driver : t1	ignition on	nbv
		engine running, above idle, operating temperature:	
		CFSV inactive	nbv
		CFSV active	0 to 12 V (switching)
		duty cycle	0 to 99%
A10	ignition coil driver : t6	ignition on	nbv
		engine running:	
		dynamic volt drop	2.0 V (max)
		primary switching	200 V (min)
A11	–		
A12	supply from main relay: t3	ignition on/engine running	nbv
A13	earth	ignition on/engine running	0.25 V (max)
A14	injector driver (cylinder 2) : t1	ignition on	nbv
		engine running:	
		cold	> 3.5 ms
		hot idle	3.5 ms
		3000 rpm	3.4 ms
		snap acceleration	20 ms (approx)
		deceleration	1 ms (approx)
A15	injector driver (cylinder 4) : t1	ignition on	nbv
		engine running:	
		cold	> 3.5 ms
		hot idle	3.5 ms
		3000 rpm	3.4 ms
		snap acceleration	20 ms (approx)
		deceleration	1 ms (approx)
A16	–		
A17	stepper motor : t6	idle speed, active	0 to 5.0 V (switching)
A18	TVPS signal : t4	engine running, hot idle, 750 rpm FCR attached to SD connector	2 to 20 steps
		A/C on, idle 850 rpm	increase 8 to 50 steps
		AT lever N to D, idle 700 rpm	increase 3 to 40 steps
A19-A21	–		
A22	air conditioning		data not available
A23-A24	–		
A25	supply from main relay: t3	ignition on/engine running	nbv
A26	earth	ignition on/engine running	0.25 V (max)

Section B

Pin	Item	Test Condition	Measurements
B1-B3	–		
B4	service adjuster (ignition timing) : t1		data not available
B5	OS heater driver : t1	ignition on	nbv
		engine running:	
		cold	1.25 V (max)
		hot	nbv
B6	SD warning lamp : t14	ignition on, lamp on	1.25 V (max)
		engine running:	
		no faults present	nbv
		faults present, lamp on	1.25 V (max)
B7	PSPS signal : t2	engine at idle speed:	
		wheels straight	nbv
		wheels turned	0.25 V (max)
B8-B11	–		
B12	SD connector : t1		data not available
B13	SD connector : t10		data not available
B14	–		
B15	air conditioning		data not available
B16	–		

Section C

Pin	Item	Test Condition	Measurements
C1	starter signal	engine cranking	nbv
C2	ATS signal : t2	ignition on/engine running	20° C: 3.00 to 3.50 V
			50° C: 2.00 to 2.30 V
C3-C5	–		
C6	OS signal : t3	ignition on, OS multiplug disconnected	0.4 to 0.5 V
		engine running, hot	200 to 1000 mV (switching)
		throttle fully-open	0.5 to 1.0 V
		deceleration (fuel cut-off)	0 to 0.5 V
		switching frequency	1 sec intervals (approx)
C7-C9	–		
C10	supply from battery : t30	ignition off/on/engine running	nbv
C11	sensor supply (MAP : t1, TPS : t1, TVPS : t1)	ignition on/engine running	5.0 V ± 0.1
C12	–		
C13	CTS signal : t2	ignition on/engine running	20° C: 2.00 to 2.50 V
			80° C: 0.70 to 1.30 V
C14	TPS signal : t2	ignition on/engine running:	
		throttle closed	0.3 to 1.0 V
		throttle fully open	4.5 to 5.5 V
C15	–		
C16	VSS signal : t3	vehicle in motion	0 to 5 V (switching)
C17	idle switch : t3	throttle closed	0 V
		throttle open	5 V
C18	OCID sensor signal: t4	engine running	0 to 5 V (switching)
C19	OCAS sensor signal : t3	engine running	0 to 5 V (switching)
C20	MAP sensor signal : t2	ignition on	5.0 V
		engine running, WOT	> 4.0 V
		250 mbar	3.4 V
		500 mbar	2.0 V
C21	automatic transmission		data not available
C22	sensor return (MAP : t3, CTS : t1 ATS : t1, OS : t4,TPS : t1, TVPS : t3)	ignition on/engine running	0.25 V (max)

Eq120006

64 pin ECM multi-plug, ECI Multi SEFi

Wiring Diagram

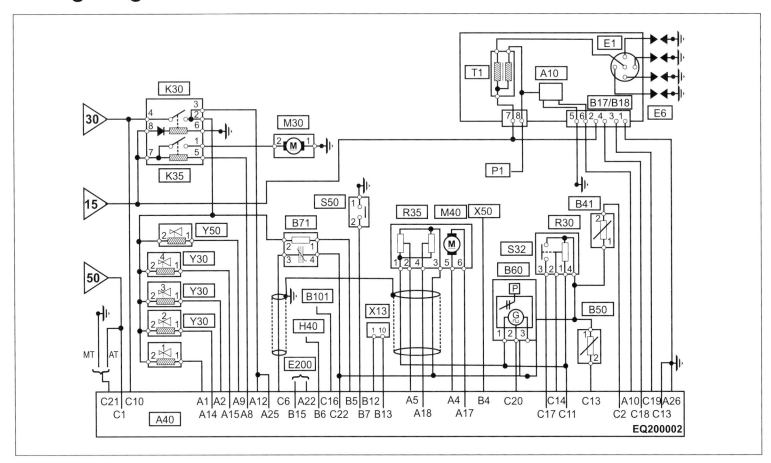

System wiring diagram, ECI Multi SEFi

Chapter 23
Renault

Contents

Index of Renault vehicles/systems

Model	Engine code	Year	System
5 1.4 cat	C3J700 (B/C/F407)	1986 to 1990	Renix SPi
5 1.4 cat	C3J760 (B/C/F407)	1990 to 1997	Renix SPi
5 1.7i cat	**F3N G716 (B/C408)**	**1987 to 1991**	**Renix SPi**
5 1.7i cat	F3N G717 (B/C409)	1987 to 1991	Renix SPi
9 1.7 cat	F3N708(L42E/C37E)	1986 to 1989	Renix MPi
9 1721 cat	F3N718(L42F/BC37F)	1986 to 1989	Renix SPi
11 1.7 cat	F3N708 L42E/C37E	1986 to 1989	Renix MPi
11 1721 cat	F3N718(L42F/BC37F)	1986 to 1989	Renix SPi
19 1.4 cat	E7J 706/740	1993 to 1996	Bosch SPi
19 1.4 cat	E7J700 (B/C/L53A)	1991 to 1995	Bosch SPi
19 1.4i cat	C3J700	1991 to 1992	Renix SPi
19 1.4i cat	C3J710 (B/C/L532)	1990 to 1992	Renix SPi
19 1.4i cat	**E7J 700**	**1991 to 1996**	**Bosch SPi**
19 1.4i ECO cat	E7J 742/745	1995 to 1996	Bosch SPi
19 1.7 DOHC 16v cat	F7P704 (X53D)	1991 to 1995	Renix MPi
19 1.7 DOHC 16v cat	F7P704(B/C/L/D53D)	1989 to 1996	Renix MPi
19 1.7 DOHC 16v	F7P700(B/C/L/D53D)	1989 to 1993	Renix MPi
19 1.7i AT cat	F3N 743 (X53C)	1990 to 1992	Renix MPi
19 1.7i cat	**F3N (740, 741)**	**1990 to 1992**	**Renix SPi**

Index of Renault vehicles/systems

Model	Engine code	Year	System
19 1.7i cat	**F3N 742 (B/C/L/X53C)**	**1990 to 1992**	**Renix MPi**
19 Chamade 1.7i AT cat	F3N 740 (B/C/L53B)	1990 to 1992	Renix SPi
19 Chamade 1.7i cat	F3N 741 (B/C/L53B)	1990 to 1992	Renix SPi
21 1.7i cat	F3N722(B/K/L/48E)	1991 to 1995	Renix MPi
21 1.7i cat	F3N723 (X48F)	1991 to 1995	Renix SPi
21 1721 cat	F3N 726(L42F/BC37F)	1986 to 1989	Renix SPi
21 2.0 & 4x4	J7R750 (B/L/K483)	1990 to 1993	Renix MPi
21 2.0 & AT 4x4	J7R751 (K483)	1986 to 1993	Renix MPi
21 2.0 12v & 4x4 cat	J7R740 (B/L/X48R)	1991 to 1995	Renix MPi
21 2.0 AT cat	J7R747 (B/K/L48C)	1991 to 1995	Renix MPi
21 2.0 cat	J7R746 (B/K/L48C)	1991 to 1995	Renix MPi
21 2.0 Turbo	**J7R 752 (L485)**	**1988 to 1992**	**Renix MPi**
21 2.0 turbo & 4x4 cat	J7R756 (L48L)	1991 to 1994	Renix MPi
21 2.0 Turbo 4x4	J7R 752 (L485)	1991 to 1992	Renix MPi
21 2.0 turbo	J7R752 (L485)	1988 to 1993	Renix MPi
21 2.0 TXi 12 valve	J7RG754(X48Q/Y/R)	1990 to 1993	Renix MPi
25 2.0 TXi 12v cat	**J7R 726 (B294)**	**1991 to 1993**	**Renix MPi**
25 2.2	J7TE706 (B29E)	1984 to 1987	Renix MPi
25 2.2	J7TJ730 (B29E)	1987 to 1990	Renix MPi
25 2.2 AT	J7TG707 (B29E)	1984 to 1987	Renix MPi
25 2.2 AT cat	J7T733 (B29B)	1987 to 1992	Renix MPi
25 2.2 AT	J7TK731 (B29E)	1987 to 1990	Renix MPi
25 2.2 cat	J7T732 (B29B)	1987 to 1992	Renix MPi
25 2.5 V6 turbo	Z7UA702 (B295	1985 to 1990	Renix MPi
25 2.5 V6 turbo cat	Z7U700 (B29G)	1989 to 1992	Renix MPi
25 V6 2.9i AT cat	Z7W 707 (B29F)	1991 to 1992	Renix MPi
25 V6 2.9i AT cat	Z7W707 (B29F)	1991 to 1992	Renix MPi
25 V6 2.9i AT	Z7W709 (B293)	1992 to 1993	Renix MPi
25 V6 2.9i cat	**Z7W 706 (B29F)**	**1991 to 1992**	**Renix MPi**
25 V6 2.9i cat	Z7W706 (B29F)	1991 to 1992	Renix MPi
Alpine 2.5 GTA V6 turbo cat	Z7U734 (D502)	1990 to 1992	Renix MPi
Alpine 2.5 GTA V6 turbo	Z7UC730 (D501)	1986 to 1992	Renix MPi
Alpine 2.5 V6 turbo cat	Z7X744 (D503)	1992 to 1997	Renix MPi
Alpine Turbo	Z7U 702	1986 to 1990	Renix MPi
Chamade 1.7i AT cat	F3N 743 X53C	1990 to 1992	Renix MPi
Chamade 1.7i cat	F3N 742 X53C	1990 to 1992	Renix MPi
Clio 1.2i cat	E7F 700, 706	1991 to 1997	Bosch SPi
Clio 1.4i cat	E7J 711-713, 719	1991 to 1997	Bosch SPi
Clio 1.8 16v DOHC cat	F7P722 (C57D)	1991 to 1997	Renix MPi
Clio 1.8 16v DOHC	F7P720 (C575)	1991 to 1993	Renix MPi
Clio 1.8i 8v cat	**F3P 710, 714**	**1991 to 1997**	**Bosch SPi**
Clio 1.8i 8v cat	**F3P 712**	**1991 to 1997**	**Renix MPi**
Clio Williams 2.0 cat	F7R 700	1993 to 1995	Renix MPi
Espace 2.0i cat	J7R 768 (J636)	1991 to 1996	Renix MPi
Espace 2.2i & 4x4 cat	**J7T 772 (J/S637)**	**1991 to 1997**	**Renix MPi**
Laguna 2.0i cat	**F3R 722**	**1994 to 1995**	**Renix MPi**
Laguna 3.0i V6	**Z7X 760 (B56E)**	**1994 to 1997**	**Siemens**
Safrane 2.0i 12v cat	J7R 734 (B542)	1993 to 1994	Renix MPi
Safrane 2.0i 12v cat	J7R 735 (B542)	1993 to 1994	Renix MPi
Safrane 2.0i AT cat	J7R 733 (B540)	1993 to 1995	Renix MPi
Safrane 2.0i cat	J7R 732 (B540)	1993 to 1997	Renix MPi
Safrane 2.2i 12v AT cat	J7T 761 (B543)	1993 to 1995	Renix MPi
Safrane 2.2i 12v cat	**J7T 760 (B543)**	**1993 to 1997**	**Renix MPi**
Savanna 1.7i cat	F3N722 (X48E)	1991 to 1995	Renix MPi
Savanna 1.7i cat	F3N723 (X48F)	1991 to 1995	Renix SPi
Savanna 2.0 & 4x4 AT	J7R751 (K483)	1986 to 1993	Renix MPi
Savanna 2.0 & 4x4	J7R750 (K483)	1986 to 1993	Renix MPi
Trafic 2.2i & 4x4 cat	J7T 780 (T/VxxA)	1989 to 1997	Renix MPi
Twingo 1.3	**C3G (C063)**	**1994 to 1997**	**Magneti-Marelli SPi**

Note: *The vehicles accentuated in bold type are the actual vehicles upon which the ECM pin tables and wiring diagrams are based. Other vehicles with the same system may be similar; but are also likely to contain some differences.*

Pin Table – Bosch SPi (19 1.4 cat, E7J700)

Pin	Item	Test Condition	Measurements
1	earth	ignition on/engine running	0.25 V (max)
2	earth	ignition on/engine running	0.25 V (max)
3	VSS signal : t3	vehicle in motion	0 to nbv (switching)
4	supply from battery : t30	ignition off/on/engine running	nbv
5	CFSV driver : t1	ignition on	nbv
		engine running, above idle, operating temperature:	
		CFSV inactive	nbv
		CFSV active	0 to 12 V (switching)
		duty cycle	0 to 99%
6	fuel pump relay driver : t2	ignition on	nbv
		engine cranking/running	1.25 V (max)
7	main relay driver : t2	ignition on/engine running	1.25 V (max)
8	–		
9	TPS signal : t2 (5 or 7 pin switch)	ignition on/engine running:	
		throttle closed	2.2 to 2.8 V
		throttle fully open	4.3 to 4.7 V (approx)
10	TPS: t4, 7 pin switch : t5, 5 pin switch, full-load contact	ignition on/engine running:	
		throttle closed/part open	3.5 to 4.0 V
		throttle fully open	0.25 V (max.)
11	CAS signal : t2	engine cranking:	> 2.0 V AC (peak to peak)
		idle:	> 11.0 V AC (peak to peak)
		cruise:	> 14.0 V AC (peak to peak)
12	AT-ECM		data not available
13	SD warning lamp (if fitted)	ignition on, lamp on	1.25 V (max)
		engine running:	
		no faults present	nbv
		faults present, lamp on	1.25 V (max)
14	ATS signal : t2	ignition on/engine running	20° C: 2.2 to 2.8 V
15	CTS signal : t2	ignition on/engine running	20° C: 1.60 to 2.50 V
			80° C: 0.20 to 0.50 V
16	MAP sensor supply : tC	ignition on/engine running	5.0 V
17	MAP sensor return : tA	ignition on/engine running	0.25 V (max)
18	SD connector : t9		data not available
19	supply from relay : t5	ignition on/engine running	nbv
20	supply from ignition switch : t15	ignition on/engine running	nbv
21	injector driver : t1	ignition on	nbv
		engine running, cold	3.0 to 3.5 ms
		engine running, hot	2.0 to 2.5 ms
		snap acceleration	6.0 ms
22	A/C control relay		data not available
23	stepper motor : t1	idle speed, active	0 to nbv (pulse)
24	stepper motor : t2	idle speed, active	0 to nbv (pulse)
25	stepper motor : t3 (idle switch)	ignition on/engine running:	
		throttle closed	0.25 V (max)
		throttle open	4.20 V
26	trip computer		data not available
27	AEI coil unit control signal : tB	ignition on	5.0 V
		engine running	0 to 5.0 V (switching)
28	CAS return : t1	engine cranking/running	0.25 V (max)
29	supply from ignition switch : t50	engine cranking	nbv
30	warning lamp unit or A/C signal		data not available
31	KS signal : t3	engine running, KS active	1.0 V (approx)
32	sensor return (ATS : t1,CTS : t1, KS : t1)	ignition on/engine running	0.25 V (max)
33	MAP sensor signal : tB	WOT/ignition on	4.0 to 4.5 V
		idle speed	1.5 to 2.0 V
34	fog lamp shunt relay or A/C thermostat signal		data not available

Pin Table – Bosch SPi (19 1.4 cat, E7J700) (continued)

Pin	Item	Test Condition	Measurements
35	OS signal : t3	ignition on, OS multiplug disconnected	0.4 to 0.5 V
		engine running, hot	200 to 1000 mV (switching)
		throttle fully-open	0.5 to 1.0 V
		deceleration (fuel cut-off)	0 to 0.5 V
		switching frequency	1 sec intervals (approx)

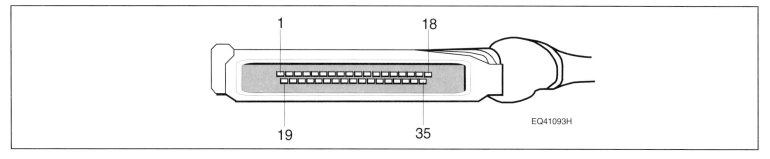

EQ41093H

35 pin ECM multi-plug, Bosch SPi

Pin Table – Bosch SPi (Clio 1.8, F3P710)

Pin	Connection	Test condition	Measurements
1	earth	ignition on/engine running	0.25 V (max)
2	earth	ignition on/engine running	0.25 V (max)
3	VSS signal : t3	vehicle in motion	0 to nbv (switching)
4	supply from battery : t30	ignition off/on/engine running	nbv
5	CFSV driver : t1	ignition on	nbv
		engine running, above idle, operating temperature:	
		CFSV inactive	nbv
		CFSV active	0 to 12 V (switching)
		duty cycle	0 to 99%
6	fuel pump relay driver : t2	ignition on	nbv
		engine cranking/running	1.25 V (max)
7	main relay driver : t2	ignition on/engine running	1.25 V (max)
8	–		
9	TPS signal : t2 (5 or 7 pin switch)	ignition on/engine running:	
		throttle closed	2.2 to 2.8 V
		throttle fully open	4.3 to 4.7 V (approx)
10	TPS: t4, 7 pin switch : t5, 5 pin switch, full-load contact	ignition on/engine running:	
		throttle closed/part open	3.5 to 4.0 V
		throttle fully open	0.25 V (max.)
11	CAS signal : t2	engine cranking:	> 2.0 V AC (peak to peak)
		idle:	> 11.0 V AC (peak to peak)
		cruise:	> 14.0 V AC (peak to peak)
12	AT-ECM		data not available
13	SD warning lamp (if fitted)	ignition on, lamp on	1.25 V (max)
		engine running:	
		no faults present	nbv
		faults present, lamp on	1.25 V (max)
14	ATS signal : t2	ignition on/engine running	20° C: 2.2 to 2.8 V
15	CTS signal : t2	ignition on/engine running	20° C: 1.60 to 2.50 V
			80° C: 0.20 to 0.50 V
16	MAP sensor supply : tC	ignition on/engine running	5.0 V
17	MAP sensor return : tA	ignition on/engine running	0.25 V (max)
18	SD connector : t9		data not available
19	supply from relay : t5	ignition on/engine running	nbv
20	supply from ignition switch : t15	ignition on/engine running	nbv

Pin	Connection	Test condition	Measurements
21	injector driver : t1	ignition on	nbv
		engine running, cold	3.0 to 3.5 ms
		engine running, hot	2.0 to 2.5 ms
		snap acceleration	6.0 ms
22	A/C control relay		data not available
23	stepper motor : t1	idle speed, active	0 to nbv (pulse)
24	stepper motor : t2	idle speed, active	0 to nbv (pulse)
25	stepper motor : t3 (idle switch)	ignition on/engine running:	
		throttle closed	0.25 V (max)
		throttle open	4.20 V
26	trip computer		data not available
27	AEI coil unit control signal : tB	ignition on	5.0 V
		engine running	0 to 5.0 V (switching)
28	CAS return : t1	engine cranking/running	0.25 V (max)
29	supply from ignition switch : t50	engine cranking	nbv
30	warning lamp unit or A/C signal		data not available
31	KS signal : t3	engine running, KS active	1.0 V AC (peak to peak)
32	sensor return (ATS : t1,CTS : t1, KS : t1)	ignition on/engine running	0.25 V (max)
33	MAP sensor signal : tB	ignition on	4.0 to 4.5 V
		engine running:	
		idle speed	1.5 to 2.0 V
		WOT	4.0 to 4.5 V
34	Fog lamp shunt relay or A/C thermostat signal		data not available
35	OS signal : t3	ignition on, OS multiplug disconnected	0.4 to 0.5 V
		engine running, hot	200 to 1000 mV (switching)
		throttle fully-open	0.5 to 1.0 V
		deceleration (fuel cut-off)	0 to 0.5 V
		switching frequency	1 sec intervals (approx)

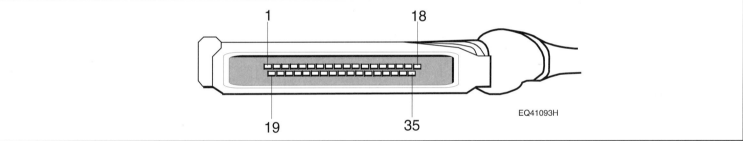

EQ41093H

35 pin ECM multi-plug, Bosch SPi

Pin Table – Magneti-Marelli SPi

Pin	Connection	Test condition	Measurements
1	–		
2	stepper motor : tB	idle speed, active	0 to 12 V (switching)
3	stepper motor : tA	idle speed, active	0 to 12 V (switching)
4	main relay driver : t2	ignition off	nbv
		ignition on/engine running	1.25 V (max)
5-7	–		
8	octane code plug	ignition on/engine running:	
		open circuit	5 V
9	–		
10	SD connector : t10		data not available
11	CAS return: t1	engine running	0.25 V (max)
12	OS return : t4	engine running	0.25 V (max)
13	CTS signal : t2	ignition on/engine running	20° C: 3.00 to 3.70 V
			40° C: 2.50 to 3.00 V
			80° C: 1.00 to 1.30 V

Pin Table – Magneti-Marelli SPi (continued)

Pin	Connection	Test condition	Measurements
14	sensor supply (MAP sensor : tA, TPS : tB)	ignition on/engine running	5.0 V ± 0.1
15	SD connector : t11		data not available
16	sensor return (CTS : t1, ATS : t1, MAP sensor : tC, TPS : A)	ignition on/engine running	0.25 V (max)
17	SD connector : t2		data not available
18	injector driver : t1	engine running, hot	
		idle	2.0 to 3.0 ms
		snap acceleration	> 6.0 ms
19	ignition coil driver : t1	ignition on	nbv
		engine running:	
		dynamic volt drop	2.0 V (max)
		primary switching	200 V (min)
20	stepper motor : tC	idle speed, active	0 to 12 V (switching)
21	stepper motor : tD	idle speed, active	0 to 12 V (switching)
22	CFSV driver : t1	ignition on	nbv
		engine running, above idle, operating temperature	
		CFSV inactive	nbv
		CFSV active	0 to 12 V (switching)
		duty cycle	0 to 54%
23	fuel pump relay driver: t2	ignition on	nbv
		engine cranking/running	1.25 V (max)
24-27	–		
28	CAS signal : t2	engine cranking	> 2.0 V AC (peak to peak)
		idle:	> 11.0 V AC (peak to peak)
		cruise	> 14.0 V AC (peak to peak)
32	OS signal : t3	ignition on, OS multiplug disconnected	0.4 to 0.5 V
		engine running, hot	200 to 1000 mV (switching)
		throttle fully-open	0.5 to 1.0 V
		deceleration (fuel cut-off)	0 to 0.5 V
		switching frequency	1 sec intervals (approx)
30	TPS signal : tC	ignition on/engine running:	
		throttle closed	0.5 V
		throttle fully open	5.0 V (max)
31	ATS signal : t2	ignition on/engine running	20° C: 3.30 to 3.70 V
			30° C: 2.70 to 3.20 V
			80° C: 1.20 to 1.50 V
32	MAP sensor signal : tB	ignition on	5.0 V
		engine running:	
		WOT	3.3 to 3.9 V
		133 mbar	2.8 to 3.6 V
		266 mbar	2.4 to 3.2 V
		400 mbar	2.0 to 2.8 V
		532 mbar	1.6 to 2.4 V
34	earth	ignition on/engine running	0.25 V (max)
35	supply from main relay : t5	ignition on/engine running	nbv

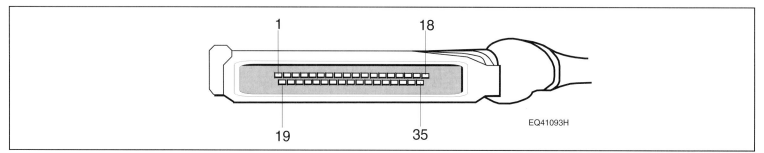

35 pin ECM multi-plug, Magneti-Marelli SPi

Pin Table – Renix MPi (19 1.7i cat, F3N742)

Pin	Item	Test Condition	Measurements
1	earth	ignition on/engine running	0.25 V (max)
2	earth	ignition on/engine running	0.25 V (max)
3	supply from ignition switch : t15	ignition on/engine running	nbv
4	supply from battery : t30	ignition off/on/engine running	nbv
5	CFSV driver : t1	engine running, above idle, operating temperature:	
		CFSV inactive	nbv
		CFSV active	0 to 12 V (switching)
		duty cycle	0 to 99%
6	fuel pump relay driver : t1	ignition on	nbv
		engine cranking/running	1.25 V (max)
7	main relay driver : t2	ignition off	nbv
		ignition on/engine running:	1.25 V (max)
8	TS, full load contact : t3	ignition on/engine running:	
		throttle closed/ part open	5 V
		throttle fully open	0 V
9	amplifier control signal : tA	engine cranking/running	0 to 5.0 V (switching)
10	park/neutral (AT)		data not available
11	CAS signal : t2	engine cranking:	> 2.0 V AC (peak to peak)
		idle:	> 11.0 V AC (peak to peak)
		cruise:	> 14.0 V AC (peak to peak)
12	AT-ECM (if fitted)		data not available
13	electric coolant pump relay driver : t2	ignition off/on	nbv
		pump actuated	1.25 V (max)
14	ATS signal : t2	ignition on/engine running	20° C : 2.2 to 2.8 V
15	CTS signal : t2	ignition on/engine running	20° C : 1.6 to 2.5 V
			80° C : 0.2 to 0.5 V
16	MAP sensor supply : tC	ignition on/engine running	5.0 V ± 0.1
17	MAP sensor return : tA	ignition on/engine running	0.25 V (max)
18	SD warning lamp/SD connector : t9	ignition on/engine running:	
		no faults present	nbv
		faults present	1.25 V (max)
19	supply from relay : t5	ignition on/engine running	nbv
20	injectors driver : t1	engine running, cold	3.5 ms
		engine running, hot	2.3 ms
		1000 rpm	2.2 ms
		2000 rpm	2.1 ms
		3000 rpm	2.0 ms
		snap acceleration	7 to 10 ms
		deceleration	0 ms
21	injectors driver : t1	engine running, cold	3.5 ms
		engine running, hot	2.3 ms
		1000 rpm	2.2 ms
		2000 rpm	2.1 ms
		3000 rpm	2.0 ms
		snap acceleration	7 to 10 ms
		deceleration	0 ms
22	air conditioning compressor relay		data not available
23	ISCV signal : t3	engine running, idle speed:	
		cold	6.0 to 6.5 V
		hot	7.0 to 9.0 V
		duty cycle	30%
24	ISCV signal : t5	engine running, idle speed:	
		cold	6.0 to 6.5 V
		hot	7.0 to 9.0 V
		duty cycle	70%
25	TS, idle contact : t2	ignition on/engine running:	
		throttle closed	0 V
		throttle part/fully open	5 V

Pin Table – Renix MPi (19 1.7i cat, F3N742)

Pin	Item	Test Condition	Measurements
26	trip computer		data not availiable
27	ignition amplifier/coil assembly : tB	engine cranking/running	0 to 5.0 V (switching)
28	CAS return : t1	engine cranking:	> 2.0 V AC (peak to peak)
		idle:	> 11.0 V AC (peak to peak)
		cruise:	> 14.0 V AC (peak to peak)
29	starter relay : t50	engine cranking	nbv
30	air conditioning (if fitted)		data not avaliable
31	KS signal : t2	engine running, KS active	1.0 V (peak to peak)
32	sensor return (CTS : t1, ATS : t1)	ignition on/running	0.25 V (max)
33	MAP sensor signal : tB	ignition on	4.0 to 4.5 V
		engine running:	
		wide open throttle (WOT)	4.0 to 4.5 V
		idle speed	1.5 to 2.0 V
34	air conditioning (if fitted)		data not avaliable
35	OS signal : t3	ignition on, OS multiplug disconnected	0.4 to 0.5 V
		engine running, hot	200 to 1000 mV (switching)
		throttle fully open	0.5 to 1.0 V
		deceleration (fuel cut-off)	0 to 0.5 V
		switching frequency	1 sec intervals (approx.)

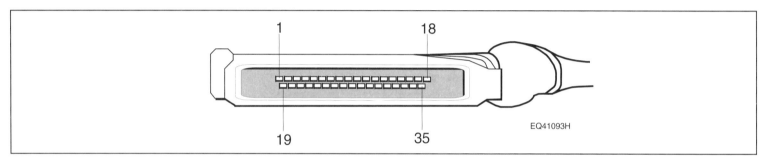

35 pin ECM multi-plug, Renix MPi (19 1.7i cat, F3N742)

Pin Table – Renix MPi (21 2.0 turbo, J7R752)

Pin	Table	Test Condition	Measurements
1	earth	ignition on/engine running	0.25 V (max)
2	earth	ignition on/engine running	0.25 V (max)
3	VSS signal : t3	vehicle in motion	0 to 12 V (switching)
4	supply from battery : t30	ignition off/on/engine running	nbv
5	SD warning lamp : t8	ignition on/engine running	
		no faults present	nbv
		faults present	0.25 V (max)
6	fuel pump relay driver : t2	ignition on	nbv
		engine cranking/running	1.25 V (max)
7	main relay driver : t2	ignition on/engine running	1.25 V (max)
8	–		
9	TPS signal : tA	ignition on/engine running:	
		throttle closed	< 1.0 V
		throttle fully open	4.25 to 4.50 V
10	earth	ignition on/engine running	0.25 V (max)
11	CAS signal : t2	engine cranking:	> 2.0 V AC (peak to peak)
		idle:	> 11.0 V AC (peak to peak)
		cruise:	> 14.0 V AC (peak to peak)
12	–		
13	air conditioning		data not available
14	ATS signal : t2	ignition on/engine running	20° C: 2.2 to 2.8 V
15	CTS signal : t2	ignition on/engine running	20° C: 1.6 to 2.5 V
			80° C: 0.2 to 0.5 V

Pin	Table	Test Condition	Measurements
16	sensor supply (MAP : tC, TPS : tB)	ignition on/engine running	5.0 V ± 0.1
17	sensor return (MAP : tA, TPS : tC)	ignition on/engine running	0.25 V (max)
18	SD warning lamp : t9	ignition on/engine running:	
		no faults present	nbv
		faults present	0.25 V (max)
19	supply from main relay : t5	ignition on/engine running	nbv
20	injectors driver : t1	engine running, cold	3.5 ms
		engine running, hot	2.3 ms
		1000 rpm	2.2 ms
		2000 rpm	2.1 ms
		3000 rpm	2.0 ms
		snap acceleration	7 to 10 ms
		deceleration	0 ms
21	injectors driver : t1	engine running, cold	3.5 ms
		engine running, hot	2.3 ms
		1000 rpm	2.2 ms
		2000 rpm	2.1 ms
		3000 rpm	2.0 ms
		snap acceleration	7 to 10 ms
		deceleration	0 ms
22	TBCV driver : t1	engine running:	
		TBCV inactive	nbv
		TBCV active	0 to 12 V (switching)
		duty cycle	0 to 99%
23	ISCV signal : t3	engine running, idle speed:	
		cold	6.0 to 6.5 V
		hot	7.0 to 9.0 V
		duty cycle	30%
24	ISCV signal : t5	engine running, idle speed:	
		cold	6.0 to 6.5 V
		hot	7.0 to 9.0 V
		duty cycle	70%
25	–		
26	trip computer		data not available
27	ignition amplifier/coil assembly : tB	engine cranking/running	0 to 5.0 V (switching)
28	CAS return : t1	ignition on/engine running	0.25 V (max)
29	cranking signal : t50	engine cranking	nbv
30	air conditioning		data not available
31	KS signal : t2	engine running, KS active	1.0 V (peak to peak)
32	sensor return (CTS : t1, ATS : t1, KS : t1)	ignition on/engine running	0.25 V (max)
33	MAP sensor signal : tB	ignition on	4.0 to 4.5 V
		engine running:	
		wide open throttle	4.0 to 4.5 V
		idle speed	1.5 to 2.0 V
34	air conditioning		data not available
35	CO pot signal : tB	ignition on/engine running:	
		open circuit	5 V
		range	0.1 to 5.0 V

EQ41093H

35 pin ECM multi-plug, Renix MPi (21 2.0 turbo, J7R752)

Pin Table – Renix MPi (25 2.0 Txi 12v cat, J7R726)

Pin	Table	Test Condition	Measurements
1	earth	ignition on/engine running	0.25 V (max)
2	earth	ignition on/engine running	0.25 V (max)
3	VSS signal : t3	vehicle in motion	0 to 12 V (switching)
4	supply from battery : t30	ignition on/off/engine running	nbv
5	–		
6	fuel pump relay driver : t2	ignition on	nbv
		engine cranking/running	1.25 V (max)
7	main relay driver : t2	ignition on/engine running	1.25 V (max)
8	–		
9	TPS signal : tA	ignition on/engine running:	
		throttle closed	< 1.0 V
		throttle fully open	4.25 to 4.50 V
10	earth	ignition on/engine running	0.25 V (max)
11	CAS signal : t2	engine cranking:	> 2.0 V AC (peak to peak)
		idle:	> 11.0 V AC (peak to peak)
		cruise:	> 14.0 V AC (peak to peak)
12-13	–		
14	ATS signal : t2	ignition on/engine running	20° C: 2.2 to 2.8 V
15	CTS signal : t2	ignition on/engine running	20° C: 1.6 to 2.5 V
			80° C: 0.2 to 0.5 V
16	sensor supply (MAP : tC, TPS : tB)	ignition on/engine running	5.0 V ± 0.1
17	sensor return (MAP : tA, TPS : tC)	ignition on/engine running	0.25 V (max)
18	SD warning lamp/SD connector : t9	ignition on/engine running:	
		no faults present	nbv
		faults present	0.25 V (max)
19	supply from main relay : t5	ignition on/engine running	nbv
20	injectors driver : t1	engine running, cold	3.5 ms
		engine running, hot	2.3 ms
		1000 rpm	2.2 ms
		2000 rpm	2.1 ms
		3000 rpm	2.0 ms
		snap acceleration	7 to 10 ms
		deceleration	0 ms
21	injectors driver : t1	engine running, cold	3.5 ms
		engine running, hot	2.3 ms
		1000 rpm	2.2 ms
		2000 rpm	2.1 ms
		3000 rpm	2.0 ms
		snap acceleration	7 to 10 ms
		deceleration	0 ms
22-23	–		
24	ISCV driver : t1	ignition on	nbv
		engine running, idle speed:	
		cold	6.0 to 6.5 V
		hot	7.0 to 9.0 V
25	pressure switch		data not available
26	trip computer		data not available
27	ignition amplifier/coil assembly : tB	engine cranking/running	0 to 5.0 V (switching)
28	CAS return : t1	ignition on/engine running	0.25 V (max)
29	cranking signal : t50	engine cranking	nbv
30	air conditioning		data not available
31	KS signal : t2	engine running, KS active	1.0 V AC (peak to peak)
32	sensor return (CTS : t1, ATS : t1)	ignition on/engine running	0.25 V (max)
33	MAP sensor signal : tB	ignition on	4.0 to 4.5 V
		engine running:	
		wide open throttle (WOT)	4.0 to 4.5 V
		idle speed	1.5 to 2.0 V
34	air conditioning		data not available

Pin	Table	Test Condition	Measurements
35	OS signal : t3	ignition on, OS multiplug disconnected	0.4 to 0.5 V
		engine running, hot	200 to 1000 mV (switching)
		throttle fully open	0.5 to 1.0 V
		deceleration (fuel cut-off)	0 to 0.5 V
		switching frequency	1 sec intervals (approx.)

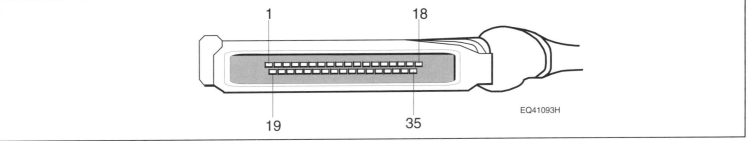

EQ41093H

35 pin ECM multi-plug, Renix MPi (25 2.0 Txi 12v cat, J7R726)

Pin Table – Renix MPi (Espace 2.2i 4x4 cat, J7T772)

Pin	Item	Test Condition	Measurements
1	earth	ignition on/engine running	0.25 V (max)
2	earth	ignition on/engine running	0.25 V (max)
3	–		
4	supply from battery : t30	ignition on/off/engine running	nbv
5	CFSV driver : t1	engine running, above idle, operating temperature:	
		CFSV inactive	nbv
		CFSV active	0 to 12V (switching)
		duty cycle	0 to 99%
6	fuel pump relay driver : t2	ignition on	nbv
		engine cranking/running	1.25 V (max)
7	main relay driver : t2	ignition on/engine running	1.25 V (max)
8	TS, full load contact : t3	ignition on/engine running:	
		throttle closed/part open	5 V
		throttle fully open	0 V
9	amplifier control signal return: tA	engine cranking/running	0.25 V (max)
10	earth	ignition on/engine running	0.25 V (max)
11	CAS signal : t2	engine cranking:	> 2.0 V AC (peak to peak)
		idle:	> 11.0 V AC (peak to peak)
		cruise:	> 14.0 V AC (peak to peak)
12	–		
13	KS return : t1	ignition on/engine running	0.25 V (max)
14	ATS signal : t2	ignition on/engine running	20° C: 2.2 to 2.8 V
15	CTS signal : t2	ignition on/engine running	20° C: 1.6 to 2.5 V
			80° C: 0.2 to 0.5 V
16	MAP sensor supply : tC	ignition on/engine running	5.0 V ± 0.1
17	MAP sensor return : tA	ignition on/engine running	0.25 V (max)
18	SD warning lamp/SD connector : t9	ignition on/engine running:	
		no faults present	nbv
		faults present	0.25 V (max)
19	supply from main relay : t5	ignition on/engine running	nbv
20	injectors driver : t1	engine running, cold	3.5 ms
		engine running, hot	2.3 ms
		1000 rpm	2.2 ms
		2000 rpm	2.1 ms
		3000 rpm	2.0 ms
		snap acceleration	7 to 10 ms
		deceleration	0 ms

Pin Table – Renix MPi (Espace 2.2i 4x4 cat, J7T772) (continued)

Pin	Item	Test Condition	Measurements
21	injectors driver : t1	engine running, cold	3.5 ms
		engine running, hot	2.3 ms
		1000 rpm	2.2 ms
		2000 rpm	2.1 ms
		3000 rpm	2.0 ms
		snap acceleration	7 to 10 ms
		deceleration	0 ms
22	–		
23	ISCV signal : t3	engine running, idle speed:	
		cold	6.0 to 6.5 V
		hot	7.0 to 9.0 V
		duty cycle	30%
24	ISCV signal : t5	engine running, idle speed:	
		cold	6.0 to 6.5 V
		hot	7.0 to 9.0 V
		duty cycle	70%
25	TS, idle contact : t2	ignition on/engine running:	
		throttle closed	0 V
		throttle part/fully open	5 V
26	–		data not available
27	ignition amplifier/coil assembly : tB	engine cranking/running	0.0 to 5.0 V (switching)
28	CAS return : t1	ignition on/engine running	0.25 V (max)
29	cranking signal : t50	engine cranking	nbv
30	air conditioning		data not available
31	KS signal : t2	engine running, KS active	1.0 V (peak to peak)
32	sensor return (CTS : t1, ATS : t1)	ignition on/engine running	0.25 V (max)
33	MAP sensor signal : tB	ignition on	4.0 to 4.5 V
		engine running:	
		wide open throttle	4.0 to 4.5 V
		idle speed	1.5 to 2.0 V
34	–		
35	OS signal : t3	ignition on, OS multiplug disconnected	0.4 to 0.5 V
		engine running, hot	200 to 1000 mV (switching)
		throttle fully open	0.5 to 1.0V
		deceleration (fuel cut-off)	0 to 0.5 V
		switching frequency	1 sec intervals (approx)

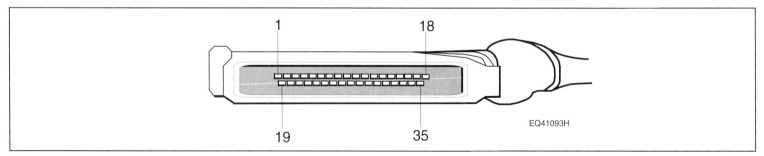

35 pin ECM multi-plug, Renix MPi (Espace 2.2i 4x4 cat, J7T772)

Pin Table – Renix MPi (Laguna 2.0i, F3R722)

Pin	Item	Test Condition	Measurement
1	earth	ignition on/engine running	0.25 V (max)
2	earth	ignition on/engine running	0.25 V (max)
3	VSS signal : t3	vehicle in motion	0 to 12 V (switching)
4	supply from battery : t30	ignition off/on/engine running	nbv

Pin	Item	Test Condition	Measurement
5	CFSV driver : t1	engine running, above idle, operating temperature:	
		CSFV inactive	nbv
		CFSV active	0 to 12 V (switching)
		duty cycle	0 to 99%
6	fuel pump relay driver : t2	ignition on	nbv
		engine cranking/running	1.25 V (max)
7	main relay driver : t2	ignition on/engine running:	1.25 V (max)
8	SD connector : t8		data not available
9	TPS signal : tA	ignition on/engine running:	
		throttle closed	< 1.0 V
		throttle fully open	4.25 to 4.50 V
10	earth	ignition on/engine running	0.25 V (max)
11	CAS signal : t2	engine cranking:	> 2.0 V AC (peak to peak)
		idle:	> 11.0 V AC (peak to peak)
		cruise:	> 14.0 V AC (peak to peak)
12	tachometer		data not available
13	SD warning lamp		data not available
14	ATS signal : t2	ignition on/engine running	20° C: 2.2 to 2.8 V
15	CTS signal : t2	ignition on/engine running	20° C: 1.6 to 2.5 V
			80° C: 0.2 to 0.5 V
16	sensor supply (MAP : tC, TPS : tB)	ignition on/engine running	5.0 V ± 0.1
17	sensor return (MAP : tA, TPS : tC)	ignition on/engine running	0.25 V (max)
18	SD connector : t9		data not available
19	supply from main relay : t5	ignition on/engine running	nbv
20	injectors driver (bank 1) : t1	engine running, cold	3.5 ms
		engine running, hot	2.3 ms
		1000 rpm	2.2 ms
		2000 rpm	2.1 ms
		3000 rpm	2.0 ms
		snap acceleration	7 to 10 ms
		deceleration	0 ms
21	injectors driver (bank 2) : t1	engine running, cold	3.5 ms
		engine running, hot	2.3 ms
		1000 rpm	2.2 ms
		2000 rpm	2.1 ms
		3000 rpm	2.0 ms
		snap acceleration	7 to 10 ms
		deceleration	0 ms
22-23	–		
24	ISCV signal : t1	idle speed	
		cold	6.0 to 6.5 V
		hot	7.0 to 9.0 V
25	–		
26	trip computer		data not available
27	ignition amplifier/coil assembly : tB	engine cranking/running	0 to 5.0 V (switching)
28	CAS return : t1	ignition on/engine running	0.25 V (max)
29	–		
30	PSPS signal	ignition on/engine running:	
		wheels straight	nbv
		wheels turned	0 V
31	KS signal : t2	engine running, KS active	1.0 V (peak to peak)
32	sensor return (CTS : t1, ATS : t1)	ignition on/running	0.25 V (max)
33	MAP sensor signal : tB	ignition on	4.0 to 4.5 V
		engine running:	
		wide open throttle	4.0 to 4.5 V
		idle speed	1.5 to 2.0 V
34	–		
35	OS signal : t3	ignition on, OS multiplug disconnected	0.4 to 0.5 V
		engine running	200 to 1000 mV (switching)
		throttle fully-open	0.5 to 1.0 V
		deceleration (fuel cut-off)	0 to 0.5 V
		switching frequency	1 sec intervals (approx.)

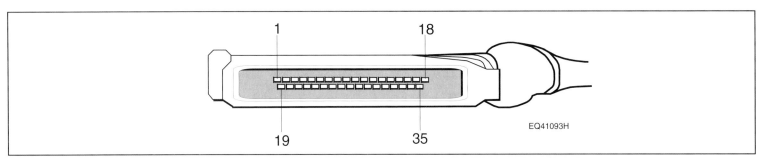

35 pin ECM multi-plug, Renix MPi (Laguna 2.0i, F3R722)

Pin Table – Renix MPi (Clio 1.8 cat, F3P712)

Pin	Item	Test Condition	Measurement
1	earth	ignition on/engine running	0.25 V (max)
2	earth	ignition on/engine running	0.25 V (max)
3	VSS signal : t3	vehicle in motion	0 to 12 V (switching)
4	supply from battery : t30	ignition off/on/engine running	nbv
5	CFSV driver : t1	engine running, above idle, operating temperature:	
		CFSV inactive	nbv
		CFSV active	0 to 12 V (switching)
		duty cycle	0 to 99%
6	fuel pump relay driver : t1	ignition on	nbv
		engine cranking/running	1.25 V (max)
7	main relay driver : t1	ignition off	nbv
		ignition on/engine running	1.25 V (max)
8	–		
9	TPS signal : tA	ignition on/engine running:	
		throttle closed	0.7 V
		throttle fully open	5.0 V
10	–		
11	CAS signal : t2	engine cranking	> 4.0 V AC (peak to peak)
		Idle	> 8.0 V AC (peak to peak)
		cruise	> 14.0 V AC (peak to peak)
12-13	–		
14	ATS signal : t2	ignition on/engine running	20° C: 2.2 to 2.8 V
15	CTS signal : t2	ignition on/engine running	20° C: 1.6 to 2.5 V
			80° C: 0.2 to 0.5 V
16	sensor supply (MAP : tC, TPS : tB)	ignition on/engine running	5.0 V ± 0.1
17	sensor return (MAP : tA, TPS : tC)	ignition on/engine running	0.25 V (max)
18	SD connector : t9	ignition on/engine running	
		no faults present	nbv
		faults present	1.25 V (max)
19	supply from main relay : t5	ignition on/engine running	nbv
20	injectors driver : t1	engine running, cold	3.5 ms
		engine running, hot	2.3 ms
		1000 rpm	2.2 ms
		2000 rpm	2.1 ms
		3000 rpm	2.0 ms
		snap acceleration	7 to 10 ms
		deceleration (fuel cut off)	0 ms (approx)
21	injectors driver : t1	engine running, cold	3.5 ms
		engine running, hot	2.3 ms
		1000 rpm	2.2 ms
		2000 rpm	2.1 ms
		3000 rpm	2.0 ms
		snap acceleration	7 to 10 ms
		deceleration (fuel cut off)	0 ms (approx)
22	–		
23	air conditioning		data not available

Pin	Item	Test Condition	Measurement
24	ISCV driver : t1	ignition on	nbv
		engine running, idle speed:	
		cold	6.0 to 6.5 V
		hot	7.0 to 9.0 V
		duty cycle	30 to 60%
25-26	–		
27	amplifier control signal : tB	engine cranking/running	0 to 5.0 V (switching)
28	CAS return : t1	engine running	0.25 V (max)
29	cranking signal : t50	engine cranking	nbv
30	air conditioning		data not available
31	KS signal : t2	engine running, KS active	1.0 to 2.0 V AC (peak to peak)
32	sensor return (CTS : t1, ATS : t1, KS : t1)	ignition on/engine running	0.25 V (max)
33	MAP sensor signal : tB	ignition on	4.0 to 4.5 V
		engine running:	
		WOT	4.0 to 4.5 V
		idle speed	1.5 to 2.0 V
34	air conditioning		data not available
35	OS signal : t3	ignition on, OS multiplug disconnected	0.4 to 0.5 V
		engine running, hot	200 to 1000 mV (switching)
		throttle fully-open	0.5 to 1.0 V
		deceleration (fuel cut-off)	0 to 0.5 V
		switching frequency	1 sec intervals (approx)

35 pin ECM multi-plug, Renix MPi (Clio 1.8 cat, F3P712)

Pin Table – Renix MPi (Safrane 2.2i 12v cat, J7T760)

Pin	Item	Test Condition	Measurements
1	earth	ignition on/engine running	0.25 V (max)
2	earth	ignition on/engine running	0.25 V (max)
3	VSS signal : t3	vehicle in motion	0 to 12 V (switching)
4	supply from battery : t30	ignition off/on/engine running	nbv
5	–		
6	fuel pump relay driver : t2	ignition on/engine running:	nbv
		engine cranking/running	1.25 V (max)
7	main relay driver : t2	ignition on	nbv briefly, then 1.25 V (max)
8	SD connector : t8		data not available
9	TPS signal : tA	ignition on/engine running:	
		throttle closed	< 1.0 V
		throttle fully open	4.25 to 4.50 V
10	–		
11	CAS signal : t2	engine cranking:	> 2.0 V AC (peak to peak)
		idle:	> 11.0 V AC (peak to peak)
		cruise:	> 14.0 V AC (peak to peak)
12	tachometer		data not available
13	SD warning lamp	ignition on/engine running:	
		no faults present	nbv
		faults present	1.25 V (max)
14	ATS signal : t2	ignition on/engine running	20° C: 2.2 to 2.8 V

Pin Table – Renix MPi (Safrane 2.2i 12v cat, J7T760) (continued)

Pin	Item	Test Condition	Measurements
15	CTS signal : t2	ignition on/engine running	20° C: 1.6 to 2.5 V
			80° C: 0.2 to 0.5 V
16	sensor supply (MAP : tC, TPS : tB)	ignition on/engine running	5.0 V ± 0.1
17	sensor return (MAP : tA, TPS : tC)	ignition on/engine running	0.25 V (max)
18	SD connector : t9	ignition on/engine running:	
		no faults present	nbv
		faults present	0.25 V (max)
19	supply from main relay : t5	ignition on/engine running	nbv
20	injectors driver : t1	engine running, cold	3.5 ms
		engine running, hot	2.3 ms
		1000 rpm	2.2 ms
		2000 rpm	2.1 ms
		3000 rpm	2.0 ms
		snap acceleration	7 to 10 ms
		deceleration	0 ms
21	injectors driver : t1	engine running, cold	3.5 ms
		engine running, hot	2.3 ms
		1000 rpm	2.2 ms
		2000 rpm	2.1 ms
		3000 rpm	2.0 ms
		snap acceleration	7 to 10 ms
		deceleration	0 ms
22-23	–		
24	ISCV driver : t1	ignition on	nbv
		engine running, idle speed:	
		cold	6.0 to 6.5 V
		hot	7.0 to 9.0 V
		duty cycle	30 to 60%
25	–		
26	trip computer		data not available
27	ignition amplifier/coil assembly : tB	engine cranking/running	0 to 5.0 V (switching)
28	CAS return : t1	ignition on/engine running	0.25 V (max)
29	–		
30	PSPS signal	ignition on/engine running:	
		wheels straight	nbv
		wheels turned	0 V
31	KS signal : t2	engine running, KS active	1.0 V AC (peak to peak)
32	sensor return (CTS : t1, ATS : t1)	ignition on/engine running	0.25 V (max)
33	MAP sensor signal : tB	ignition on	4.0 to 4.5 V
		engine running:	
		WOT	4.0 to 4.5 V
		idle speed	1.5 to 2.0 V
34	–		
35	OS signal : t3	ignition on, OS multiplug disconnected	0.4 to 0.5 V
		engine running, hot	200 to 1000 mV (switching)
		throttle fully open	0.5 to 1.0 V
		deceleration (fuel cut-off)	0 to 0.5 V
		switching frequency	1 sec intervals (approx.)

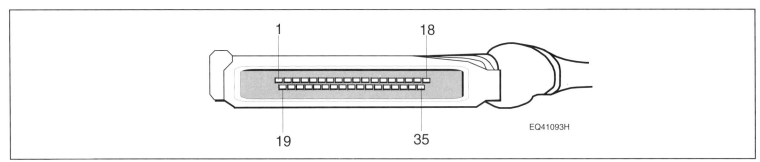

EQ41093H

35 pin ECM multi-plug, Renix MPi (Safrane 2.2i 12v cat, J7T760)

Pin Table – Renix MPi (25 2.9 V6, Z7W706)

Pin	Item	Test Condition	Measurements
1	earth	ignition on/engine running	0.25 V (max)
2	earth	ignition on/engine running	0.25 V (max)
3	VSS signal: t3	vehicle in motion	0 to 12 V (switching)
4	supply from battery : t30	ignition off/on/engine running	nbv
5	–		
6	fuel pump relay driver : t2	engine cranking/running	nbv
7	main relay driver : t2	ignition on/engine running	1.25 V (max)
8	–		
9	TPS signal : tA	ignition on/engine running:	
		throttle closed	< 1.0 V
		throttle fully open	4.25 to 4.50 V
10	earth	ignition on/engine running	0.25 V (max)
11	CAS signal : t2	engine cranking:	> 2.0 V AC (peak to peak)
		idle:	> 11.0 V AC (peak to peak)
		cruise:	> 14.0 V AC (peak to peak)
12	–		
13	SD warning lamp : t8	ignition on, lamp on	1.25 V (max)
		engine running:	
		no fault present	nbv
		fault present, lamp on	1.25 V (max)
14	ATS signal : t2	ignition on/engine running	20° C: 2.2 to 2.8 V
15	CTS signal : t2	ignition on/engine running	20° C: 1.6 to 2.5 V
			80° C: 0.2 to 0.5 V
16	sensor supply (MAP : tC, TPS : tB)	ignition on/engine running	5.0 V ± 0.1
17	sensor return (MAP : tA, TPS : tC)	ignition on/engine running	0.25 V (max)
18	SD connector : t9	ignition on/engine running:	
		no faults present	nbv
		faults present	0.25 V (max)
19	supply from main relay : t5	ignition on/engine running	nbv
20	injectors driver : t1	engine running, cold	3.5 ms
		engine running, hot	2.3 ms
		1000 rpm	2.2 ms
		2000 rpm	2.1 ms
		3000 rpm	2.0 ms
		snap acceleration	7 to 10 ms
		deceleration	0 ms
21	injectors driver : t1	engine running, cold	3.5 ms
		engine running, hot	2.3 ms
		1000 rpm	2.2 ms
		2000 rpm	2.1 ms
		3000 rpm	2.0 ms
		snap acceleration	at least 25 ms
22	–		
23	ISCV signal : t3	engine running, idle speed:	
		cold	6.0 to 6.5 V
		hot	7.0 to 9.0 V
		duty cycle	30%
24	ISCV signal : t5	engine running, idle speed:	
		cold	6.0 to 6.5 V
		hot	7.0 to 9.0 V
		duty cycle	70%
25	–		
26	trip computer		data not available
27	ignition amplifier/coil assembly : tB	engine cranking/running	0.0 to 5.0 V (switching)
28	CAS return : t1	ignition on/engine running	0.25 V (max)
29	starter relay : t50	engine cranking	nbv
30	air conditioning		data not available
31	KS signal : t2	engine running, KS active	1.0 V AC (peak to peak)

Pin Table – Renix MPi (25 2.9 V6, Z7W706) (continued)

Pin	Item	Test Condition	Measurements
32	sensor return (CTS : t1, ATS : t1)	ignition on/running	0.25 V (max)
33	MAP sensor signal : tB	ignition on	4.0 to 4.5 V
		engine running:	
		WOT	4.0 to 4.5 V
		idle speed	1.5 to 2.0 V
34	air conditioning		data not available
35	OS signal : t3	ignition on, OS multiplug disconnected	0.4 to 0.5 V
		engine running, hot	200 to 1000 mV (switching)
		throttle fully open	0.5 to 1.0 V
		deceleration (fuel cut-off)	0 to 0.5 V
		switching frequency	1 sec intervals (approx)

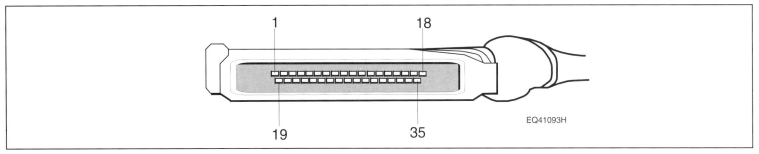

EQ41093H

35 pin ECM multi-plug, Renix MPi (25 2.9 V6, Z7W706)

Pin Table – Renix SPi (5 1.7i cat, F3N G716)

Pin	Connection	Test condition	Measurements
1	earth	ignition on/engine running	0.25 V (max)
2	earth	ignition on/engine running	0.25 V (max)
3	supply from ignition switch : t15	ignition on/engine running	nbv
4	supply from battery : t30	ignition off/on/engine running	nbv
5	CFSV driver : t1	ignition on	nbv
		engine running, above idle, operating temperature:	
		CFSV inactive	nbv
		CFSV active	0 to 12 V (switching)
		duty cycle	0 to 99%
6	fuel pump relay driver : t2	ignition on	nbv
		engine cranking/running	1.25 V (max)
7	main relay driver : t2	ignition on/engine running	1.25 V (max)
8	TS, full-load contact : t3	ignition on/engine running:	
		closed (throttle fully open)	0.25 V (max)
		open (throttle closed or part open)	5.0 V
9	AEI coil unit control signal return : tA	engine running	0.25 V (max)
10	earth	ignition on/engine running	0.25 V (max)
11	CAS signal : t2	engine cranking:	> 2.0 V AC (peak to peak)
		Idle:	> 11.0 V AC (peak to peak)
		cruise:	> 14.0 V AC (peak to peak)
12	earth	ignition on/engine running	0.25 V (max)
13	sensor return (KS : t3)	ignition on/engine running	0.25 V (max)
14	ATS signal : t2	ignition on/engine running	20° C: 2.2 to 2.8 V
15	CTS signal : t2	ignition on/engine running	20° C: 1.60 to 2.50 V
			80° C: 0.20 to 0.50 V
16	MAP sensor supply : tC	ignition on/engine running	5.0 V
17	MAP sensor return : tA	ignition on/engine running	0.25 V (max)
18	SD connector : t9		data not available

Pin	Connection	Test condition	Measurements
19	supply from relay : t5	ignition on/engine running	nbv
20	–		
21	injector driver : t1	ignition on	nbv
		engine running, hot	1.4 ms
		snap acceleration	11.0 ms
		deceleration	< 1.0 ms
22	–		
23	stepper motor : t1	idle speed, active	0 to nbv (switching)
24	stepper motor : t2	idle speed, active	0 to nbv (switching)
25	idle switch : t3	engine running, idle speed:	
		throttle closed	0.25 V (max)
		throttle open	4.20 V
26	–		
27	AEI coil unit control signal : tB	ignition on	5.0 V
		engine running	0 to 5.0 V (switching)
28	CAS return : t1	engine cranking/running	0.25 V (max)
29	cranking signal : t50	engine cranking	nbv
30	–		
31	KS signal : t1	engine running, KS active	1.0 V AC (peak to peak)
32	sensor return (ATS : t1, CTS : t1)	ignition on/engine running	0.25 V (max)
33	MAP sensor signal : tB	ignition on	4.0 to 4.5 V
		engine running:	
		WOT	4.0 to 4.5 V
		idle speed	1.5 to 2.0 V
34	–		
35	OS signal : t3	ignition on, OS multiplug disconnected	0.4 to 0.5 V
		engine running	200 to 1000 mV (switching)
		throttle fully-open	0.5 to 1.0 V
		deceleration (fuel cut-off)	0 to 0.5 V
		switching frequency	1 sec intervals (approx)

EQ41093H

35 pin ECM multi-plug, Renix SPi (5 1.7i cat, F3N G716)

Pin Table – Renix SPi (19 1.7i cat, F3N740)

Pin	Connection	Test condition	Measurements
1	earth	ignition on/engine running	0.25 V (max)
2	earth	ignition on/engine running	0.25 V (max)
3	VSS signal : t3	vehicle in motion	0 to 12 V (switching)
4	supply from battery : t30	ignition off/on/engine running	nbv
5	CFSV driver : t1	ignition on	nbv
		engine running, above idle, operating temperature:	
		CFSV inactive	nbv
		CFSV active	0 to 12 V (switching)
		duty cycle	0 to 99%
6	fuel pump relay driver : t2	ignition on	nbv
		engine cranking/running	1.25 V (max)
7	main relay driver : t2	ignition on/engine running	1.25 V (max)

Pin Table – Renix SPi (19 1.7i cat, F3N740) (continued)

Pin	Connection	Test condition	Measurements
8	TS, full-load switch : t3	ignition on/engine running:	
		throttle fully open	0.25 V (max)
		throttle closed/part open	5.0 V
9-10	–		
11	CAS signal : t2	engine cranking:	> 2.0 V AC (peak to peak)
		Idle:	> 11.0 V AC (peak to peak)
		cruise:	> 14.0 V AC (peak to peak)
12	earth	ignition on/engine running	0.25 V (max)
13	–		
14	ATS signal : t2	ignition on/engine running	20° C: 2.2 to 2.8 V
15	CTS signal : t2	ignition on/engine running	20° C: 1.60 to 2.50 V
			80° C: 0.20 to 0.50 V
16	MAP sensor supply : tC	ignition on/engine running	5.0 V
17	MAP sensor return : tA	ignition on/ engine running	0.25 V (max)
18	SD connector : t9		data not available
19	supply from relay : t5	ignition on/engine running	nbv
20	injector driver : t1	ignition on	nbv
		engine running, hot	1.4 ms
		snap acceleration	11.0 ms
		deceleration	< 1.0 ms
21	injector driver : t1	ignition on	nbv
		engine running, hot	1.4 ms
		snap acceleration	11.0 ms
		deceleration	< 1.0 ms
22	–		
23	stepper motor : t1	idle speed, active	0 to nbv (switching)
24	stepper motor : t2	idle speed, active	0 to nbv (switching)
25	idle switch : t3	ignition on/engine running:	
		throttle closed	0.25 V (max)
		throttle open	4.20 V
26	–		
27	AEI coil unit control signal : tB	ignition on	5.0 V
		engine running	0 to 5.0 V (switching)
28	CAS return : t1	engine cranking/running	0.25 V (max)
29	cranking signal : t50	engine cranking	nbv
30	–		
31	KS signal : t3	engine running, KS active	1.0 V AC (peak to peak)
32	sensor return (ATS: t1, CTS: t1, KS: t1)	ignition on/engine running	0.25 V (max)
33	MAP sensor signal : tB	ignition on	4.0 to 4.5 V
		engine running:	
		WOT	4.0 to 4.5 V
		idle speed	1.5 to 2.0 V
34	–		
35	OS signal : t3	ignition on, OS multiplug disconnected	0.4 to 0.5 V
		engine running	200 to 1000 mV (switching)
		throttle fully-open	0.5 to 1.0 V
		deceleration (fuel cut-off)	0 to 0.5 V
		switching frequency	1 sec intervals (approx.)

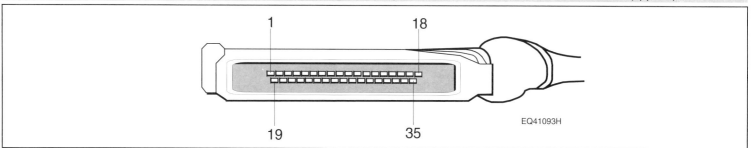

35 pin ECM multi-plug, Renix SPi (19 1.7i cat, F3N740)

Pin Table – Siemens (Laguna 3.0 V6, Z7X)

Pin	Connection	Test condition	Measurements
1	amplifier control signal : t5	engine cranking/running	0 to 5.0 V (switching)
2	earth	ignition on/engine running	0.25 V (max)
3	earth	ignition on/engine running	0.25 V (max)
4	injector driver : t1	engine running, cold	3.0 to 3.5 ms
		engine running, hot	2.0 to 2.5 ms
		snap acceleration	6.0 ms
		deceleration	1 ms (approx)
5	heated rear window		data not available
6	air conditioning		data not available
7	–		
8	KS signal : t2	engine running, KS active	1.0 V AC (peak to peak)
9-10	–		data not available
11	SD connector : t11		data not available
12	VSS signal : t3	vehicle in motion	0 to 12 V (switching)
13	trip computer		data not available
14	–		
15	CTS signal : t2	ignition on/engine running	20° C: 2.00 to 2.50 V
			80° C: 1.00 to 1.30 V
16	MAP sensor signal : t3	ignition on	5.0 V
		engine running, WOT	5.0 V
		idle speed	not stated, expect 1.25 V (approx)
17	OS signal : t3	ignition on, OS multiplug disconnected	0.4 to 0.5 V
		engine running, hot	200 to 1000 mV (switching)
		throttle fully-open	0.5 to 1.0 V
		deceleration (fuel cut-off)	0 to 0.5 V
		switching frequency	1 sec intervals (approx)
18	earth	ignition on/engine running	0.25 V (max)
19	TPS signal : tA	ignition on/engine running:	
		throttle closed	0.5 V
		throttle open	5.0 V
20	ATS signal : t2	ignition on/engine running	20° C: 3.00 to 3.50 V
			50° C: 2.00 to 2.30 V
21-22	–		
23	anti-percolation relay driver : t2	ignition on	nbv
		engine running, active	1.25 V (max)
24	supply from ignition switch : t15	ignition on/engine running	nbv
25	–		
26	SD warning lamp : t1	ignition on, lamp on	1.25 V (max)
		engine running:	
		no faults present	nbv
		faults present, lamp on	1.25 V (max)
27	–		
28	amplifier control signal : t5	engine cranking/running	0 to 5.0 V (switching)
29	amplifier control signal : t4	engine cranking/running	0 to 5.0 V (switching)
30	injector driver : t1	engine running, cold	3.0 to 3.5 ms
		engine running, hot	2.0 to 2.5 ms
		snap acceleration	6.0 ms
		deceleration	1 ms (approx)
31	sensor shield (KS1 : t3, KS2 : t3)	ignition on/engine running	0.25 V (max)
32	SD connector		data not available
33	CAS return: t1	engine running	0.25 V (max)
34	CAS signal : t2	cranking:	> 4.0 V AC (peak to peak)
		Idle:	> 8.0 V AC (peak to peak)
		cruise:	> 14.0 V AC (peak to peak)
35	wash/wipe switch		data not available
36	KS signal : t2	engine running, KS active	1.0 V AC (peak to peak)
37	–		
38	SD connection : t10		data not available

Pin Table – Siemens (Laguna 3.0 V6, Z7X) (continued)

Pin	Connection	Test condition	Measurements
39-40	–		
41	variable damping control		data not available
42	–		
43	tachometer		data not available
44	sensor return (KS1 : t1, KS2 : t1, MAP sensor : tA, CTS : t1)	ignition on/engine running	0.25 V (max)
45	sensor supply, (MAP sensor : tC, TPS : tC)	ignition on/engine running	5.0 V ± 0.1
46	sensor return (TPS : tB, ATS : t1)	ignition on/engine running	0.25 V (max)
47	main relay driver : t2	ignition off	nbv
		ignition on/engine running	1.25 V (max)
48	fuel pump relay driver: t2	ignition on	nbv
		engine cranking/running	1.25 V (max)
49	–		
50	CFSV driver : t1	engine running, above idle, operating temperature	
		CFSV inactive	nbv
		CFSV active	0 to 12 V (switching)
		duty cycle	0 to 99%
51	air conditioning		data not available
52	supply from fuel pump relay :t5	ignition on	nbv
53	–		
54	ISCV driver : t1	ignition on	nbv
		engine running, idle speed:	
		cold	6.0 to 6.5 V
		hot	7.0 to 9.0 V
		duty cycle	30 to 60%

27   1

55   EQ120059   28

55 pin ECM multi-plug, Siemens

Wiring Diagrams

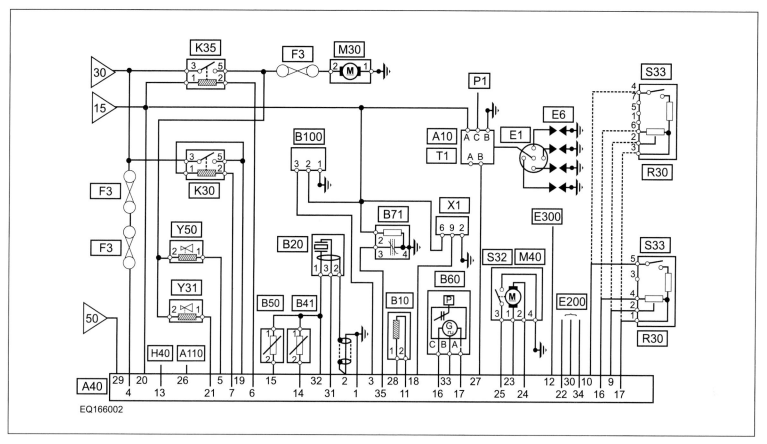

System wiring diagram, Bosch SPi (19 1.4 cat, E7J700)

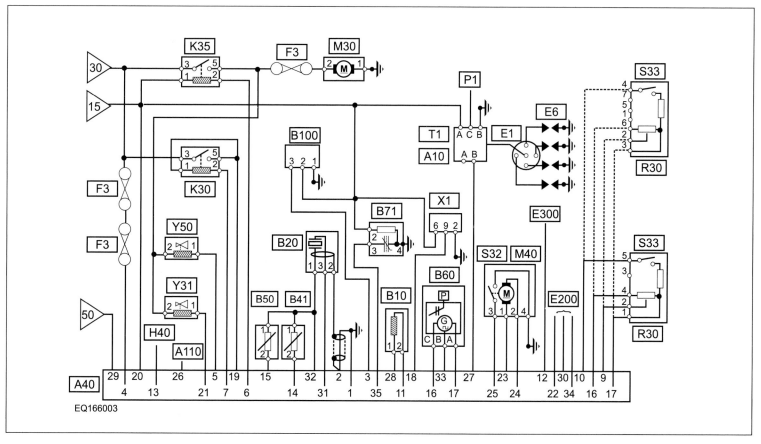

System wiring diagram, Bosch SPi (Clio 1.8, F3P710)

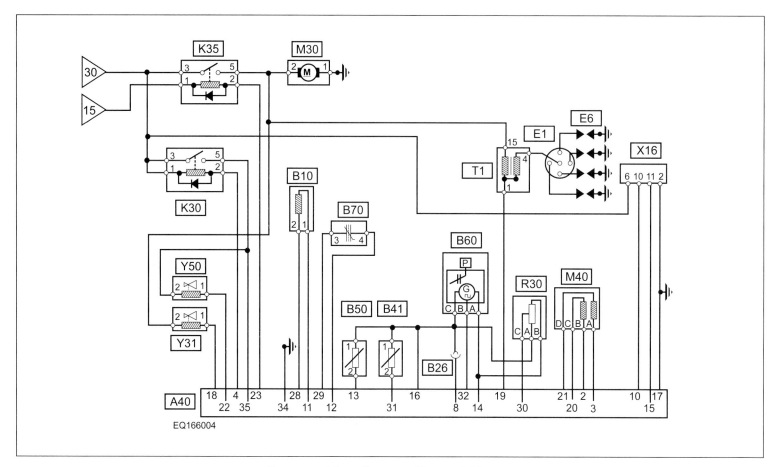

System wiring diagram, Magneti-Marelli

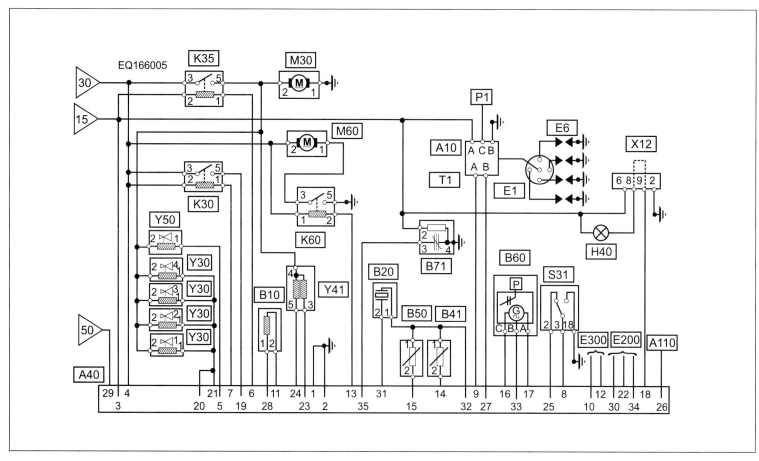

System wiring diagram, Renix MPi (19 1.7i cat, F3N742)

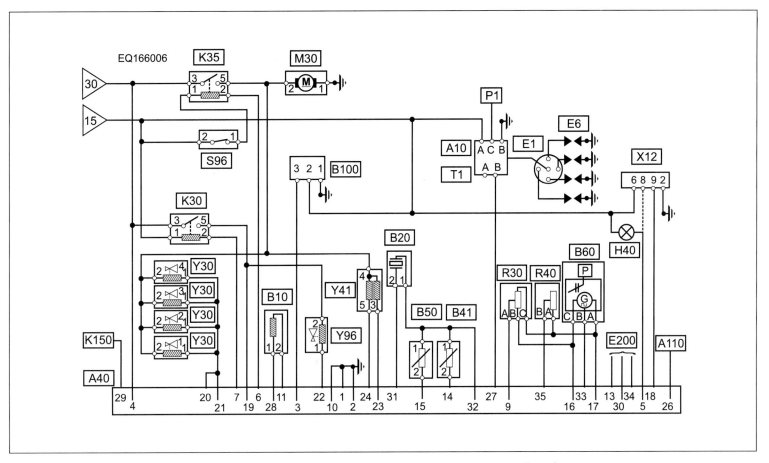

System wiring diagram, Renix MPi (21 2.0 turbo, J7R752)

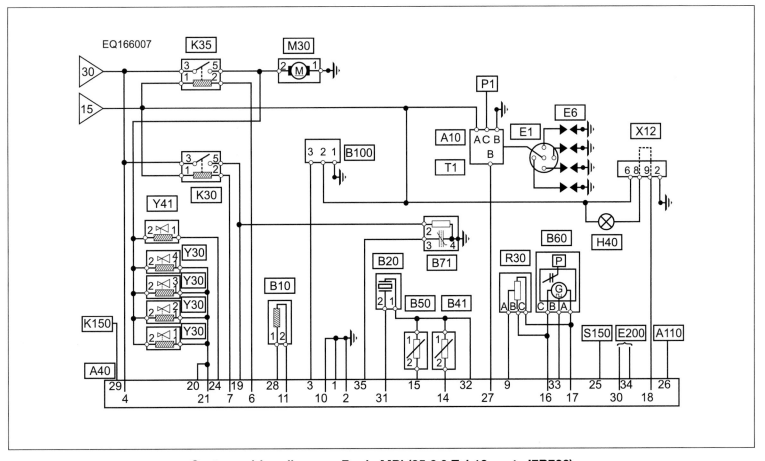

System wiring diagram, Renix MPi (25 2.0 Txi 12v cat, J7R726)

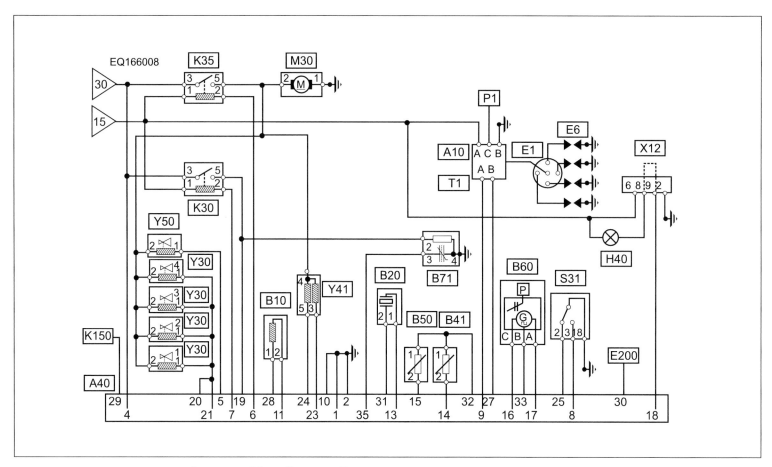

System wiring diagram, Renix MPi (Espace 2.2i 4x4 cat, J7T772)

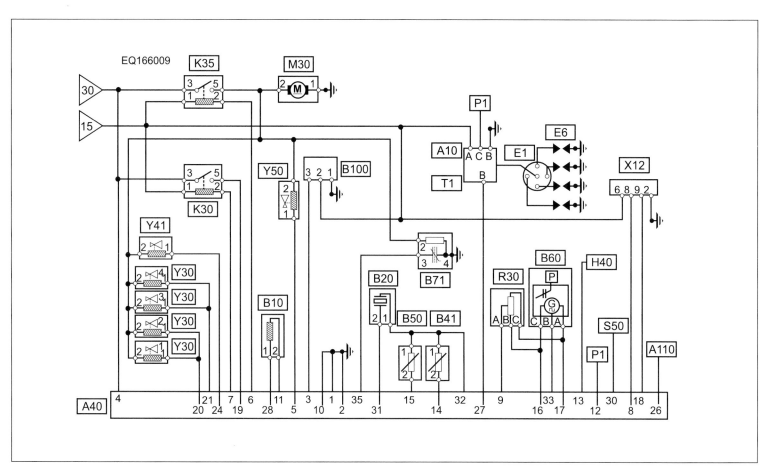

System wiring diagram, Renix MPi (Laguna 2.0i, F3R722)

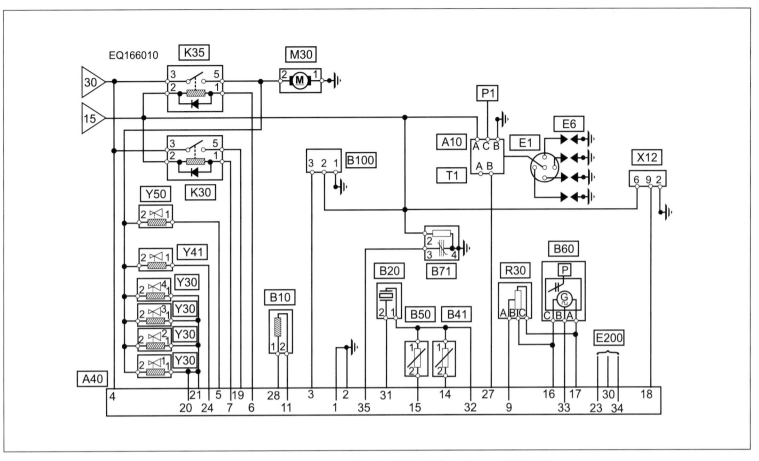

System wiring diagram, Renix MPi (Clio 1.8 cat, F3P712)

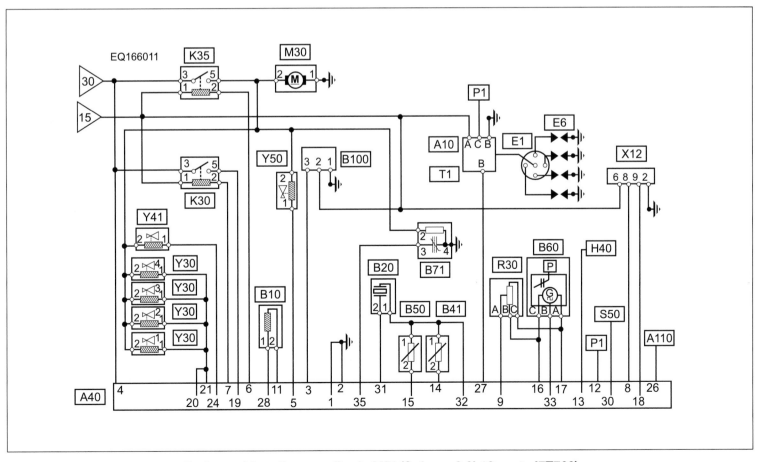

System wiring diagram, Renix MPi (Safrane 2.2i 12v cat, J7T760)

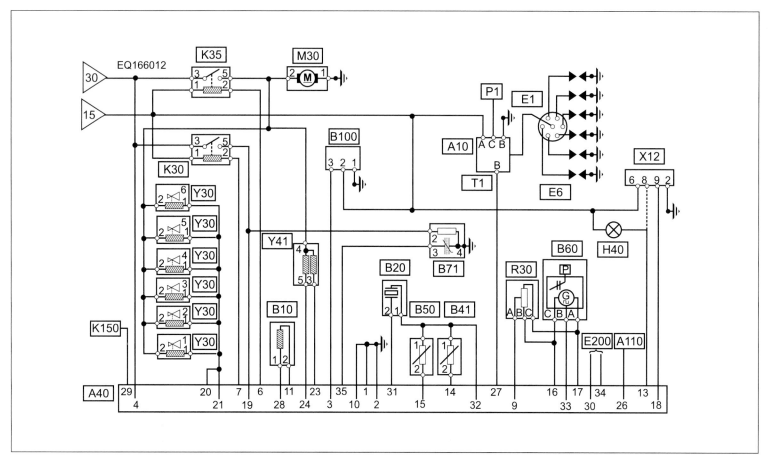

System wiring diagram, Renix MPi (25 2.9 V6, Z7W706)

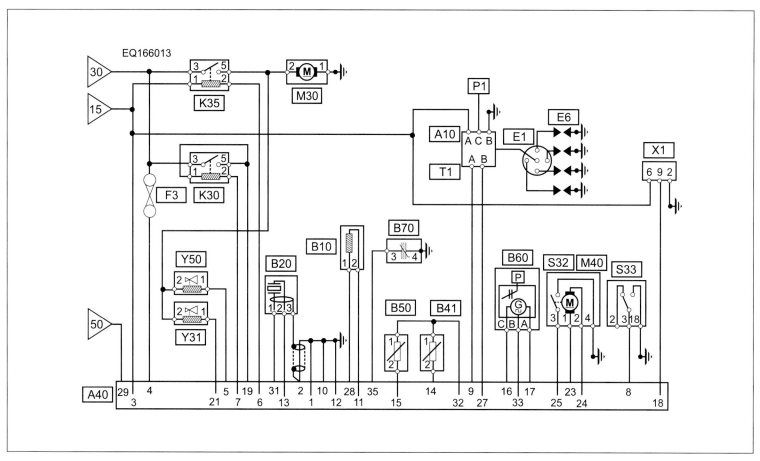

System wiring diagram, Renix SPi (5 1.7i cat, F3N G716)

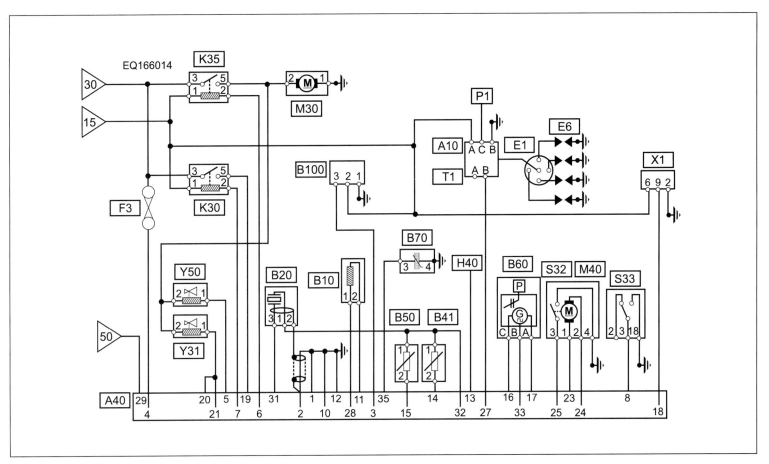

System wiring diagram, Renix SPi (19 1.7i cat, F3N740)

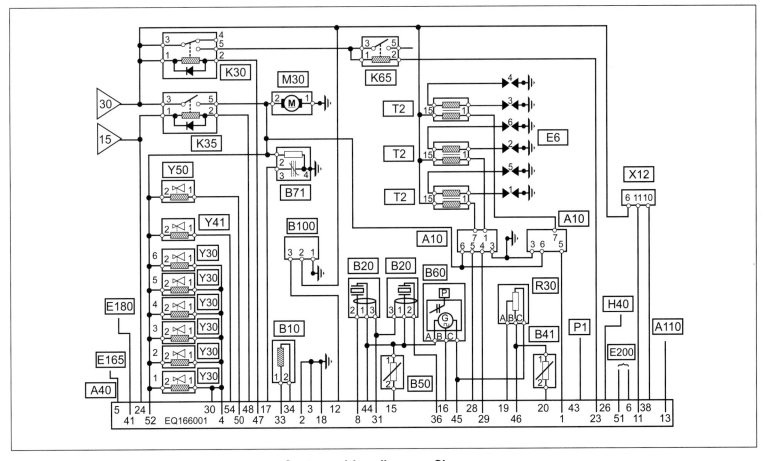

System wiring diagram, Siemens

Notes

Chapter 24
Rover

Contents

Index of Rover vehicles/systems

Model	Engine code	Year	System
111 1.1 SOHC	K8	1995 to 1998	Rover MEMS SPi
114 1.4 SOHC	**K8**	**1995 to 1997**	**Rover MEMS SPi**
200 vi DOHC 16v	18K16	1995 to 1997	Rover MEMS MPi
200 Vi DOHC 16v	18K16	1997 to 1999	Rover MEMS MPi
214 16v cat	**K16**	**1993 onwards**	**Rover MEMS MPi**
214 cat	K16	1990 to 1992	Rover MEMS SPi
214	**K16**	**1989 to 1992**	**Rover MEMS SPi**
216 SOHC 16v	D16A7	1989 to 1996	Honda PGMFI (4-cyl)
216 SOHC 16v cat	D16A6	1989 to 1996	Honda PGMFI (4-cyl)
216 SOHC 16v AT cat	D16Z2	1989 to 1996	Honda PGMFI (4-cyl)
216 DOHC 16v	D16A9	1990 to 1994	Honda PGMFI (4-cyl)
216 DOHC 16v AT	D16Z4	1990 to 1994	Honda PGMFI (4-cyl)
216 DOHC 16v cat	D16A8	1990 to 1994	Honda PGMFI (4-cyl)
216 DOHC 16v	16K16	1995 to 1997	Rover MEMS MPi
218is DOHC 16v	18K16	1997 to 1999	Rover MEMS MPi
220 GTi 16v	20M4	1991 to 1994	Rover MEMS MPi
220 GTi 16v	20M4	1993 onwards	Rover MEMS MPi
220 Turbo cat	20T16	1992 onwards	Rover MEMS MPi

Index of Rover vehicles/systems (continued)

Model	Engine code	Year	System
414 16v cat	K16	1993 onwards	Rover MEMS MPi
414 cat	K16	1990 to 1992	Rover MEMS SPi
414	K16	1990 to 1992	Rover MEMS SPi
416 SOHC 16v	D16A7	1989 to 1996	Honda PGMFI (4-cyl)
416 SOHC 16v cat	D16A6	1989 to 1996	Honda PGMFI (4-cyl)
416 DOHC 16v	D16A9	1990 to 1994	Honda PGMFI (4-cyl)
416 DOHC 16v AT	D16Z4	1990 to 1994	Honda PGMFI (4-cyl)
416 DOHC 16v cat	D16A8	1990 to 1994	Honda PGMFI (4-cyl)
416i AT SOHC 16V	D16Y3	1995 to 1998	Honda PGMFI (4-cyl)
416i AT SOHC 16V	D16B2	1997 to 1999	Honda PGMFI (4-cyl)
416I auto SOHC 16v	D16	1995 to 1996	Honda PGMFI (4-cyl)
420 i 2.0 16v	20M4	1991 to 1994	Rover MEMS MPi
420 i 2.0 16v	20M4	1992 onwards	Rover MEMS MPi
420 Turbo cat	20T16	1992 onwards	Rover MEMS MPi
618 SOHC 16v	**F18A3**	**1996 to 1998**	**Honda PGMFI (4-cyl)**
620 2.0 DOHC 16v turbo	20T4 T16	1994 to 1997	Rover MEMS MPi
620I SOHC 16v	F20Z2	1996 to 1998	Honda PGMFI (4-cyl)
620iS SOHC 16v	F20Z1	1996 to 1998	Honda PGMFI (4-cyl)
623I DOHC 16v	H23A3	1996 to 1998	Honda PGMFI (4-cyl)
800 Vitesse Sport Sterling	20T4	1994 to 1999	Rover MEMS MPi
820E 2.0 DOHC	**20HD M16e**	**1986 to 1990**	**Lucas 10CU SPi**
820i 16v Vitesse turbo	20T4	1992 onwards	Rover MEMS MPi
820i 16v	20T4	1991 to 1992	Rover MEMS MPi
820i 16v	20T4	1993 onwards	Rover MEMS MPi
820i 2.0 DOHC cat	**20HD M16**	**1988 to 1991**	**Lucas 14CUX MPi**
820SE 2.0 DOHC	20HD M16e	1986 to 1990	Lucas 10CU SPi
820Si 2.0 DOHC cat	20HD M16	1988 to 1991	Lucas 14CUX MPi
825 Sterling V6	**KV6**	**1996 to 1997**	**Rover MEMS MPi**
827 V6 SOHC 24v cat	V6 2.7	1988 to 1990	Honda PGMFI (6-cyl)
827 V6 SOHC 24v cat	V6 2.7	1990 to 1991	Honda PGMFI (6-cyl)
827 V6 SOHC 24v cat	V6 2.7	1991 to 1996	Honda PGMFI (6-cyl)
827 V6 SOHC 24v	**V6 2.7**	**1988 to 1990**	**Honda PGMFI (6-cyl)**
827 V6 SOHC 24v	V6 2.7	1990 to 1991	Honda PGMFI (6-cyl)
Cabrio 1.6	16K16	1996 to 1999	Rover MEMS MPi
Cabrio 1.8	18K16	1995 to 1999	Rover MEMS MPi
Coupe 1.6	16K16	1996 to 1999	Rover MEMS MPi
Coupe 1.8	18K16	1996 to 1997	Rover MEMS MPi
Maestro-MG 2.0 EFi	20H	1984 to 1989	Lucas 11CU MPi
Maestro-MG 2.0 EFi	20HE99	1989 to 1992	Lucas 11CU MPi
Metro 1.1i SOHC cat	K8	1991 to 1994	Rover MEMS SPi
Metro 1.4 16v	K16	1990 to 1992	Rover MEMS SPi
Metro 1.4 cat	K16	1990 to 1992	Rover MEMS SPi
Metro 1.4 cat	**K16**	**1993 on**	**Rover MEMS SPi**
Metro 1.4i 16v	K16	1991 to 1992	Rover MEMS MPi
Metro 1.4i 16v	K16	1993 onwards	Rover MEMS MPi
Metro 1.4i SOHC	K8	1991 to 1992	Rover MEMS SPi
Metro 1.4i SOHC cat	K8	1991 to 1994	Rover MEMS SPi
MGF 1.8 VVC DOHC 16v	K16	1995 to 1999	Rover MEMS MPi
Mini Cooper 1.3i AT	12A2DF76	1991 to 1992	Rover MEMS SPi
Mini Cooper 1.3i MT	12A2DF75	1991 to 1992	Rover MEMS SPi
Mini Cooper 1.3i cabriolet	2A2EF77	1993 on	Rover MEMS SPi
Montego 2.0 EFi AT	20HE14	1989 to 1993	Lucas 11CU MPi
Montego 2.0 EFi	20HE13	1989 to 1993	Lucas 11CU MPi
Montego 2.0 EFi	**20HE99**	**1989 to 1993**	**Lucas 11CU MPi**
Montego 2.0i AT	20 HE 37	1989 to 1992	Rover MEMS MPi
Montego 2.0i MT	20 HE 36	1989 to 1992	Rover MEMS MPi
Tourer 1.6	16K16	1996 to 1999	Rover MEMS MPi
Tourer 1.8	18K16	1996 to 1997	Rover MEMS MPi

Note: The vehicles accentuated in bold type are the actual vehicles upon which the ECM pin tables and wiring diagrams are based. Other vehicles with the same system may be similar; but are also likely to contain some differences.

Pin Table – Honda PGMFI (4-cyl)

Pin	Item	Test Condition	Measurements
A1	supply from main relay : t87	ignition on/engine running	nbv
A2	earth	ignition on/engine running	0.25 V (max)
A3	amplifier control signal	engine cranking/running	0 to 12 V (switching)
A4	intake air bypass solenoid driver : t1	ignition on	nbv
		engine running:	
		by-pass solenoid non-active	nbv
		by-pass solenoid active	1.25 V (max)
A5	–		
A6	automatic transmission		data not available
A7	SD warning lamp : t1	ignition on, lamp on	1.25 V (max)
		engine running:	
		no faults present	nbv
		faults present, lamp on	1.25 V (max)
A8	OS heater driver : t1	ignition on	nbv
		engine running:	
		OS heater active	1.25 V (max)
		OS heater inactive	nbv
A9	ISCV driver : t1	ignition on	nbv
		engine hot:	
		no load	30% (approx)
		under load	37% (approx)
A10	fuel pump relay driver : t85	engine cranking (starter supply)	1.25 V (max)
		engine running (pump relay)	1.25 V (max)
A11	injector driver (cyl 3) : t1	ignition on	nbv
		engine running, cold	3.0 to 4.0 ms
		engine running, hot	2.1 to 2.6 ms
		snap acceleration	> 8.0 ms
A12	injector driver (cyl 2) : t1	ignition on	nbv
		engine running, cold	3.0 to 4.0 ms
		engine running, hot	2.1 to 2.6 ms
		snap acceleration	> 8.0 ms
A13	injector driver (cyl 1) : t1	ignition on	nbv
		engine running, cold	3.0 to 4.0 ms
		engine running, hot	2.1 to 2.6 ms
		snap acceleration	> 8.0 ms
A14	shield return	ignition on/engine running	0.25 V (max)
A15	earth	ignition on/engine running	0.25 V (max)
A16	–		
A17	CFSV driver : t1	ignition on	nbv
		engine running, above idle, operating temperature	
		CFSV inactive	nbv
		CFSV active	0 to 12 V (switching)
		duty cycle	0 to 99%
A18	automatic transmission		data not available
A19-A20	–		
A21	ICOV driver : t1	ignition on	nbv
		engine running:	
		ICOV driver non-active	nbv
		ICOV driver active	1.25 V (max)
A22	engine mount solenoid driver : t1	ignition on	nbv
		engine running:	
		mount solenoid inactive	nbv
		mount solenoid active	1.25 V (max)
A23	–		
A24	EGR solenoid valve driver : t1	ignition on	nbv
		engine running:	
		EGR inactive	nbv
		EGR active	1.25 V (max)

Pin Table – Honda PGMFI (4-cyl) (continued)

Pin	Item	Test Condition	Measurements
A25	–		
A26	injector driver (cyl 4) : t1	ignition on	nbv
		engine running, cold	3.0 to 4.0 ms
		engine running, hot	2.1 to 2.6 ms
		snap acceleration	> 8.0 ms
B1	RPM sensor return: t1	engine running	0.25 V (max)
B2	TDC sensor return : t1	engine running	0.25 V (max)
B3	CID sensor return : t1	engine running	0.25 V (max)
B4	starter circuit : t50	engine cranking/running	nbv
B5	automatic transmission		data not available
B6	air conditioning		data not available
B7	automatic transmission		data not available
B8	supply from main relay : t87	ignition on/engine running	nbv
B9	RPM sensor signal : t2	engine cranking:	> 4.0 V AC (peak to peak)
		idle:	> 8.0 V AC (peak to peak)
		cruise:	> 14.0 V AC (peak to peak)
B10	TDC sensor signal : t2	engine cranking:	> 2.0 V AC (peak to peak)
		idle:	> 11.0 V AC (peak to peak)
		cruise:	> 14.0 V AC (peak to peak)
B11	CID signal : t2	engine cranking:	> 4.0 V AC (peak to peak)
		idle:	> 8.0 V AC (peak to peak)
		cruise:	> 14.0 V AC (peak to peak)
B12	VSS signal : t3	vehicle in motion	0 to 5 V (switching)
B13-B14	–		
B15	automatic transmission		data not available
B16	shield return	ignition on/engine running	0.25 V (max)
D1	MAP sensor return : t2	ignition on/engine running	0.25 V (max)
D2	MAP sensor supply : t3	ignition on/engine running	5.0 V ± 0.1
D3	MAP sensor signal : t1	WOT/ignition on	2.75 to 2.95 V
		idle speed	0.6 to 0.8 V (approx)
D4	ATS signal : t2	ignition on/engine running	20° C: 3.00 to 3.50 V
			50° C: 2.00 to 2.30 V
D5	automatic transmission		data not available
D6	automatic transmission		data not available
D7	alternator	engine running	nbv
D8	SD connector		data not available
D9-D10	–		
D11	supply from battery : t30	ignition off/on/engine running	nbv
D12	sensor return (ATS : t1, CTS : t1, linear EGR sensor : t1, TPS : t1)	ignition on/engine running	0.25 V (max)
D13	sensor supply : (TPS : t2, linear EGR sensor : t2)	ignition on/engine running	5.0 V ± 0.1
D14	automatic transmission		data not available
D15	–		
D16	OS signal : t3	ignition on, OS multiplug disconnected	0.4 to 0.5 V
		engine running, hot	200 to 1000 mV (switching)
		throttle fully-open	0.5 to 1.0 V
		deceleration (fuel cut-off)	0 to 0.5 V
		switching frequency	1 sec intervals (approx)
D17	linear EGR sensor signal : t3	engine running, EGR active	0.1 to 4.9 V (variable)
D18-D20	–		
D21	automatic transmission		data not available

eq34093

76 pin ECM multi-plug, Honda PGMFI (4-cyl)

Pin Table – Honda PGMFI (6-cyl)

Pin	Item	Test Condition	Measurements
A1	vacuum control box : t4 (secondary air injection solenoid valve)	ignition on	nbv
		engine running:	
		valve non-active	nbv
		valve active	1.25 V (max)
A2	vacuum control box (ICOV driver : t6)	ignition on	nbv
		engine running:	
		ICOV non-active	nbv
		ICOV active	1.25 V (max)
A4	neutral switch MT : t4		data not available
A5	cruise control		data not available
A6	VSS signal	vehicle in motion	0 to 12 V (switching)
A7	ignition switch : t50	engine cranking	nbv
A8	amplifier control signal : tB	engine cranking/running	0 to 12 V (switching)
A10	RPM sensor signal : t2	engine cranking:	> 4.0 V AC (peak to peak)
		idle:	> 8.0 V AC (peak to peak)
		cruise:	> 14.0 V AC (peak to peak)
A11	air conditioning		data not available
A12	supply from main relay : t87	ignition on/engine running	nbv
A13	SD warning lamp : t1	ignition on, lamp on	1.25 V (max)
		engine running:	
		no faults present	nbv
		faults present, lamp on	1.25 V (max)
A14	air conditioning		data not available
A15	air conditioning		data not available
A16	PSPS signal : t2	ignition on/engine running:	
		wheels straight	0.25 V (max)
		wheels turned	nbv
A17	alternator	engine running	nbv
A18	amplifier control signal : tB	engine cranking/running	0 to 12.0 V (switching)
A19	Ignition timing adjustment pot : t3	ignition on/engine running	0.1 to 4.9 V (variable)
A20	RPM sensor return : t1	engine cranking/running	0.25 V (max)
A21	CID sensor signal : t2	engine cranking:	> 2.0 V AC (peak to peak)
		idle:	> 11.0 V AC (peak to peak)
		cruise:	> 14.0 V AC (peak to peak)
A22	TDC sensor signal : t2	engine cranking:	> 2.0 V AC (peak to peak)
		idle:	> 11.0 V AC (peak to peak)
		cruise:	> 14.0 V AC (peak to peak)
A23	ATS signal : t2	ignition on/engine running	20 to 40° C: 1.0 to 3.0 V
A24	TPS signal : t3	ignition on/engine running:	
		throttle closed	0.5 V
		throttle fully open	4.50 V (approx)
A25	BPS signal : t3	ignition on/engine running:	
		1013 mbar	4.0 V
		970 mbar	3.7 V
		900 mbar	3.0 V
		800 mbar	2.1 V
		700 mbar	1.3 V
A26	MAP sensor signal : t3	WOT/ignition on	2.75 to 2.95 V
		idle speed	0.6 to 0.8 V
A27	sensor supply (MAP : t2, BPS : t2, TPS : t2, linear EGR sensor : t2, timing adjust : t2)	ignition on/engine running	5.0 V ± 0.1
A28	sensor supply (MAP : t2, BPS : t2, TPS : t2, linear EGR sensor : t2, timing adjust : t2)	ignition on/engine running	5.0 V ± 0.1
A29	CID sensor return : t1	engine cranking/running	0.25 V (max)
A30	TDC sensor return : t1	engine cranking/running	0.25 V (max)
A31	CTS signal : t2	ignition on/engine running	0 to 20° C: 2.0 to 3.5 V 80 to 100° C: 0.5 to 0.8 V

Pin Table – Honda PGMFI (6-cyl) (continued)

Pin	Item	Test Condition	Measurements
A32	linear EGR sensor signal : t3	engine running, EGR active	0.4 to 4.0 V (variable)
A33	oxygen sensor signal (rear) : t1	ignition on, OS multiplug disconnected	0.4 to 0.5 V
		engine running, hot	200 to 1000 mV (switching)
		throttle fully-open	0.5 to 1.0 V
		fuel cut-off	0 to 0.5 V
		switching frequency	1 sec intervals (approx)
A34	oxygen sensor signal (front) : t1	ignition on, OS multiplug disconnected	0.4 to 0.5 V
		engine running, hot	200 to 1000 mV (switching)
		throttle fully-open	0.5 to 1.0 V
		fuel cut-off	0 to 0.5 V
		switching frequency	1 sec intervals (approx)
A35	sensor return, (CTS : t1, MAP : t1, ATS : t1, TPS : t1, BPS : t1, linear EGR sensor : t1, timing adjuster : t1)	ignition on/engine running	0.25 V (max)
A36	sensor return, (CTS : t1, MAP : t1, ATS : t1, TPS : t1, BPS : t1, linear EGR sensor : t1, timing adjuster : t1)	ignition on/engine running	0.25 V (max)
B1	shield earth	ignition on/engine running	0.25 V (max)
B2	shield earth	ignition on/engine running	0.25 V (max)
B3	vacuum control box (ICOV driver : t5)	ignition on	nbv
		engine running:	
		ICOV inactive	nbv
		ICOV active	1.25 V (max)
B4	fuel pump relay driver: t85	ignition on	nbv
		engine cranking/running	1.25 V (max)
B5	vacuum control box : t2 (EGR solenoid valve driver : t1)	ignition on	nbv
		engine running:	
		EGR inactive	nbv
		EGR active	1.25 V (max)
B6	injector driver, (cylinder 5) : t1	ignition on	nbv
		engine running, cold	3.5 ms
		engine running, hot	2.4 to 2.7 ms
		snap acceleration	> 8 ms
		deceleration	1 ms (approx)
B7	injector driver (cylinder 6) : t1	ignition on	nbv
		engine running, cold	3.5 ms
		engine running, hot	2.4 to 2.7 ms
		snap acceleration	> 8 ms
		deceleration	1 ms (approx)
B8	main relay driver : t85	ignition on	nbv, briefly, then 1.25 V (max)
		engine running	1.25 V (max)
B9	main relay driver : t85	ignition on	nbv, briefly, then 1.25 V (max)
		engine running	1.25 V (max)
B10	supply from battery : t30	ignition off/on/engine running	nbv
B11	supply from relay : t87	ignition on/engine running	nbv
B12	vacuum control box : t1 (fuel pressure solenoid valve : t1)	ignition on	nbv
		engine running:	
		valve inactive	nbv
		valve active	1.25 V (max)
B13	ISCV driver : t1	ignition on	nbv
		engine running, idle speed	
		cold	6.0 to 6.5 V
		hot	7.0 to 9.0 V
		duty cycle	30 to 60%

Pin	Item	Test Condition	Measurements
B14	injector driver (cylinder 4) : t1	ignition on	nbv
		engine running, cold	3.5 ms
		engine running, hot	2.4 to 2.7 ms
		snap acceleration	> 8 ms
		deceleration	1 ms (approx)
B15	injector driver (cylinder 3) : t1	ignition on	nbv
		engine running, cold	3.5 ms
		engine running, hot	2.4 to 2.7 ms
		snap acceleration	> 8 ms
		deceleration	1 ms (approx)
B16	injector driver (cylinder 2) : t1	ignition on	nbv
		engine running, cold	3.5 ms
		engine running, hot	2.4 to 2.7 ms
		snap acceleration	> 8 ms
		deceleration	1 ms (approx)
B17	injector driver (cylinder 1) : t1	ignition on	nbv
		engine running, cold	3.5 ms
		engine running, hot	2.4 to 2.7 ms
		snap acceleration	> 8 ms
		deceleration	1 ms (approx)

53 pin ECM multi-plug, Honda PGMFI (6-cyl)

Pin Table – Lucas 10CU SPi

Pin	Item	Test Condition	Measurements
1-2	–		
3	supply from battery : t30	ignition on/off/engine running	nbv
4	supply from ignition switch : t15	ignition on/engine running	nbv
5	TS, idle contact : t2	ignition on/engine running:	
		throttle closed	0 V
		throttle open	5 V
6	–		
7	SD connector		data not available
8	SD connector		data not available
9	sensor earth return : t1	ignition on/engine running	0.25 V (max)
10	–		
11	CTS signal : t2	ignition on/engine running	20° C: 2.70 V
			80° C: 0.75 V
12	TPS signal : t3	ignition on/engine running:	
		throttle closed	0.30 to 0.70 V
		throttle fully open	4.50 V (approx)
13	earth	ignition on/engine running	0.25 V (max)
14	injector driver : t1	ignition on	nbv
		engine running, cold	> 3.0 ms
		engine running, hot	2.0 ms
		snap acceleration	> 5 ms
15	earth	ignition on/engine running	0.25 V (max)
16	TPS supply : t2	ignition on/engine running	5.0 V ± 0.1
17	ambient ATS signal : t2	ignition on/engine running	20° C: 1.055 to 1.435 V
			50° C: 0.31 to 0.55 V
18	supply from starter circuit : t50	engine cranking	nbv

Pin Table – Lucas 10CU SPi (continued)

Pin	Item	Test Condition	Measurements
19	CAS signal : t2	engine cranking:	> 2.0 V AC (peak to peak)
		idle:	> 11.0 V AC (peak to peak)
		cruise:	> 14.0 V AC (peak to peak)
20	knock sensor signal : t2	engine running, KS active	1.0 V AC (peak to peak)
21	CAS return : t1	ignition on/engine running	0.25 V (max)
22-23	–		
24	SD connector		data not available
25	supply from relay : t87	ignition on/engine running	nbv
26	–		
27	stepper motor phase 5	idle speed, active	0 to nbv (switching)
28	stepper motor phase 4	idle speed, active	0 to nbv (switching)
29	stepper motor phase 3	idle speed, active	0 to nbv (switching)
30	main relay driver : t85	ignition off	nbv
		ignition on/engine running	1.25 V (max)
31	stepper motor phase 2	idle speed, active	0 to nbv (switching)
32	–		
33	temperature gauge	ignition on/engine running	
		cold	8.0 to 9.0 V (average)
		hot	6.0 to 7.0 (average)
34	–		
35	stepper motor supply : t1	idle speed, active	0 to nbv (switching)
36-37	–		
38	ATS signal : t2	ignition on/engine running	20° C: 2.50 V
			60° C: 0.55 to 0.65 V
39	–		
40	ignition coil driver : t1	igntion on	nbv
		dynamic volt drop	2.0 V (max)
		primary switching wire	200 V (min)

40 pin ECM multi-plug, Lucas 10CU SPi

Pin Table – Lucas 11CU MPi

Pin	Item	Test Condition	Measurements
1	injectors driver : t1	ignition on	nbv
		engine running, cold	3.8 ms
		engine running hot:	
		idle	2.4 ms
		2000 rpm	2.2 ms
		3000 rpm	2.1 ms
		snap acceleration	> 6.0 ms
		deceleration	0 ms
2	stepper motor : t1	idle speed, active	0 to 12 V (switching)
3	stepper motor : t3	idle speed, active	0 to 12 V (switching)
4	MFU main relay driver : t6/3	ignition off	nbv
		ignition on/engine running	1.25 V (max)
5	earth	ignition on/engine running	0.25 V (max)
6	VSS signal : t3	vehicle in motion	5.0 to 7.0 V (average)

Pin	Item	Test Condition	Measurements
7	instrument panel (temperature gauge drive)	ignition on/engine running	
		cold	8.0 to 9.0 V (average)
		hot	6.0 to 7.0 (average)
8	–		
9	TPS supply : t2	ignition on/engine running	5.0 V ± 0.1
10	CTS signal : t2	ignition on/engine running	20° C: 2.70 V
			80° C: 0.75 V
11	–		
12	sensor return	ignition on/engine running	0.25 V (max)
13	Ignition coil driver : t1 (via ballast resistor)	ignition on/engine running	nbv
		dynamic volt drop	2.0 V (max)
		primary switching	200 V (min)
14	stepper motor : t2	idle speed, active	0 to 12 V (switching)
15	stepper motor : t4	idle speed, active	0 to 12 V (switching)
16	fuel pump relay driver : t6/1	ignition on	nbv
		engine cranking/running	1.25 V (max)
17	earth	ignition on/engine running	0.25 V (max)
18	inertia switch : t1 (ignition supply)	inertia switch closed	nbv
		inertia switch open	0 V
19	supply from battery : t30	ignition off/on/engine running	nbv
20	flat timing signal (ignition ECM : t8)	engine cranking/running	0 V to nbv (switching)
21	MAF sensor signal : t3	ignition on	0.20 to 0.70 V
		idle	1.5 V
		3000 rpm	2.4 V
		snap throttle open	> 4.0 V
		full load	> 6.00 V
22	TPS signal : t3	ignition on/engine running	
		throttle closed	0.325 ± 0.010 V
		throttle fully open	4.20 to 4.90 V (approx)
23	supply from main relay : t8/8	ignition on/engine running	nbv
24	earth	ignition on/engine running	0.25 V (max)
25	earth	ignition on/engine running	0.25 V (max)

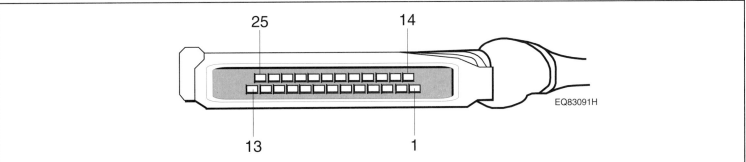

25 pin ECM multi-plug, Lucas 11CU MPi

Pin Table – Lucas 14CUX MPi

Pin	Item	Test Condition	Measurements
1	stepper motor : t4	idle speed, active	0 to 12 V (switching)
2	supply from main relay : t87	ignition on/engine running	nbv
3	TPS supply : t3	ignition on/engine running	5.0 V ± 0.1
4	OS return : t4	ignition on/engine running	0.25 V (max)
5	heated rear window input		data not available
6	VSS signal : t3	vehicle in motion	5.0 to 7.0 V (average)
7	CTS signal : t2	ignition on/engine running	20° C: 2.70 V
			80° C: 0.75 V
8	–		

Pin Table – Lucas 14CUX MPi (continued)

Pin	Item	Test Condition	Measurements
9	SD connector : t5	ignition on	nbv
10	–		
11	instrument panel (temperature gauge drive)	ignition on/engine running:	
		cold	8.0 to 9.0 V (average)
		hot	6.0 to 7.0 V (average)
12	main relay driver : t85	ignition off	nbv
		ignition on	1.25 V (max)
13	injectors driver : t1	ignition on	nbv
		engine running, cold	3.8 ms
		engine running, hot:	
		idle	2.4 ms
		2000 rpm	2.2 ms
		3000 rpm	2.1 ms
		snap acceleration	> 6.0 ms
		deceleration (fuel cut off)	0 ms
14	earth	ignition on/engine running	0.25 V (max)
15	supply from battery : t30	ignition off/on/engine running	nbv
16	fuel pump relay driver : t85	ignition on	nbv
		engine cranking/running	1.25 V (max)
17	flat timing signal to ignition ECM : t8	engine running, idle	0 V nbv (switching)
18	SD connector : t4	ignition on	nbv
19	inertia switch : t1 (ignition supply)	inertia switch closed	nbv
		inertia switch open	0 V
20	TPS signal : t2	ignition on/engine running:	
		throttle closed	0.325 V ± 0.01
		throttle fully open	4.20 to 4.90 V (approx)
21	AC magnetic clutch relay : t87		data not available
22	–		
23	OS sensor : t3	ignition on, OS multiplug disconnected	0.4 to 0.5 V
		engine running, hot	200 to 1000 mV (switching)
		throttle fully-open	0.5 to 1.0 V
		deceleration (fuel cut-off)	0 to 0.5 V
		switching frequency	1 sec intervals (approx)
24	FRTS signal : t2	ignition on/engine running	26° C: 2.6 V
25	sensor return	ignition on/engine running	0.25 V (max)
26	stepper motor : t3	idle speed, active	0 to 12 V (switching)
27	earth: diagnostic connector : t3	ignition on/engine running	0.25 V (max)
28	stepper motor : t2	idle speed, active	0 to 12 V (switching)
29	stepper motor : t1	idle speed, active	0 to 12 V (switching)
30	–		
31	SD connector : t1	ignition on	nbv
32	–		
33	CFSV driver : t1	ignition on	nbv
		engine running, above idle, operating temperature:	
		CFSV inactive	nbv
		CFSV active	0 to 12 V (switching)
		duty cycle	0 to 99%
34	starter relay driver : t85	engine cranking	1.25 V (max)
35	MAF sensor signal : t2	ignition on	0.20 to 0.70 V
		idle	1.50 V
		3000 rpm	2.40 V
		snap open throttle	> 4.50 V
		full load	> 6.00 V
36	CFSV driver : t1	ignition on	nbv
		engine running, above idle, operating temperature:	
		CFSV inactive	nbv
		CFSV active	0 to 12 V (switching)
		duty cycle	0 to 99%

Pin	Item	Test Condition	Measurements
37	SD connector : t2	ignition on	nbv
38	–		
39	engine speed signal from ignition ECM : t11	engine cranking/running	4.0 to 6.0 V (average)
40	earth	ignition on/engine running	0.25 V (max)

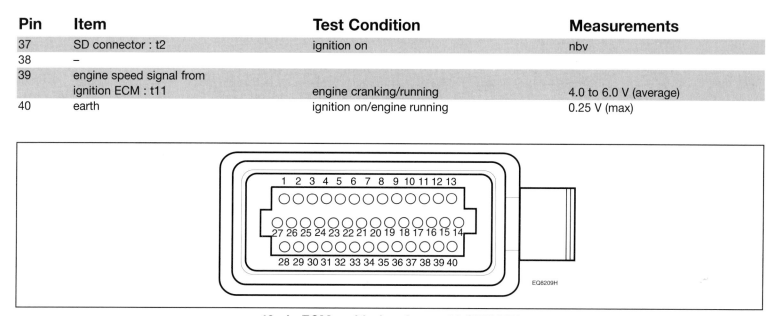

40 pin ECM multi-plug, Lucas 14 CUX MPi

Pin Table – Rover MEMS MPi (Rover 214i, K16)

Pin	Item	Test Condition	Measurements
1	injector driver (cyl 4) : t1	ignition on	nbv
		engine running, cold	3.0 to 3.5 ms
		engine running, hot:	
		idle	2.0 to 2.5 ms
		2000 rpm	2.0 to 2.5 ms
		3000 rpm	2.0 to 2.5 ms
		snap acceleration	6.0 ms
		deceleration (fuel cut off)	0 V
2	stepper motor phase 2	idle speed, active	0 to nbv (switching)
3	stepper motor phase 1	idle speed, active	0 to nbv (switching)
4	main relay driver : t85	ignition off	nbv
		ignition on/engine running	1.25 V (max)
5-6	–		
7	OS signal : t3	ignition on, OS multiplug disconnected	0.4 to 0.5 V
		engine running, hot	200 to 1000 mV (switching)
		throttle fully-open	0.5 to 1.0 V
		deceleration (fuel cut-off)	0 to 0.5 V
		switching frequency	1 sec intervals (approx)
8	TPS signal : t3	ignition on/engine running:	
		throttle closed	0.40 to 0.60 V
		throttle fully open	4.25 to 4.50 V
9	TPS supply : t2	ignition on/engine running	5.0 V ± 0.1
10	SD connector : t10		data not available
11	supply from ignition switch : t15	ignition on/engine running	nbv
12-13	–		
14	earth	ignition on/engine running	0.25 V (max)
15	diagnostics input : t15	ignition on/engine running	5.0 V ± 0.1
16	ATS signal : t2	ignition on/engine running	20° C: 3.00 V
			78° C: 0.78 V
17	–		
18	oxygen sensor return : t4	ignition on/engine running	0.25 V (max)
19	AC magnetic clutch relay		data not available
20	fuel pump relay driver : t85	ignition on	nbv
		engine cranking/running	1.25 V (max)

Pin Table – Rover MEMS MPi (Rover 214i, K16) (continued)

Pin	Item	Test Condition	Measurements
21	CFSV driver : t1	ignition on	nbv
		engine running, above idle, operating temperature:	
		CFSV inactive	nbv
		CFSV active	0 to 12 V (switching)
		duty cycle	0 to 99%
22	stepper motor phase 3	idle speed, active	0 to nbv
23	injector driver (cyl 2) : t1	ignition on	nbv
		engine running, cold	3.0 to 3.5 ms
		engine running, hot:	
		idle	2.0 to 2.5 ms
		2000 rpm	2.0 to 2.5 ms
		3000 rpm	2.0 to 2.5 ms
		snap acceleration	6.0 ms
		deceleration (fuel cut off)	0 V
24	injector driver (cyl 1) : t1	ignition on	nbv
		engine running, cold	3.0 to 3.5 ms
		engine running, hot:	
		idle	2.0 to 2.5 ms
		2000 rpm	2.0 to 2.5 ms
		3000 rpm	2.0 to 2.5 ms
		snap acceleration	6.0 ms
		deceleration (fuel cut off)	0 V
25	ignition coil driver : t1	ignition on	nbv
		engine running:	
		dynamic volt drop	2.0 V (max)
		primary switching	200 V (min)
26	injector driver (cyl 3) : t1	ignition on	nbv
		engine running, cold	3.0 to 3.5 ms
		engine running, hot:	
		idle	2.0 to 2.5 ms
		2000 rpm	2.0 to 2.5 ms
		3000 rpm	2.0 to 2.5 ms
		snap acceleration	6.0 ms
		deceleration (fuel cut off)	0 V
27	stepper motor phase 4	idle speed, active	nbv to 0 V
28	supply from main relay : t87	ignition on/engine running	nbv
29	ECM earth	ignition on/engine running	0.25 V (max)
30	sensor return	ignition on/engine running	0.25 V (max)
31	CAS signal : t2	engine cranking :	> 2.0 V AC (peak to peak)
		idle :	> 11.0 V AC (peak to peak)
		cruise :	> 14.0 V AC (peak to peak)
32	CAS return : t1	ignition on/engine running	0.25 V (max)
33	CTS signal : t2	ignition on/engine running	20° C: 3.00 V
			78° C: 0.78 V
34	–		
35	AC high pressure, safety switch		data not available
36	OS relay driver : t85	ignition on	nbv
		engine running	0.25 V (max)

24.6 36 pin ECM multi-plug, Rover MEMS MPi (Rover 214i, K16)

Pin Table – Rover MEMS MPi (825 Sterling V6)

Terminal A, black

Pin	Item	Test Condition	Measurements
1	injector driver (cylinder 5) : t1	ignition on	nbv
		engine running, cold	> 3.5 ms
		engine running, hot	3.5 ms
		snap acceleration	20 ms (approx)
		deceleration	1 ms (approx)
2	ICOV 1 driver : t1	ignition on	nbv
		engine running	
		ICOV inactive	nbv
		ICOV active	1.25 V (max)
3	–		
4	engine cooling fan relay		data not available
5-7	–		
8	MAP sensor signal : t3	ignition on	5.0 V
		engine running:	
		WOT	5.0 V
		idle speed	1.25 to 1.30 V
9	–		
10	OTS signal : t2	ignition on/engine running	15 to 30° C: 2.0 to 3.0 V
			80° C: 0.5 to 1.0 V
11	–		
12	TPS signal : t3	ignition on/engine running:	
		throttle closed	0.40 to 0.60 V
		throttle open	4.25 to 4.50 V
13	sensor return (MAP sensor : t1, TPS : t1, CTS : t1, ATS : t1, OTS : t1, FTS : t1)	ignition on/engine running	0.25 V (max)
14	ATS signal : t2	ignition on/engine running	20° C: 3.00 V
15	CTS signal : t2	ignition on/engine running	20° C: 2.00 to 2.50 V
			80° C: 0.78 V
16-17	–		
18	TPS supply : t2	ignition on/engine running	5.0 V ± 0.1
19	air conditioning		data not available
20	–		
21	earth	ignition on/engine running	0.25 V (max)
22	main relay driver : t85	ignition off	nbv
		ignition on/engine running	1.25 V (max)
23	ICOV 2 driver : t1	ignition on	nbv
		engine running:	
		ICOV inactive	nbv
		ICOV active	1.25 V (max)
24	injector driver (cylinder 4) : t1	ignition on	nbv
		engine running, cold	> 3.5 ms
		engine running, hot	3.5 ms
		snap acceleration	20 ms (approx)
		deceleration	1 ms (approx)
25	ignition coil 3 driver : t1	ignition on	nbv
		engine running:	
		dynamic volt drop	2.0 V (max)
		primary switching	200 V (min)
26	ignition coil 2 driver : t1	ignition on	nbv
		engine running:	
		dynamic volt drop	2.0 V (max)
		primary switching	200 V (min)
27	–		
28	engine cooling fan relay		data not available
29	air conditioning		data not available
30	fuel pump relay driver: t85	ignition on	nbv
		engine cranking/running	1.25 V (max)

Pin Table – Rover MEMS MPi (825 Sterling V6) (continued)

Terminal A, black (continued)

Pin	Item	Test Condition	Measurements
31-32	–		
33	supply from ignition switch : t15	ignition on/engine running	nbv
34	FTS signal : t2	ignition on/engine running	26°C: 2.6 V
35	–		
36	MAP sensor supply : t2	ignition on/engine running	5.0 V ± 0.1

Terminal B, red

Pin	Item	Test Condition	Measurements
1	camshaft sensor (inductive) signal : t1	idle speed	8.0 V AC (peak to peak)
2	camshaft sensor (inductive) return : t2	ignition on/engine running	0.25 V (max)
3-4	–		
5	OS signal 2 : t3	ignition on, OS multiplug disconnected	0.4 to 0.5 V
		engine running, hot	200 to 1000 mV (switching)
		throttle fully-open	0.5 to 1.0 V
		deceleration (fuel cut-off)	0 to 0.5 V
		switching frequency	1 sec intervals (approx)
6	OS return : t4	ignition on/engine running	0.25 V (max)
7-8	–		
9	tachometer		data not available
10	stepper motor : t6	idle speed, active	0 to 5.0 V (switching)
11	–		
12	injector driver (cylinder 1) : t1	ignition on	nbv
		engine running, cold	> 3.5 ms
		engine running, hot	3.5 ms
		snap acceleration	20 ms (approx)
		deceleration	1 ms (approx)
13	injector driver (cylinder 2) : t1	ignition on	nbv
		engine running, cold	> 3.5 ms
		engine running, hot	3.5 ms
		snap acceleration	20 ms (approx)
		deceleration	1 ms (approx)
14	injector driver (cylinder 3) : t1	ignition on	nbv
		engine running, cold	> 3.5 ms
		engine running, hot	3.5 ms
		snap acceleration	20 ms (approx)
		deceleration	1 ms (approx)
15	stepper motor : t4	idle speed, active	0 to 5.0 V (switching)
16	earth	ignition on/engine running	0.25 V (max)
17	CFSV driver : t1	ignition on	nbv
		engine running, above idle, operating temperature	
		CFSV inactive	nbv
		CFSV active	0 to 12 V (switching)
		duty cycle	0 to 99%
18	cruise control		data not available
19	air conditioning		data not available
20-22	–		
23	shield return	ignition on/engine running	0.25 V (max)
24	earth	ignition on/engine running	0.25 V (max)
25	CAS signal : t1	engine cranking:	> 4.0 V AC (peak to peak)
		idle:	> 8.0 V AC (peak to peak)
		cruise:	> 14.0 V AC (peak to peak)
26	CAS return: t2	engine running	0.25 V (max)
27	OS signal 1 : t3	ignition on, OS multiplug disconnected	0.4 to 0.5 V
		engine running, hot	200 to 1000 mV (switching)
		throttle fully-open	0.5 to 1.0 V
		deceleration (fuel cut-off)	0 to 0.5 V
		switching frequency	1 sec intervals (approx)

Pin	Item	Test Condition	Measurements
28	OS return : t4	ignition on/engine running	0.25 V (max)
29	–		
30	air conditioning		data not available
31	SD connector : t7		data not available
32	–		
33	stepper motor : t3	idle speed, active	0 to 5.0 V (switching)
34	stepper motor : t1	idle speed, active	0 to 5.0 V (switching)
35	injector driver (cylinder 6) : t1	ignition on	nbv
		engine running, cold	> 3.5 ms
		engine running, hot	3.5 ms
		snap acceleration	20 ms (approx)
		deceleration	1 ms (approx)
36	ignition coil 1 driver : t1	ignition on	nbv
		engine running:	
		dynamic volt drop	2.0 V (max)
		primary switching	200 V (min)

1   EQ20092H   12

24 ——   —— 13

25   36

36+36 pin ECM multi-plug, Rover MEMS MPi (825 Sterling V6)

Pin Table – Rover MEMS SPi (Rover 114)

Pin	Item	Test Condition	Measurements
1	injector supply	ignition on/engine running	nbv
2	stepper motor phase 4	idle speed, active	0 to nbv (switching)
3	stepper motor phase 3	idle speed, active	0 to nbv (switching)
4	MFU main relay driver : t85	ignition off	nbv
		ignition on/engine running	1.25 V (max)
5	–		
6	MFU manifold relay driver : t85	ignition on	nbv
		engine running:	
		cold:	1.25 V (max)
		hot:	nbv
7	oxygen sensor return : t4	ignition on/engine running	0.25 V (max)
8	TPS signal : t3	ignition on/engine running	
		throttle closed	0.20 to 0.60 V
		throttle fully open	4.25 to 4.50 V
9	TPS supply : t2	ignition on/engine running	5.0 V ± 0.1
10	diagnostic connector, output		data not available
11	supply from ignition switch : t15	ignition on/engine running	nbv
12	–		
13	engine immobiliser		data not available
14	–		
15	diagnostic connector, input	ignition on/engine running	5.0 V ± 0.1
16	ATS signal: t2	ignition on/engine running	20° C: 3.00 V
			78° C: 0.78 V
17	–		
18	oxygen sensor signal : t3	ignition on, OS multiplug disconnected	0.8 V
		engine running, hot	200 to 1000 mV (switching)
		throttle fully open	0.5 to 1.0 V
		fuel cut-off	0 to 0.5 V
		switching frequency	1 sec intervals (approx)

Pin Table – Rover MEMS SPi (Rover 114) (continued)

Pin	Item	Test Condition	Measurements
19	–		
20	MFU pump relay driver : t86	ignition on	nbv
		engine cranking/running	1.25 V (max)
21	CFSV driver : t1	ignition on	nbv
		engine running, above idle, operating temperature:	
		CFSV inactive	nbv
		CFSV active	0 to 12 V (switching)
		duty cycle	0 to 99%
22	stepper motor phase 1	idle speed, active	0 to nbv (switching)
23	–		
24	injector driver : t1	ignition on	nbv
		engine cranking, cold	14.8 ms
		engine running, cold	2.2 ms
		engine running, hot:	
		idle	2.0 ms
		2000 rpm	1.8 ms
		3000 rpm	1.8 ms
25	ignition coil driver : t1	ignition on	nbv
		engine running:	
		dynamic volt drop	2.0 V (max)
		primary switching	200 V (min)
26	–		
27	stepper motor phase 2	idle speed, active	0 to nbv (switching)
28	supply from MFU main relay : t87	ignition on/engine running	nbv
29	main ECM earth	ignition on/engine running	0.25 V (max)
30	sensor return (TPS : t1, CTS : t1, ATS : t1)	ignition on/engine running	0.25 V (max)
31	CAS signal : t2	engine cranking:	> AC 2.0 V (peak to peak)
		idle:	> AC 11.0 V (peak to peak)
		cruise:	> AC 14.0 V (peak to peak)
32	CAS return : t1	ignition on/engine running	0.25 V (max)
33	CTS signal : t2	ignition on/engine running	20°C: 3.00 V
			78°C: 0.78 V
34	–		
35	–		
36	OS relay driver : t86	ignition on	nbv
		engine running, OS heater active	1.25 V (max)

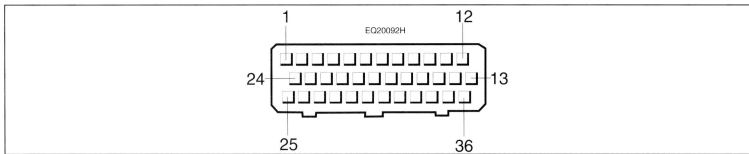

36 pin ECM multi-plug, Rover MEMS SPi (Rover 114)

Pin Table – Rover MEMS SPi (Metro K16)

Pin	Item	Test Condition	Measurements
1	–		
2	stepper motor : t2	idle speed, active	0 to 12 V (switching)
3	stepper motor : t1	idle speed, active	0 to 12 V (switching)
4	MFU main relay driver : t6/3	ignition off	nbv
		ignition on/engine running	1.25 V (max)
5	–		

Pin	Item	Test Condition	Measurements
6	MFU manifold relay driver : t6/5	ignition on	nbv
		engine running:	
		cold:	1.25 V (max)
		hot:	nbv
7	oxygen sensor return : t4	ignition on/engine running	0.25 V (max)
8	TPS signal : t3	ignition on/engine running:	
		throttle closed	0.20 to 0.60 V
		throttle fully open	4.25 to 4.50 V
9	TPS supply : t2	ignition on/engine running	5.0 V ± 0.1
10	SD connector : t2		data not available
11	supply from ignition switch : t15	ignition on/engine running	nbv
12	–		
13	TS, idle contact : t2	ignition on/engine running:	
		throttle closed	0 V
		throttle open	5.0 V ± 0.1
14	AT: P/N sensor		data not available
15	SD connector	ignition on/engine running	5.0 V ± 0.1
16	ATS signal : t2	ignition on/engine running	20° C: 3.00 V
			78° C: 0.78 V
17	–		
18	oxygen sensor signal : t3	ignition on, OS multiplug disconnected	0.4 to 0.5 V
		engine running, hot	200 to 1000 mV (switching)
		throttle fully-open	0.5 to 1.0 V
		deceleration (fuel cut-off)	0 to 0.5 V
		switching frequency	1 sec intervals (approx)
19	–		
20	MFU pump relay driver : t6/1	ignition off	nbv
		engine cranking/running	1.25 V (max)
21	CFSV driver : t1	ignition on	nbv
		engine running, above idle, operating temperature:	
		CFSV inactive	nbv
		CFSV active	0 to 12 V (switching)
		duty cycle	0 to 99%
22	stepper motor : t3	idle speed, active	0 to 12 V (switching)
23	–		
24	injector driver : t1	ignition on	nbv
		engine cranking, cold	14.8 ms
		engine running, cold	2.2 ms
		engine running, hot	2.0 ms
		2000 rpm	1.8 ms
		3000 rpm	1.8 ms
25	ignition coil driver : t1	ignition on	nbv
		engine running:	
		dynamic volt drop	2.0 V (max)
		primary switching	200 V (min)
26	–		
27	stepper motor : t4	idle speed, active	0 to 12 V (switching)
28	supply from main relay : t8/1	ignition on/engine running	nbv
29	main ECM earth A	ignition on/engine running	0.25 V (max)
30	sensor return (CTS : t1, ATS : t1, SD connector : t1, TPS : t1)	ignition on/engine running	0.25 V (max)
31	CAS signal : t2	engine cranking:	> 2.0 V AC (peak to peak)
		idle:	> 11.0 V AC (peak to peak)
		cruise:	> 14.0 V AC (peak to peak)
32	CAS return : t1	ignition on/engine running	0.25 V (max)
33	CTS signal : t2	ignition on/engine running	20° C: 3.00 V
			78° C: 0.78 V
34-35	–		
36	OS relay driver : t85	ignition off	nbv
		engine running, hot	1.25 V (max)

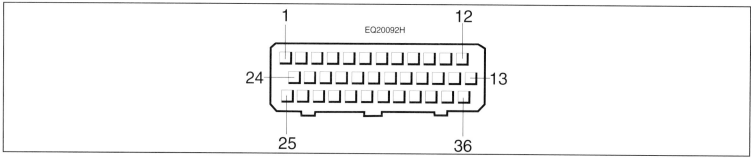

36 pin ECM multi-plug, Rover MEMS SPi (Metro K16)

Pin Table – Rover MEMS SPi (Rover 214, K16)

Pin	Item	Test Condition	Measurements
1	–		
2	stepper motor : t2	idle speed, active	0 to 12 V (switching)
3	stepper motor : t1	idle speed, active	0 to 12 V (switching)
4	main relay driver : t85	ignition off	nbv
		ignition on/engine running	1.25 V (max)
5	–		
6	manifold heater relay driver : t85	ignition on	nbv
		engine running	
		cold	1.25 V (max)
		hot	nbv
7	–		
8	TPS signal : t3	ignition on/engine running:	
		throttle closed	0.20 to 0.60 V
		throttle fully open	4.25 to 4.50 V
9	TPS supply : t2	ignition on/engine running	5.0 V ± 0.1
10	SD connector : t2	ignition on/engine running	5.0 V ± 0.1
11	supply from ignition switch : t15	ignition on/engine running	nbv
12	–		
13	TS, idle contact : t2	ignition on/engine running:	
		throttle closed	0 V
		throttle open	5.0 V ± 0.1
14	AT : P/N sense		data not available
15	SD connector : t3	ignition on/engine running	5.0 V ± 0.1
16	ATS signal : t2	ignition on/engine running	20° C: 3.00 V
			78° C: 0.78 V
17-18	–		
19	A/C active		data not available
20	fuel pump relay driver : t85	ignition off	nbv
		engine cranking/running	1.25 V (max)
21	–		
22	stepper motor : t3	idle speed, active	0 to 12 V (switching)
23	–		
24	injector driver : t1	ignition on	nbv
		engine cranking, cold	14.8 ms
		engine running, cold	2.2 ms
		engine running, hot	2.0 ms
		2000 rpm	1.8 ms
		3000 rpm	1.8 ms
25	ignition coil driver : t1	ignition on	nbv
		engine cranking/running	200 V (min)
		dynamic volt drop	2.0 V (max)
26	–		
27	stepper motor : t4	idle speed, active	0 to 12 V (switching)
28	supply from main relay : t87	ignition on/engine running	nbv
29	main ECM earth	ignition on/engine running	0.25 V (max)

Pin	Item	Test Condition	Measurements
30	sensor return (CTS : t1, ATS: t1, TPS : t1, SD connector : t1)	ignition on/engine running	0.25 V (max)
31	CAS signal : t2	engine cranking :	> 2.0 V AC (peak to peak)
		idle :	> 11.0 V AC (peak to peak)
		cruise :	> 14.0 V AC (peak to peak)
32	CAS return : t1	ignition on/engine running	0.25 V (max)
33	CTS signal : t2	ignition on/engine running	20° C: 3.00 V
			78° C: 0.78 V
34	–		
35	A/C sensor		data not available
36	–		

EQ20092H

36 pin ECM multi-plug, Rover MEMS SPi (Rover 214, K16)

Wiring Diagrams

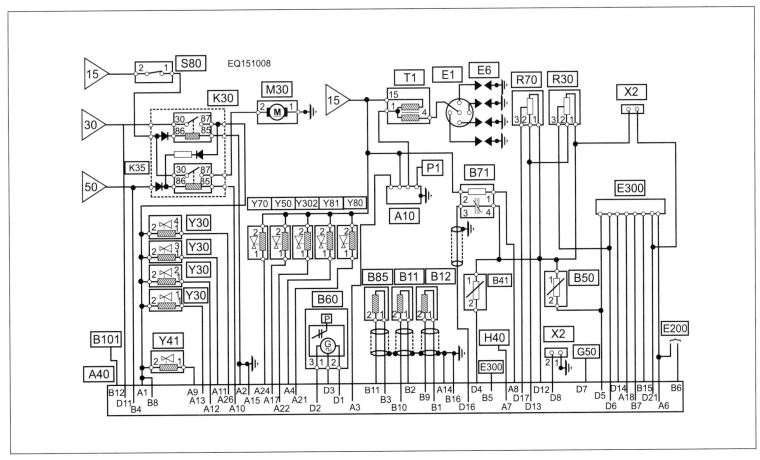

EQ151008

System wiring diagram, Honda PGMFI (4-cyl)

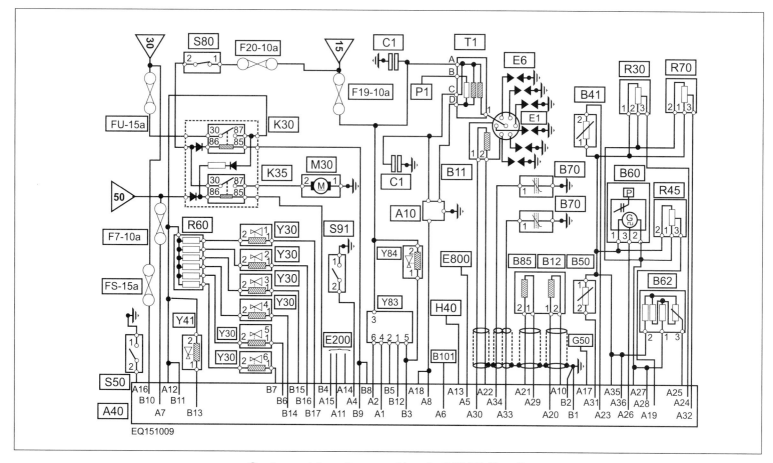

System wiring diagram, Honda PGMFI (6-cyl)

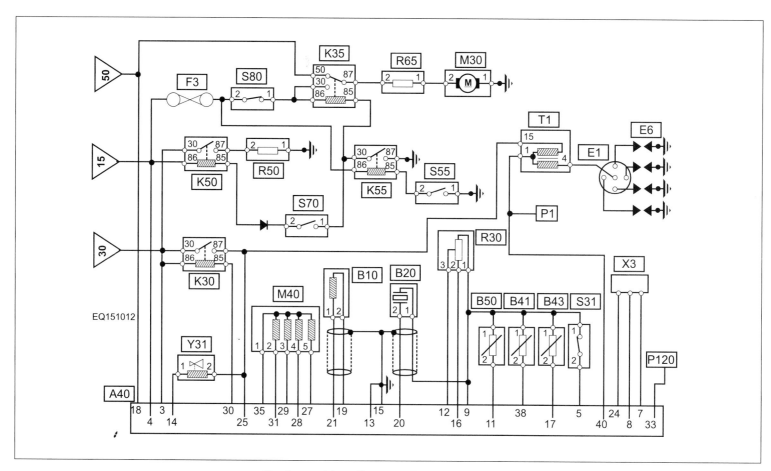

System wiring diagram, Lucas 10CU SPi

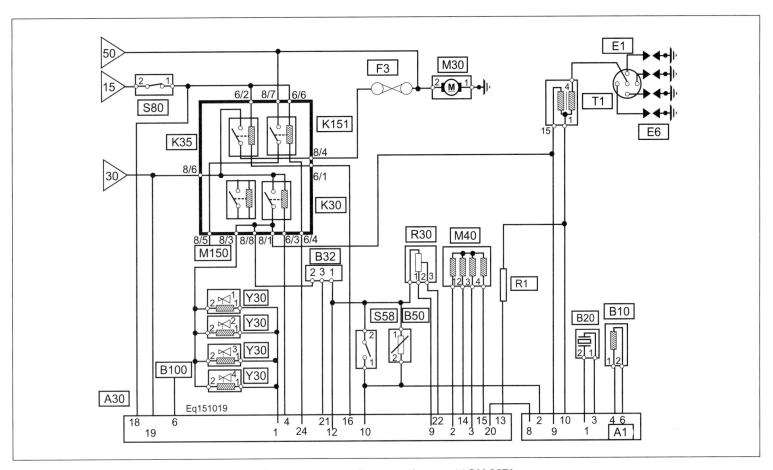

System wiring diagram, Lucas 11CU MPi

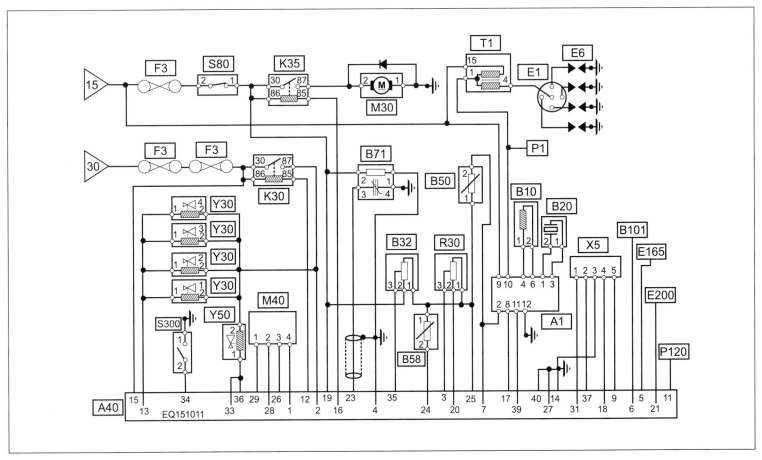

System wiring diagram, Lucas 14CUX MPi

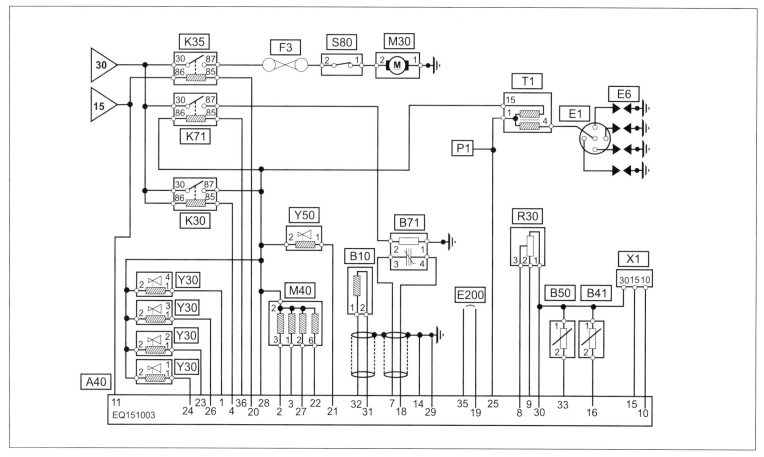

System wiring diagram, Rover MEMS MPi (Rover 214i, K16)

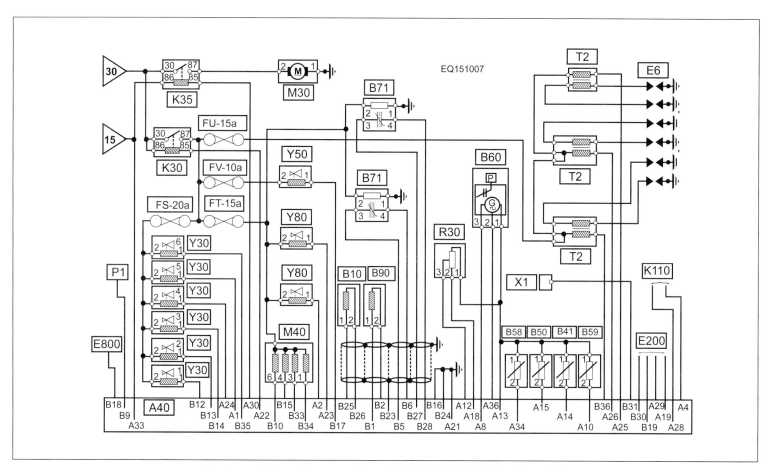

System wiring diagram, Rover MEMS MPi (825 Sterling V6)

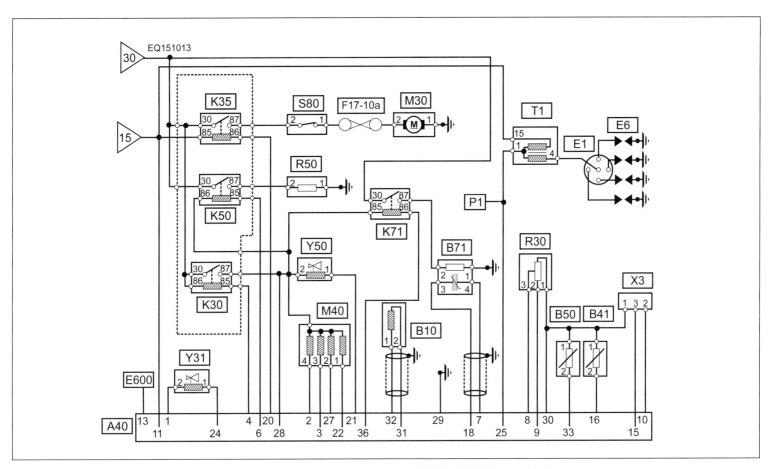

System wiring diagram, Rover MEMS SPi (Rover 114)

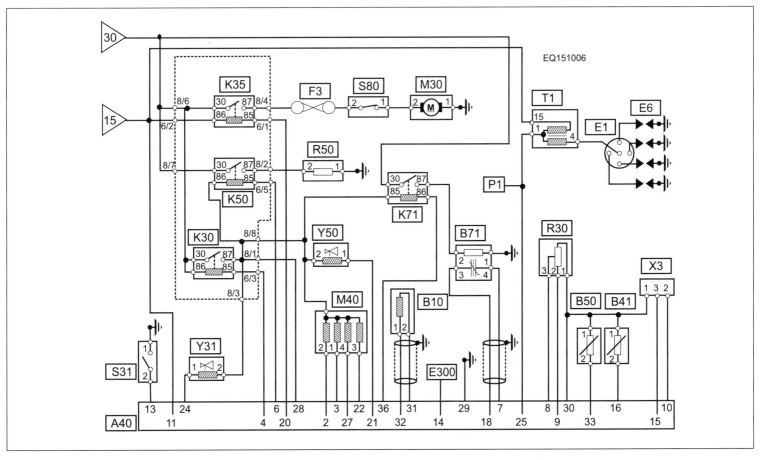

System wiring diagram, Rover MEMS SPi (Metro K16)

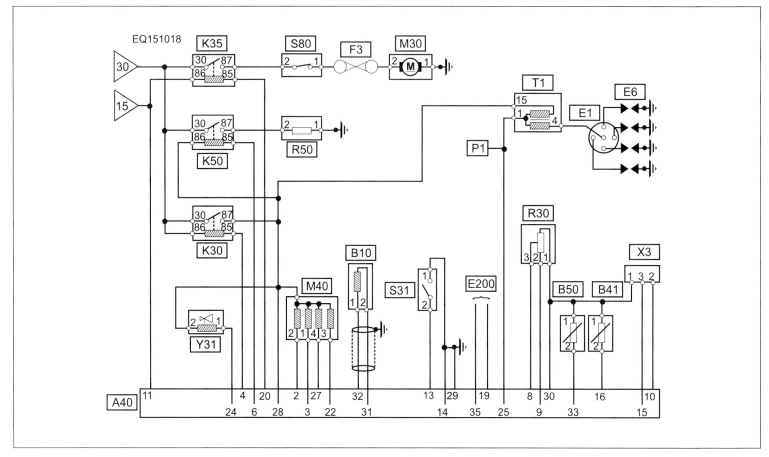

System wiring diagram, Rover MEMS SPi (Rover 214, K16)

Chapter 25
Saab

Contents

Index of Saab vehicles/systems

Model	Engine code	Year	System
900 2.0 16V DOHC cat	B202 2L	1989 to 1993	Bosch LH Jetronic 2.0
900 2.0i Cat	B204I	1995 to 1998	Bosch Motronic 2.10.2
900 2.0i Cat	**B206I**	**1993 to 1994**	**Bosch Motronic 2.10.2**
900 2.0i Turbo	**B204L**	**1993 to 1998**	**Saab Trionic**
900 2.1 16v	B212	1991 to 1993	Bosch LH Jetronic 2.0
900 2.3i Cat	B234I	1993 to 1998	Bosch Motronic 2.10.2
900 2.3i 16v DOHC	B234I	1993 to 1997	Bosch Motronic 2.10.2
900 2.5i V6	**B258I**	**1993 to 1998**	**Bosch Motronic 2.8.1**
900 16v Cat	B202	1989 to 1993	Lucas CU 14 LH Jetronic
900 16v Cat	**B202**	**1989 to 1993**	**Lucas CU 14 LH Jetronic**
900 Turbo 16c Cat	B202	1990 to 1993	Lucas CU 14 LH Jetronic
900 Turbo 16v Cat	B202L	1990 to 1993	Lucas CU 14 LH Jetronic
900 Turbo 16v Cat	B202LTT	1990 to 1993	Bosch LH Jetronic 2.0
900 Turbo 16v DOHC	B202 2S	1988 to 1990	Bosch LH Jetronic 2.0
900i 16v DOHC	**B202i**	**1989 to 1990**	**Bosch LH Jetronic 2.2**
900i 16v DOHC cat	B202i	1990 to 1993	Bosch LH Jetronic 2.0
900S Turbo cat	B202I	1990 to 1993	Bosch LH Jetronic 2.0
9000 2.0 Ecopower	B202S	1992 to 1994	Bosch LH Jetronic 2.4
9000 2.0 Turbo cat	B204S	1994 to 1995	Saab Trionic
9000 2.0 Turbo Intercooler	B204L	1994 to 1997	Saab Trionic
9000 2.0i cat	B204i	1994 to 1998	Saab Trionic
9000 2.0i Turbo	B204E	1996 to 1998	Saab Trionic
9000 2.0i 16v cat	**B202I**	**1988 to 1993**	**Bosch LH Jetronic 2.4**
9000i 16v cat	B202I	1986 to 1987	Bosch LH Jetronic 2.2
9000i 16v Cat	B202I	1988 to 1993	Bosch LH Jetronic 2.4
9000 Turbo 16	B202	1985 to 1990	Bosch LH Jetronic 2.2
9000 Turbo 16	B202	1991 to 1993	Bosch LH Jetronic 2.4.2
9000 Turbo Cat	B202L	1989 to 1993	Bosch LH Jetronic 2.0
9000 Turbo 16 cat	B202	1986 to 1988	Bosch LH Jetronic 2.2
9000 Turbo 16 cat	B202	1989 to 1993	Bosch LH Jetronic 2.4
9000I 2.3 cat	B234I	1990 to 1991	Bosch LH Jetronic 2.4.1
9000I 2.3 cat	B234I	1991 to 1993	Bosch LH Jetronic 2.4.2
9000 2.3i cat	B234i	1994 to 1998	Saab Trionic
9000 2.3-16 Cat	B234	1990 to 1994	Bosch LH Jetronic 2.0
9000 2.3 Ecopower L/P Turbo	B234E	1994 to 1998	Saab Trionic
9000 2.3 Turbo	B234	1991 to 1992	Bosch LH Jetronic 2.0
9000 2.3 Turbo	B234	1993 to 1994	Saab Trionic
9000 2.3 Turbo cat	B234L	1991 to 1993	Bosch LH Jetronic 2.0
9000 2.3 Turbo cat	B234L	1994 to 1998	Saab Trionic
9000 2.3 Turbo cat	B234R	1994 to 1998	Saab Trionic
9000 3.0i V6	B308i	1995 to 1997	Bosch Motronic 2.8.1

Note: *The vehicles accentuated in bold type are the actual vehicles upon which the ECM pin tables and wiring diagrams are based. Other vehicle with the same system may be similar; but are also likely to contain some differences.*

Pin Table – Bosch LH Jetronic 2.2

Pin	Item	Test Condition	Measurements
1	–		
2	CTS signal : t1	ignition on/engine running	20° C: 2.0 V
			80° C: 0.5 V
3	TS, idle contact : t1	ignition on/idle speed:	
		throttle closed	0 V
		throttle open	5.0 V
4	AT		data not available
5	earth	ignition on/engine running	0.25 V (max)
6	MAF sensor return : t3	ignition on/engine running	0.25 V (max)
7	MAF sensor signal : t5	ignition on	1.3 V
		engine running:	
		idle	2.0 to 2.3 V
		3000 rpm	2.75 V
		snap accelerate	3.00 to 3.50 V (approx)
8	MAF hot wire burn-off : t1	coolant above 65° C, rpm above 2000, switch off engine, after 4 seconds hot wire glows for 1.0 second	2.0 to 5.0 V
9	supply from main relay : t87	ignition on/engine running	nbv
10	ISCV driver : t1	ignition on	nbv
		engine running, idle speed:	
		cold	6.0 to 6.5 V
		hot	7.0 to 9.0 V
		duty cycle	60%
11	earth	ignition on/engine running	0.25 V (max)
12	TS, full load contact : t3	ignition on/engine running:	
		throttle closed	5.0 V
		throttle fully open	0 V
13	injector driver : t1	ignition on	nbv briefly then 0 V
		engine running, cold	3.0 to 3.5 ms
		engine running, hot	2.0 to 2.5 ms
		snap acceleration	6.0 ms
		deceleration	0 ms (approx)
14	MAF sensor return : t6	ignition on/engine running	0.25 V (max)
15	earth (9000 turbo cat)	ignition on/engine running	0.25 V (max)
16	air conditioning		data not available
17	fuel pump relay driver : t85	ignition on	nbv
		engine cranking/running	1.25 V (max)
18	supply from ignition switch : t15	ignition on/engine running	nbv
19	SD connector		data not available
20	OS signal : t3	ignition on (OS multiplug disconnected)	0.4 to 0.5 V
		engine running, hot	200 to 1000 mV (switching)
		throttle fully open	0.5 to 1.0 V
		deceleration (fuel cut-off)	0 to 0.5 V
21	main relay driver : t85	ignition on	nbv
		engine cranking/running	1.25 V (max)
22	SD connector (some models)		data not available
23	ISCV driver : t3	ignition on	nbv
		engine running, idle speed:	
		cold	6.0 to 6.5 V
		hot	7.0 to 9.0 V
		duty cycle	40%
24	signal from ignition ECM : t8	ignition on	10 V
		engine cranking/running	0.25 V
		frequency	15 Hz
25	earth	ignition on/engine running	0.25 V (max)

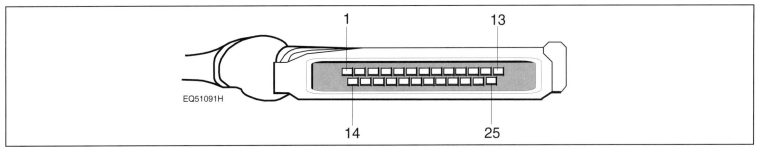

25 pin ECM multi-plug, Bosch LH Jetronic 2.2

Pin Table – Bosch LH Jetronic 2.4/2.4.1/2.4.2

Pin	Item	Test Condition	Measurement
1	rpm signal from ignition ECM : t17	ignition on	700 mV
		engine cranking/running	8 V
		frequency	30Hz
2	TS, idle contact : t1	ignition on/engine running:	
		throttle closed	0 V
		throttle open	12.0 V
3	TS, full load contact : t3	ignition on/engine running:	
		throttle closed	12.0 V
		throttle fully open	0 V
4	supply from battery : t30	ignition off/on/engine running	nbv
5	earth	ignition on/engine running	0.25 V (max)
6	MAF return : t2	ignition on/engine running	0.25 V (max)
7	MAF sensor signal : t3	ignition on	1.3 V
		engine cranking/idle	2.0 to 2.3 V
		3000 rpm	2.75 V
		snap accelerate	3.00 to 3.50 V (approx)
8	MAF hot wire burn-off : t4	coolant above 65° C, rpm above 2000, switch off engine, after 4 seconds hot wire glows for 1.0 second	2.0 to 5.0 V
9	supply from main relay : t87	ignition on/engine running	nbv
10-11	–		
12	SD connector		data not available
13	CTS signal : t2	ignition on/engine running	20°C: 2.0 V
			80°C: 0.5 V
14	A/C compressor		
15	supply from main relay : t87	ignition on/engine running	nbv
16	SD connector		data not available
17	earth	ignition on/engine running	0.25 V (max)
18	injector driver : t1	ignition on	nbv
		engine running, cold	3.0 to 3.5 ms
		engine running, hot	2.0 to 2.5 ms
		snap acceleration	> 6.0 ms
		deceleration	0 ms (approx)
19	–		
20	fuel pump relay driver : t85	ignition off/on	nbv
		engine cranking/running	1.25 V (max)
21	main relay driver : t85	ignition on	nbv
		engine cranking/running	1.25 V (max)
22	SD connector/warning lamp	ignition on, lamp on	1.25 V (max)
		engine running:	
		no faults present	nbv
		faults present, lamp on	1.25 max
23	–		
24	OS signal (cat models) : t3	ignition on (OS multiplug disconnected)	0.4 to 0.5 V
		engine running, hot	200 to 1000 mV (switching)
		throttle fully open	0.5 to 1.0 V
		deceleration (fuel cut-off)	0 to 0.5 V

Pin Table – Bosch LH Jetronic 2.4/2.4.1/2.4.2 (continued)

Pin	Item	Test Condition	Measurement
25	signal from ignition ECM : t8	ignition on	10 V
		engine cranking/running	0.25 V
		frequency	15 Hz
26	–		
27	CFSV driver : t1	ignition on	nbv
		engine running, above idle, operating temperature:	
		CFSV inactive	nbv
		CFSV active	0 to 12 V (switching)
		duty cycle	0 to 99%
28-29	–		
30	AT		data not available
31	–		
32	cold start valve driver	ignition on/engine running	nbv
		engine cranking	1.25 V (max)
33	ISCV driver : t1	ignition on	nbv
		engine running, idle speed:	
		cold	6.0 to 6.5 V
		hot	7.0 to 9.0 V
		duty cycle	30 to 60%
34	–		
35	supply from ignition switch : t15	ignition on/engine running	nbv

35 pin ECM multi-plug, Bosch LH Jetronic 2.4

Pin Table – Bosch Motronic 2.8.1

Pin	Item	Test Condition	Measurement
1	amplifier control signal (cyls 1 and 4) : t3	engine cranking/running	0 to 5.0 V (switching)
2	earth	ignition on/engine running	0.25 V (max)
3	fuel pump relay driver : t85	ignition on	nbv
		engine cranking/running	1.25 V (max)
4	ISCV driver : t1	ignition on	nbv
		engine running :	
		cold	6.0 to 6.5 V
		hot	7.0 to 9.0 V
		engine running:	
		frequency	100 to 110 Hz
		duty cycle	56 to 58%
		engine hot duty cycle, no load	40 to 44%
		duty cycle, under load	44 to 50%
5	CFSV driver : t1	ignition on	nbv
		engine running, above idle, operating temperature:	
		CFSV inactive	nbv
		CFSV active	0 to 12 V (switching)
		duty cycle	0 to 99%
6	–		

Pin	Item	Test Condition	Measurement
7	MAF sensor signal : t1	engine running:	
		idle	0.7 V
		3000 rpm	1.25 V
		snap accelerate	3.00 to 3.50 V (approx)
8	camshaft sensor signal : t2	engine running	0 to 5 V (switching)
9	VSS signal : t3	vehicle in motion	0 to 12 V (switching)
10	earth	ignition on/engine running	0.25 V (max)
11	KS1 signal : t2	engine running, KS active	1.0 to 2.0 V AC (peak to peak)
12	TPS supply : t2	ignition on/engine running	5.0 V ± 0.1
13	SD connector : tL		data not available
14	earth	ignition on/engine running	0.25 V (max)
15	injector driver (cylinder. 5) : t1	ignition on	nbv
		cold idle	> 4.5 ms
		hot idle	3.1 to 3.3 ms
16	injector driver (cylinder 2) : t1	ignition on	nbv
		cold idle	> 4.5 ms
		hot idle	3.1 to 3.3 ms
17	injector driver (cylinder 1) : t1	ignition on	nbv
		cold idle	> 4.5 ms
		hot idle	3.1 to 3.3 ms
18	supply from battery : t30	ignition off/on/engine running	nbv
19	earth	ignition on/engine running	0.25 V (max)
20	amplifier control signal (cyls 2 and 5) : t1	engine cranking/running	0 to 5.0 V (switching)
21	amplifier control signal (cyls 3 and 6) : t2	engine cranking/running	0 to 5.0 V (switching)
22	SD warning lamp	engine running:	
		no faults present	nbv
		faults present, lamp on	0.25 V (max)
23	–		
24	earth	ignition on/engine running	0.25 V (max)
25	air conditioning		data not available
26	secondary air pump relay driver : t85	ignition on	nbv
		engine running:	
		pump inactive	nbv
		pump active	1.25 V (max)
27	supply from ignition switch : t15	ignition on/engine running	nbv
28	oxygen sensor 1 signal : t3	ignition on	0.4 to 0.5 V
		engine running	200 to 1000 mV (switching)
		throttle fully-open	0.5 to 1.0 V
		deceleration (fuel cut-off)	0 to 0.5 V
		switching frequency	1 sec intervals (approx)
29	KS2 signal : t2	engine running, KS active	1.0 to 2.0 V AC (peak to peak)
30	sensor return (ATS : t1, CTS : t1, TPS : t1, MAF : t2, KS1: t2, KS2 : t2)	ignition on/engine running	0.25 V (max)
31-32	–		
33	injector driver (cylinder 6) : t1	ignition on	nbv
		engine running, cold idle	> 4.5 ms
		engine running, hot idle	3.1 to 3.3 ms
34	injector driver (cylinder 4) : t1	ignition on	nbv
		engine running, cold idle	> 4.5 ms
		engine running, hot idle	3.1 to 3.3 ms
35	injector driver (cylinder 3) : t1	ignition on	nbv
		engine running, cold idle	> 4.5 ms
		engine running, hot idle	3.1 to 3.3 ms
36	–		
37	supply from relay : t87	ignition on/engine running	nbv
38	AT		data not available
39	–		
40	air conditioning		data not available
41	–		

Pin Table – Bosch Motronic 2.8.1 (continued)

Pin	Item	Test Condition	Measurement
42	earth	ignition on/engine running	0.25 V (max)
43	tachometer		data not available
44	ATS signal : t2	ignition on/engine running	20° C: 3.00 to 3.50 V
			80° C: 1.00 to 1.30 V
45	CTS signal : t2	ignition on/engine running	20° C: 3.00 to 3.50 V
			80° C: 1.00 to 1.30 V
46	main relay driver : t85	ignition off	nbv
		ignition on/engine running	1.25 V (max)
47	oxygen sensor 2 signal : t1	ignition on	0.4 to 0.5 V
		engine running	200 to 1000 mV (switching)
		throttle fully-open	0.5 to 1.0 V
		deceleration (fuel cut-off)	0 to 0.5 V
		switching frequency	1 sec intervals (approx)
48	CAS earth : t2	engine running	0.25 V (max)
49	CAS signal : t1	engine cranking:	> 4.0 V AC (peak to peak)
		idle:	> 8.0 V AC (peak to peak)
		cruise:	> 14.0 V AC (peak to peak)
50	–		
51	AT		data not available
52	–		
53	TPS signal : t3	ignition on/engine running:	
		throttle closed	0.1 to 0.7 V
		throttle fully open	3.9 to 4.8 V
54	AT		data not available
55	SD connector : tK		data not available

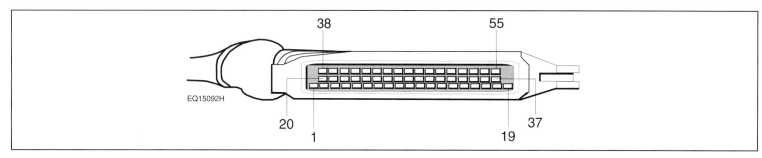

EQ15092H

55 pin ECM multi-plug, Bosch Motronic 2.8.1

Pin Table – Bosch Motronic 2.10.2

Pin	Item	Test Condition	Measurement
1	ignition coil driver : t1	ignition on	nbv
		engine running:	
		dynamic volt drop	2.0 V (max)
		primary switching	300 V (min)
2	earth	ignition on/engine running	0.25 V (max)
3	fuel pump relay driver : t85	ignition on	nbv
		engine cranking/running	1.25 V (max)
4	ISCV driver : t3	ignition on	nbv
		idle speed	6 to 12 V (switching)
		duty cycle, idle speed range	20% to 60%
		frequency	100 Hz
5	CFSV driver : t1	ignition on	nbv
		engine running, above idle, operating temperature:	
		CFSV inactive	nbv
		CFSV active	0 to 12 V (switching)
		duty cycle	0 to 99%

Pin	Item	Test Condition	Measurement
6	tachometer output (countries without leaded fuel)	engine running, idle	3 V (approx)
		frequency, idle	30 Hz
		frequency, 2500 rpm	85 Hz
7	MAF sensor signal : t4	ignition on	data not available
		idle	1.0 to 2.0 V
		2500 rpm	1.5 V
		snap accelerate	3.00 to 3.50 V (approx)
8	camshaft sensor signal : t2	engine running	0 to 5 V (switching)
		frequency	7.5 Hz
9	VSS	vehicle in motion	0 to 12 V (switching)
10	earth	ignition on/engine running	0.25 V (max)
11	KS signal : t1	engine running, KS active	1.0 V AC (peak to peak)
12	sensor supply (TPS t3, camshaft sensor : t2)	ignition on/engine running	5.0 V ± 0.1
13	SD connector : t6		data not available
14	earth	ignition on/engine running	0.25 V (max)
15	–		
16	injector driver (cyl 3) : t1	ignition on	nbv
		engine running, cold idle	> 3.5 ms
		engine running, hot idle	3.1 to 3.3 ms
17	injector driver (cyl 1) : t1	ignition on	nbv
		engine running, cold idle	> 3.5 ms
		engine running, hot idle	3.1 to 3.3 ms
18	supply from battery : t30	ignition off/on/engine running	nbv
19	earth	ignition on/engine running	0.25 V (max)
20	–		
21	SD warning lamp : t1	ignition on, lamp on	1.25 V (max)
		engine running: no faults present	nbv
		faults present, lamp on	1.25 V (max)
22	ISCV driver : t1	ignition on	nbv
		idle speed	6 to 12 V (switching)
		duty cycle, idle speed range	20% to 60%
		frequency	100 Hz
23	secondary air pump relay driver : t85	ignition on	nbv
		engine running:	
		pump inactive	nbv
		active, < 60 seconds, cold engine	1.25 V (max)
24	earth	ignition on/engine running	0.25 V (max)
25	–		
26	MAF sensor return : t2	ignition on/engine running	0.25 V (max)
27	supply from ignition switch : t15	ignition on/engine running	nbv
28	OS signal : t3	ignition on, OS multiplug disconnected	0.4 to 0.5 V
		engine running, hot	200 to 1000 mV (switching)
		throttle fully open	0.5 to 1.0 V
		deceleration (fuel cut-off)	0 to 0.5 V
		switching frequency	1 sec intervals (approx)
29	–		
30	sensor return (TPS : t1, MAF : 1, camshaft sensor : t1, KS : t1)	ignition on/engine running	0.25 V (max)
31-32	–		
33	air conditioning		data not available
34	injector driver (cyl 2) : t1	ignition on	nbv
		engine running, cold idle	> 3.5 ms
		engine running, hot idle	3.1 to 3.3 ms
35	injector driver (cyl 4) : t1	ignition on	nbv
		engine running, cold idle	> 3.5 ms
		engine running, hot idle	3.1 to 3.3 ms
36	main relay driver : t85	ignition off	nbv
		ignition on/engine running	1.25 V (max)
37	supply from main relay : t87	ignition on/engine running	nbv

Pin Table – Bosch Motronic 2.10.2 (continued)

Pin	Item	Test Condition	Measurement
38-39	–		
40	supply from main relay (AT) : t87	ignition on/engine running	nbv
40	pin not connected (MT)	ignition on/engine running	0 V
41	air conditioning		data not available
42-43	–		
44	radiator fan electrical load : t10	ignition on/engine running:	
		fan active	nbv
		fan inactive	0 V
45	CTS signal : t2	ignition on/engine running	20° C: 3.00 to 3.50 V
			80° C: 1.00 to 1.30 V
46	–		
47	AT		data not available
48	CAS signal : t2	engine cranking	> 4.0 V AC (peak to peak)
		idle	> 8.0 V AC (peak to peak)
		cruise	> 14.0 V AC (peak to peak)
49	CAS return : t1	engine running	0.25 V (max)
50	–		
51	AT		data not available
52	AT		data not available
53	TPS signal : t3	ignition on/engine running:	
		throttle closed	0.35 to 0.87 V
		throttle fully open	> 4.25 V
54	ECM coding : t1		data not available
55	SD connector : t7		data not available

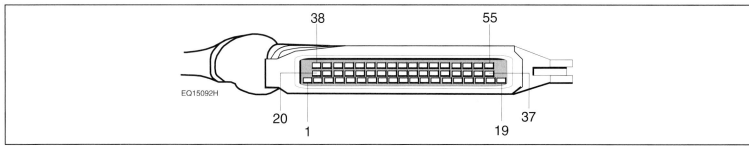

55 pin ECM multi-plug, Bosch Motronic 2.10.2

Pin Table – Lucas LH Jetronic CU 14

Pin	Item	Test Condition	Measurement
1	stepper motor : tD	idle speed, active	0 to nbv (switching)
2	supply from main relay : t87a	ignition on/engine running	nbv
3	TPS supply : t3	ignition on/engine running	5.0 V ± 0.1
4	earth	ignition on/engine running	0.25 V (max)
5	idle switch	ignition on/engine running:	
		throttle closed	0 V
		throttle open	5.0 V
6	VSS signal : t3	drive wheels rotating or vehicle in motion	0 to 12 V (switching)
7	CTS signal : t2	ignition on/engine running	20° C: 2.00 to 2.50 V
			80° C: 1.00 to 1.30 V
8	–		
9	SD connector : t1		data not available
10	SD warning lamp	ignition on, lamp on	1.25 V (max)
		engine running:	
		no faults present	nbv
		faults present, lamp on	1.25 V (max)
11	injector resistor : t1	ignition on	nbv
12	main relay driver : t85	ignition off	
		ignition on/engine running	1.25 V (max)

Pin	Item	Test Condition	Measurement
13	injector driver (cyls 1, 2, 3, 4) : t1	ignition on	nbv
		engine running, cold	> 3.5 ms
		engine running, hot	3.5 ms
		snap acceleration	20 ms (approx)
		deceleration	0 ms (approx)
14	earth	ignition on/engine running	0.25 V (max)
15	supply from battery : t30	ignition off/on/engine running	nbv
16	fuel pump relay driver : t85	ignition on	nbv
		cranking/running	1.25 max
17	CFSV driver : t1	ignition on	nbv
		engine running, above idle, operating temperature:	
		CFSV inactive	nbv
		CFSV active	0 to 12 V (switching)
		duty cycle	0 to 99%
18	SD connector : t2		data not available
19	supply from ignition switch : t15	ignition on/engine running	nbv
20	TPS signal : t2	ignition on/engine running:	
		throttle closed	0.5 V
		throttle fully open	5.0 V
21	air conditioning		data not available
22	MAF sensor return : t2	ignition on/engine running	0.25 V (max)
23	OS signal : t3	ignition on, OS multiplug disconnected	0.4 to 0.5 V
		engine running, hot	200 to 1000 mV (switching)
		throttle fully open	0.5 to 1.0 V
		deceleration (fuel cut-off)	0 to 0.5 V
		switching frequency	1 sec intervals (approx)
24	–		
25	sensor return (MAF sensor : t2, TPS : t1, CTS : t1)	ignition on/engine running	0.25 V (max)
26	stepper motor : tC	idle speed, active	0 to nbv (switching)
27	earth	ignition on/running	0.25 V (max)
28	stepper motor : tB	idle speed, active	0 to nbv (switching)
29	stepper motor : tA	idle speed, active	0 to nbv (switching)
30	SD connector : t3		data not available
31	SD connector : t1		data not available
32	SD connector : t2		data not available
33-34	–		
35	MAF sensor signal : t3	engine running:	
		idle speed	0.7 V
		3000 rpm	1.25 V
		snap accelerate	3.00 to 3.50 V (approx)
36	air conditioning		data not available
37-38	–		
39	engine speed signal from amplifier : t7	engine cranking/running	4.0 to 6.0 V
40	earth	ignition on/engine running	0.25 V (max)

EQ8209H

40 pin ECM multi-plug, Lucas LH Jetronic CU14

Pin Table – Saab Trionic

Pin	Item	Test Condition	Measurement
1	supply from battery : t30	ignition off/on/engine running	nbv
2	TBCV driver : t3	engine running, 900 rpm:	
		frequency	90 Hz
		duty cycle	17.5%
		pulse duration	1.9 ms
		engine running, 1000 to 1500 rpm:	
		frequency	90 Hz
		duty cycle	2.0%
		pulse duration	0.2 ms
3	injector driver (cylinder 1) : t1	ignition on	nbv
		engine running, 900 rpm:	
		pulse duration	2.5 ms
		frequency	7.5 Hz
4	injector driver (cylinder 2) : t1	ignition on	nbv
		engine running, 900 rpm:	
		pulse duration	2.5 ms
		frequency	7.5 Hz
5	injector driver (cylinder 3) : t1	ignition on	nbv
		engine running, 900 rpm:	
		pulse duration	2.5 ms
		frequency	7.5 Hz
6	injector driver (cylinder 4) : t1	ignition on	nbv
		engine running, 900 rpm:	
		pulse duration	2.5 ms
		frequency	7.5 Hz
7-8	–		
9	ignition cartridge (trigger 1) : t2	engine running, 900 rpm:	
		voltage	1.2 V
		frequency	7.5 Hz
		duty cycle	8.3%
		pulse duration	11 ms
10	ignition cartridge (trigger 2) : t3	engine running, 900 rpm:	
		voltage	1.2 V
		frequency	7.5 Hz
		duty cycle	8.3%
		pulse duration	11 ms
11	ignition cartridge (trigger 3) : t4	engine running, 900 rpm:	
		voltage	1.2 V
		frequency	7.5 Hz
		duty cycle	8.3%
		pulse duration	11 ms
12	ignition cartridge (trigger 4) : t5	engine running, 900 rpm:	
		voltage	1.2 V
		frequency	7.5 Hz
		duty cycle	8.3%
		pulse duration	11 ms
13	torque limitation		data not available
14	gear lever switch		data not available
15	brake light switch		data not available
16	–		
17	ignition cartridge (cyls 1 and 2) : t8	engine running: 900 rpm:	
		voltage	1.5 V
		frequency	15 to 30 Hz
18	ignition cartridge (cyls 3 and 4) : t9	engine running: 900 rpm:	
		voltage	1.5 V
		frequency	15 to 30 Hz
19	–		
20	pressure signal, ECM to instrument cluster		data not available

Pin	Item	Test Condition	Measurement
21	CFSV driver : t1	ignition on	nbv
		engine running, above idle, operating temperature:	
		CFSV inactive	nbv
		CFSV active	0 to 12 V (switching)
		duty cycle	8 Hz, 50%
		pulse duration	60 ms
22	MAP sensor signal : t2	ignition on:	
		–750 mbar	0.48 V
		–500 mbar	0.95 V
		0 bar	1.9 V
		250 mbar	2.4 V
		500 mbar	2.8 V
		750 mbar	3.3V
23	OS signal : t4	ignition on (OS multiplug disconnected)	0.4 to 0.5 V
		engine running, hot	200 to 1000 mV (switching)
		throttle fully-open	0.5 to 1.0 V
		deceleration (fuel cut-off)	0 to 0.5 V
		switching frequency	1 sec intervals (approx)
24	earth	ignition on/engine running	0.25 V (max)
25	earth	ignition on/engine running	0.25 V (max)
26	TBCV driver : t1	ignition on/engine running	
		1000 to 1500 rpm	90 Hz
			17.5%
			1.9 ms
27	CFSV driver : t1	ignition on	nbv
		engine running, above idle, operating temperature:	
		CFSV inactive	nbv
		CFSV active	0 to 12 V (switching)
		duty cycle	8 Hz, 50%
		pulse duration	60 ms
28-30	–		
31	main relay driver : t85	ignition off	nbv
		ignition on/engine running	1.25 V (max)
32	SD warning lamp : t1	ignition on, lamp on	1.25 V (max)
		engine running:	
		no faults present	nbv
		faults present, lamp on	1.25 V (max)
33	SD connection : t7		data not available
34	–		
35	cruise control		data not available
36	cruise control		data not available
37-38	–		
39	VSS signal : t3	vehicle in motion	0 to 12 V (switching 29 times/rpm)
40	–		
41	CAS signal : t1	engine cranking:	> 4.0 V AC (peak to peak)
		idle:	> 8.0 V AC (peak to peak)
		cruise:	> 14.0 V AC (peak to peak)
42	TPS supply : t1	ignition on/engine running	5.0 V ± 0.1
43	MAP sensor supply : t3	ignition on/engine running	5.0 V ± 0.1
44	ignition cartridge : t7	knock signal from ignition cartridge	data not available
45	TPS signal : t3	ignition on/engine running:	
		idle speed	0.5 V
		throttle fully open	5.0 V
46	ATS signal (AFS : t2)	ignition on/engine running	20° C: 2.4 V
			80° C: 0.54 V
47	production plug earth	ignition on/engine running	0.25 V (max)
48	supply from battery : t30	ignition off/on/engine running	nbv

Pin Table – Saab Trionic

Pin	Item	Test Condition	Measurement
49	ISCV driver : t1	ignition on	nbv
		engine running, idle speed, hot	3.5 to 5.5 V
		duty cycle	25 to 45%
50	OS heater driver : t1	engine running:	
		900 rpm ± 50	0.3 V (approx)
51-53	–		
54	A/C		data not available
55	Change gear indicator, light load high speed indication in instrument cluster		data not available
56	fuel pump relay driver : t85	ignition on	nbv briefly, then 0 V
		engine cranking/running	1.25 V (max)
57	cruise control		data not available
58	engine speed signal to instrument cluster	data not available	
59	A/C		data not available
60	supply from ignition switch : t15	ignition on/engine running	nbv
61	–		
62	production plug		data not available
63	production plug		data not available
64	–		
65	production plug		data not available
66	sensor return (MAP sensor : t1, CTS : t1, TPS : t1, ATS : t1, CAS : t2)	ignition on/engine running	0.25 V (max)
67	sensor return (MAP sensor : t1, CTS : t1, TPS : t1, ATS : t1, CAS : t2)	ignition on/engine running	0.25 V (max)
68	CTS signal : t2	ignition on/engine running	20° C: 2.40 V
			80° C: 0.54 V
69-70	–		

Eq120009

70 pin ECM multi-plug, Saab Trionic

Wiring Diagrams

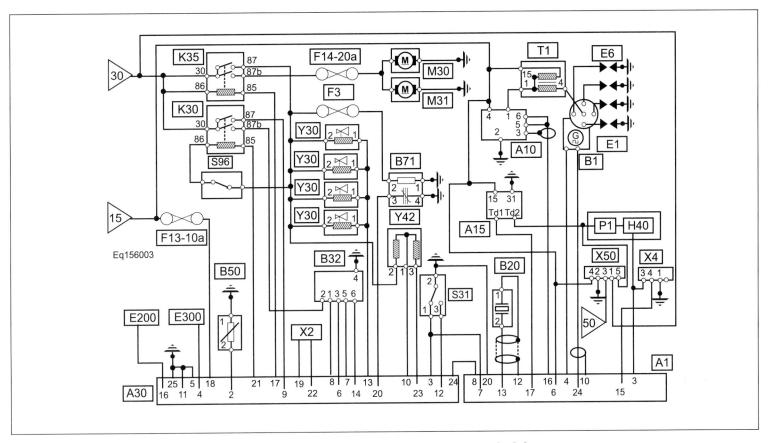

System wiring diagram, Bosch LH Jetronic 2.2

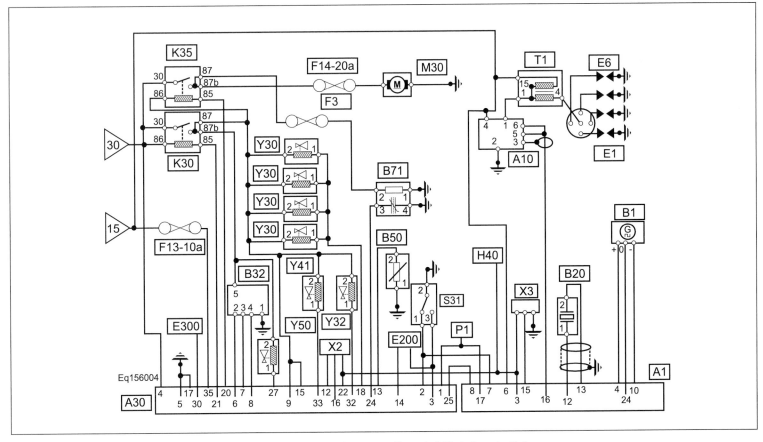

System wiring diagram, Bosch LH Jetronic 2.4

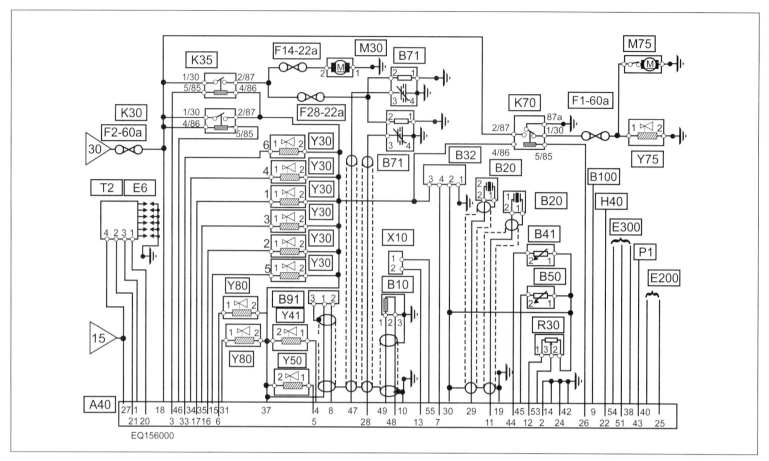

System wiring diagram, Bosch Motronic 2.8.1

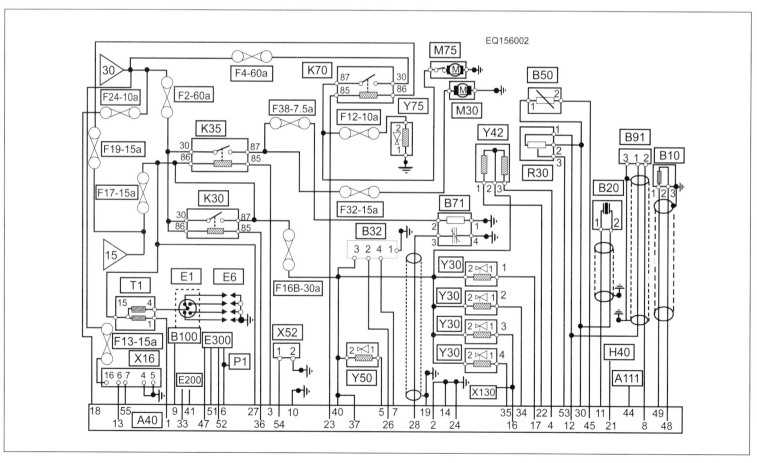

System wiring diagram, Bosch Motronic 2.10.2

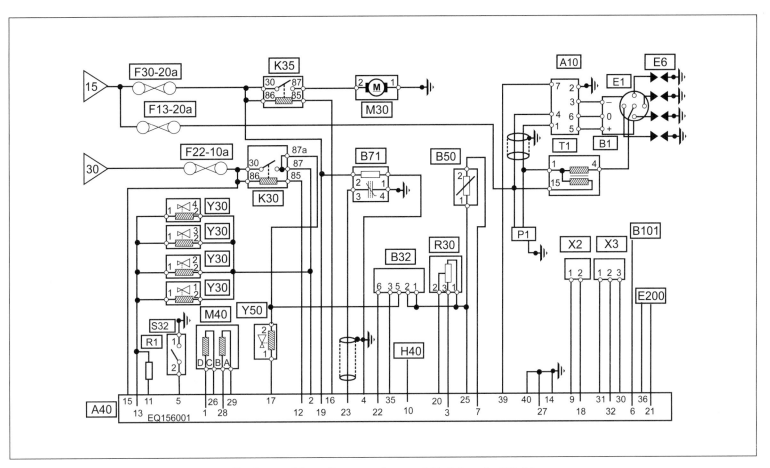

System wiring diagram, Lucas LH Jetronic CU 14

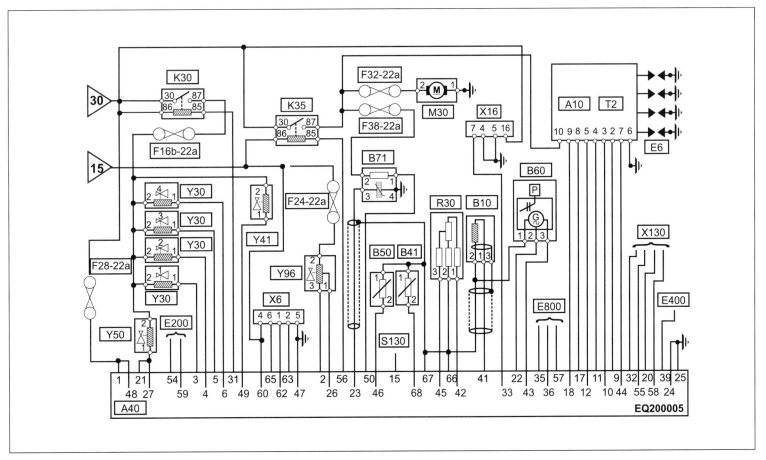

System wiring diagram, Saab Trionic

Notes

Chapter 26
Seat

Contents

Index of Seat vehicles/systems

Model	Engine code	Year	System
Alhambra 2.0	ADY	1996 to 1997	Simos 4S
Arosa 1.0	AER	1997 to 1998	Bosch Motronic MP 9.0
Arosa 1.4	AEX	1997 to 1998	Bosch Motronic MP 9.0
Cordoba 1.4i SOHC 8V	ABD	1994 to 1997	Bosch Mono-Motronic 1.2.3
Cordoba 1.6i SOHC 8V	1F	1995 to 1998	Bosch Mono-Motronic 1.2.3
Cordoba 1.6i SOHC 8V	ABU	1993 to 1997	Bosch Mono-Motronic 1.2.3
Cordoba 1.8i 16V	ADL	1994 to 1997	VAG Digifant (45 pin)
Cordoba 1.8i SOHC 8V	**ABS**	**1993 to 1995**	**Bosch Mono-Motronic 1.2.3**
Cordoba 2.0i SOHC 8V	**2E**	**1993 to 1997**	**VAG Digifant (45 pin)**
Cordoba 2.0i	ABF	1994 to 1996	VAG Digifant (68 pin)
Cordoba 2.0i	ADY	1996 to 1997	Simos 4S
Cordoba 2.0i	**AGG**	**1996 to 1997**	**Simos 4S**
Ibiza 1.05i SOHC 8v	AAU	1993 to 1997	Bosch Mono-Motronic 1.2.3
Ibiza 1.2i R-cat	**021.C.1000**	**1989 to 1993**	**Bosch LU2 Jetronic**
Ibiza 1.3i US83	AAV	1993 to 1994	Bosch Mono-Motronic 1.2.3
Ibiza 1.4i SOHC 8V	ABD	1994 to 1997	Bosch Mono-Motronic 1.2.3
Ibiza 1.5 SXi	021.A.2000	1988 to 1991	Bosch LE2 Jetronic
Ibiza 1.5i R-cat	021.C.2000	1989 to 1993	Bosch LU2 Jetronic
Ibiza 1.6i SOHC 8V	ABU	1993 to 1997	Bosch Mono-Motronic 1.2.3
Ibiza 1.7i Sportline R-cat	021.C.3000	1992 to 1993	Bosch LU2 Jetronic
Ibiza 1.8i 16V	ADL	1994 to 1997	VAG Digifant (45 pin)
Ibiza 1.8i SOHC 8V	ABS	1993 to 1995	Bosch Mono-Motronic 1.2.3
Ibiza 2.0i SOHC 8V	2E	1993 to 1997	VAG Digifant (45 pin)
Ibiza 2.0i	ABF	1994 to 1996	VAG Digifant (68 pin)
Ibiza 2.0i	ADY	1996 to 1997	Simos 4S
Ibiza 2.0i	AGG	1996 to 1997	Simos 4S

Index of Seat vehicles/systems (continued)

Model	Engine code	Year	System
Inca 1.4i	**AEX**	**1995 to 1998**	**Bosch Motronic MP 9.0**
Inca 1.6i	1F	1995 to 1998	Bosch Mono-Motronic 1.2.3
Malaga 1.2i R-cat	021.C.1000	1989 to 1993	Bosch LU2 Jetronic
Malaga 1.5i	**021.A.2000**	**1989 to 1994**	**Bosch LE-Jetronic**
Malaga 1.5i R-cat	021.C.2000	1989 to 1993	Bosch LU2 Jetronic
Malaga 1.5i	021.A.2000	1985 to 1991	Bosch LE2 Jetronic
Malaga Sportline 1.7i R-cat	021.C.3000	1993 to 1994	Bosch LU2 Jetronic
Toledo 1.6i cat SOHC	**1F**	**1991 to 1994**	**Bosch Mono-Jetronic**
Toledo 1.6i SOHC	1F	1994 to 1997	Bosch Mono-Motronic 1.2.3
Toledo 1.8i cat SOHC	**RP**	**1991 to 1994**	**Bosch Mono-Jetronic**
Toledo 1.8i cat SOHC	RP	1994 to 1996	Bosch Mono-Motronic 1.2.3
Toledo 1.8i SOHC	RP	1991 to 1994	Bosch Mono-Jetronic
Toledo 1.8i SOHC 8v	ABS	1994 to 1997	Bosch Mono-Motronic 1.2.3
Toledo 1.8l 16v	**PL**	**1991 to 1994**	**Bosch KE-Jetronic**
Toledo 2.0i	2E	1991 to 1998	VAG Digifant (45 pin)
Toledo 2.0i	**ABF**	**1994 to 1998**	**VAG Digifant (68 pin)**

Note: The vehicles accentuated in bold type are the actual vehicles upon which the ECM pin tables and wiring diagrams are based. Other vehicle with the same system may be similar; but are also likely to contain some differences.

Pin Table – Bosch KE-Jetronic

Pin	Item	Test Condition	Measurements
1	supply from ignition : t15	ignition on/engine running	nbv
2	earth	ignition on/engine running	0.25 V (max)
3	ISCV driver : t3	ignition on	nbv
		engine running, idle speed:	
		cold	6.0 to 6.5 V
		hot	7.0 to 9.0 V
		duty cycle	30 to 60%
4	ISCV driver : t1	ignition on	nbv
		engine running, idle speed:	
		cold	6.0 to 6.5 V
		hot	7.0 to 9.0 V
		duty cycle	30 to 60%
5	TS, full load contact : t3	ignition on/engine running:	
		throttle closed/part open	5 V
		throttle fully open	0 V
6	–		
7	earth (OS shield)	ignition on/engine running	0.25 V (max)
8	OS signal : t2	ignition on, OS multiplug disconnected	0.4 to 0.5 V
		engine running, hot	200 to 1000 mV (switching)
		throttle fully open	0.5 to 1.0 V
		deceleration (fuel cut-off)	0 to 0.5 V
		switching frequency	1 sec intervals (approx)
9	earth	ignition on/engine running	0.25 V (max)
10	differential pressure regulator	idle speed, cold	55 to 75 mA (approx)
		idle speed, hot	0 to 1 mA (approx)
		deceleration from 3000 rpm	–40 mA (approx)
11	–		
12	differential pressure regulator	idle speed, cold	55 to 75 mA (approx)
		idle speed, hot	0 to 1 mA (approx)
		deceleration from 3000 rpm	–40 mA (approx)
13	TS, idle contact : t1	ignition on/engine running:	
		throttle closed	0 V
		throttle part/fully open	5 V

Pin	Item	Test Condition	Measurements
14	AFS signal : t3	ignition on/engine running:	
		sensor plate closed	0.20 to 0.30 V
		voltage range	0.1 to 4.5 V (approx)
		open/close sensor plate	voltage increase/decrease
15	earth	ignition on/engine running	0.25 V (max)
16	–		
17	AFS supply : t2	ignition on/engine running	5.0 V ± 0.1
18	AFS return : t1	ignition on/engine running	0.25 V (max)
19	–		
20	earth	ignition on/engine running	0.25 V (max)
21	CTS signal : t2	ignition on/engine running	20° C: 2.5 to 3.0 V
			80° C: 0.3 to 0.6 V
22	earth	ignition on/engine running	0.25 V (max)
23	–		
24	cranking supply : t50	engine cranking	nbv
25	tachometer		data not available

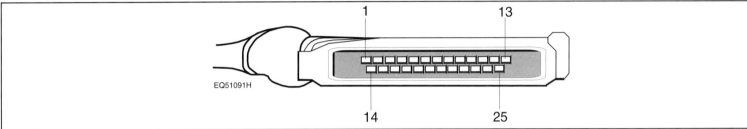

25 pin ECM multi-plug, Bosch KE-Jetronic

Pin Table – Bosch LE Jetronic

Pin	Connection	Test condition	Measurements
1	engine speed signal, ignition control unit : t5	engine cranking/running	3 V
2	TS, idle contact : t2	engine running:	
		throttle closed	nbv
		throttle part/fully open	0 V
3	TS, full-load contact : t3	engine running:	
		throttle closed/part open	0 V
		throttle fully open	nbv
4	cranking supply : t50	engine cranking	nbv
5	earth	ignition on/engine running	0.25 V (max)
6	ignition ECM : t15	engine cranking/running	0 to nbv (switching)
7	AFS signal : t7	relay pins 30 & 87 bridged:	
		AFS flap closed	1.8 V
		AFS flap fully open	6.5 V
8	ATS signal (AFS : t8)	engine running	20° C: 9.0 to 10.0 V
9	supply from main relay : t87	engine cranking/running	nbv
10	CTS signal : t2	engine running	0° C: 9.0 to 10.0 V
			20° C: 7.0 to 8.0 V
			40° C: 3.0 to 4.0 V
			80° C: 1.5 to 2.0 V
11	–		
12	injector driver : t1	engine cranking, cold	> 2.5 ms
		idle	2.5 ms
		1000 rpm	2.4 ms
		2000 rpm	2.3 ms
		3000 rpm	2.2 ms
		snap acceleration	> 6.0 ms
		deceleration	0 ms
13	earth : t1	ignition on/engine running	0.25 V (max)

Pin Table – Bosch LE Jetronic (continued)

Pin	Connection	Test condition	Measurements
14-19	–		
20	OS signal : t3 (LU2 only)	ignition on, OS multiplug disconnected	0.4 to 0.5 V
		engine running, hot	200 to 1000 mV (switching)
		throttle fully open	0.5 to 1.0 V
		deceleration (fuel cut-off)	0 to 0.5 V
		switching frequency	1 sec intervals (approx)
21	–		
22	CO verification signal (LU2 only)	engine at operating temperature, ignition timing & idle speed within operating parameters.	
		OS disconnected	6.3 V
		OS reconnected	7.8 to 5.8 V (6.3 V ideal)
23-25	–		

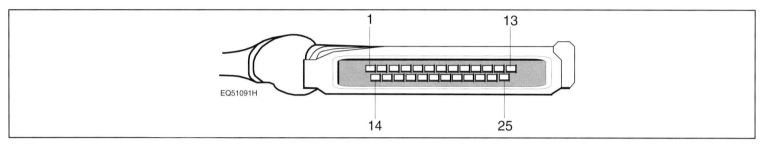

EQ51091H

25 pin ECM multi-plug, Bosch LE Jetronic

Pin Table – Bosch Mono-Jetronic

Pin	Connection	Test condition	Measurements
1	timing signal (amplifier : t7)	engine running	0 to nbv (switching)
2	CTS signal : t2	ignition on/engine running	20° C: 2.5 to 3.0 V
			80° C: 0.3 to 0.6 V
3	idle switch (stepper motor : t3), timing control valve : t1	ignition on/engine running:	
		idle switch closed	0.25 V (max)
		idle switch open	nbv
4	supply from battery : t30	ignition off/on/engine running	nbv
5	earth	ignition on/engine running	0.25 V (max)
6	P/N switch (AT) or earth	ignition on/engine running	0.25 V (max)
7	TPS signal : t2	ignition on/engine running:	
		throttle closed	1.0 V
		throttle fully open	4.50 V (approx)
8	TPS supply : t5	ignition on/engine running	5.0 V ± 0.1
9	supply from ignition switch : t15	ignition on/engine running	nbv
10	–		
11	earth	ignition on/engine running	0.25 V (max)
12	CFSV driver : t1	ignition on	nbv
		engine running, above idle, operating temperature:	
		CFSV inactive	nbv
		CFSV active	0 to 12 V (switching)
		duty cycle	0 to 99%
13	injector driver : t2	engine cranking, cold	3.0 to 4.0 ms
		engine running, cold	3.0 to 4.0 ms
		engine cranking, hot	1.5 to 2.5 ms
		engine running, hot	1.5 to 2.5 ms
		2000 rpm	1.5 to 2.5 ms
		3000 rpm	1.5 to 2.5 ms
		snap acceleration	10 to 15 ms
		deceleration	0 ms

Pin	Connection	Test condition	Measurements
14	ATS signal : t4	ignition on/engine running	20° C: 2.5 to 3.0 V
			80° C: 0.3 to 0.6 V
15-16	–		
17	fuel pump relay driver : t85	ignition on	nbv
		engine cranking/running	1.25 V (max)
18	TPS signal : t4	ignition on/engine running:	
		throttle closed	0 V
		throttle fully open	4.00 V (approx)
19	–		data not available
20	OS signal : t3	ignition on, OS multiplug disconnected	0.4 to 0.5 V
		engine running, hot	200 to 1000 mV (switching)
		throttle fully-open	0.5 to 1.0 V
		deceleration (fuel cut-off)	0 to 0.5 V
		switching frequency	1 sec intervals (approx)
21	–		
22	SD connector	ignition on/engine running:	
		no faults present	nbv
		faults present	0.25 V (max)
23	stepper motor : t2	idle speed, active	0 to 5.0 V (switching)
24	stepper motor : t1	idle speed, active	0 to 5.0 V (switching)
25	earth	ignition on/engine running	0.25 V (max)

EQ51091H

25 pin ECM multi-plug, Bosch Mono-Jetronic

Pin Table – Bosch Mono-Motronic 1.2.3

Pin	Connection	Test condition	Measurements
1	earth	ignition on/engine running	0.25 V (max)
2	stepper motor : t2	idle speed, active	0 to 5.0 V (switching)
3	CFSV driver : t1	ignition on	nbv
		engine running, above idle, operating temperature:	
		CFSV inactive	nbv
		CFSV active	0 to 12 V (switching)
		duty cycle	0 to 99%
4-6	–		
7	injector driver : t3	engine cranking, cold	> 3.0 to 4.0 ms
		engine running, cold	3.0 to 4.0 ms
		engine cranking, hot	> 2.5 ms
		running hot	1.5 to 2.5 ms
		deceleration	0 ms
8	HES supply : t3	engine cranking/running	9.0 V (min)
9	tachometer		data not available
10	idle switch : t3	ignition on/engine running:	
		throttle closed	0.25 V (max)
		throttle open	nbv
11	–		
12	earth	ignition on/engine running	0.25 V (max)

Pin Table – Bosch Mono-Motronic 1.2.3 (continued)

Pin	Connection	Test condition	Measurements
13	HES signal : t2	ignition on:	
		multiplug disconnected	5.0 to 10.0 V
		multiplug connected:	
		trigger vane cut-out space in air gap	< 700 mV
		trigger vane diverting hall voltage	5.0 to 10.0 V
		engine running	5.0 to 7.0 (average)
14	TPS supply : t5	ignition on/engine running	5.0 V ± 0.1
15	OS return : t4	ignition on/engine running	0.25 V (max)
16	–		
17	sensor return (CTS : t1, ATS : t1,TPS : t1)	ignition on/engine running	0.25 V (max)
18	TPS signal : t4	ignition on/engine running:	
		throttle closed	0 V
		throttle fully open	4.00 V (approx)
19	–		
20	earth	ignition on/engine running	0.25 V (max)
21	supply from battery : t30	ignition off/on/engine running	nbv
22	–		
23	supply from ignition switch : t15	ignition on/engine running	nbv
24	amplifier control signal : t2	engine cranking/running	0 to nbv (switching)
25	fuel pump relay driver : t3	ignition on	nbv
		engine cranking/running	1.25 V (max)
26	stepper motor : t1	idle speed, active	0 to 5.0 V (switching)
27	–		
28	manifold heater relay driver : t86	ignition on	nbv
		engine running, cold	1.25 V (max)
		engine running, hot	nbv
29	SD connector		data not available
30-35	–		
36	VSS signal	vehicle in motion	0 to 12 V (switching)
37	–		
38	OS signal : t4	ignition on, OS multiplug disconnected	0.4 to 0.5 V
		engine running, hot	200 to 1000 mV (switching)
		throttle fully-open	0.5 to 1.0 V
		deceleration (fuel cut-off)	0 to 0.5 V
		switching frequency	1 sec intervals (approx)
39-40	–		
41	TPS signal : t2	ignition on/engine running:	
		throttle closed	1.0 V
		throttle fully open	4.50 V (approx)
42	CTS signal : t2	ignition on/engine running	20° C: 2.5 to 3.0 V
			80° C: 0.3 to 0.6 V
43	ATS signal : t4	ignition on/engine running	20° C: 2.5 to 3.0 V
			80° C: 0.3 to 0.6 V
44-45	–		

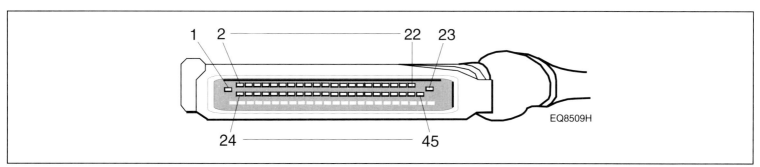

45 pin ECM multi-plug, Bosch Mono-Motronic 1.2.3

Pin Table – Bosch Motronic MP9.0

Pin	Connection	Test condition	Measurements
1	earth	ignition on/engine running	0.25 V (max)
2	stepper motor (TCA : t1)	idle speed, active	0 to 5.0 V (switching)
		frequency	500 Hz
		duty cycle	30%
3	CFSV driver : t1	engine running, above idle, operating temperature:	
		CFSV inactive	nbv
		CFSV active	0 to 12 V (switching)
		duty cycle	0 to 99%
4	injector driver (cylinder 4) : t1	engine running:	
		range	3.9 to 8 ms
5	–		
6	injector driver (cylinder 2) : t1	engine running:	
		range	3.9 to 8 ms
7	injector driver (cylinder 1) : t1	engine running:	
		range	3.9 to 8 ms
8	HES supply : t3	ignition on/engine running	9.0 V (min)
9	tachometer		data not available
10	idle switch (TCA : t3)	ignition on/engine running:	
		throttle closed	0.25 V (max)
		throttle open	nbv
11-12	–		
13	HES signal : t2	ignition on:	
		multiplug disconnected	5.0 to 10.0 V
		multiplug connected:	
		trigger vane cut-out space in air gap	< 700 mV
		trigger vane diverting hall voltage	5.0 to 10.0 V
		engine running	5.0 to 7.0 (average)
14	TPS supply (TCA : t4)	ignition on	5.0 V ± 0.1
15	OS signal : t3	engine running	
		non-active (open loop)	0.45 to 0.50 V
		active (closed loop)	0.0 – 0.3 to 0.7 – 1.0 V (switching)
16	TVPS signal (TCA : t8)	ignition on/running	0.5 to 4.0 V slight variation on move throttle
17	sensor return (CTS: t1, HES: t1, MAP/ATS assembly: t1, TCA : t7)	ignition on/engine running	0.25 V (max)
18	MAP signal (MAP/ATS assembly : t4)	ignition on	4.50 V (approx)
		engine running:	
		WOT	4.50 V (approx)
		idle speed	0.25 to 0.6 V
19	KS return : t2	engine running, KS active	0.25 V (max)
20	–		
21	supply from battery : t30	ignition off/on/engine running	nbv
22	–		
23	supply from ignition switch : t15	ignition on/engine running	nbv
24	amplifier control signal : t2	engine cranking/running	0 to 5.0 V (switching)
25	fuel pump relay driver : t85	ignition on	nbv
		engine cranking/running	1.25 V (max)
26	stepper motor (TCA : t2)	idle speed, active	0 to 5.0 V (switching)
		frequency	500 Hz
		duty cycle	60%
27	–		
28	injector driver (cylinder 3) : t1	engine running:	
		range	3.9 to 8 ms
29	immobiliser control unit		data not available
30-32	–		
33	A/C		data not available
34	–		

Pin Table – Bosch Motronic MP9.0 (continued)

Pin	Connection	Test condition	Measurements
35	A/C		data not available
36	VSS signal	vehicle in motion	0 to 4.5 V (switching)
37	MAP supply (MAP/ATS assembly) : t3	ignition on/engine running	5.0 V ± 0.5
38	OS return : t4	engine running	0.25 V (max)
39	KS signal : t1	engine running, idle, KS active	0.4 to 2.0 V AC
40	–		
41	TPS signal (TCA : t5)	ignition on/engine running	4.0 to 0.75 V
42	CTS signal : t2	ignition on/engine running	20° C: 2.5 to 3.0 V
			80° C: 0.3 to 0.6 V
43	ATS signal (MAP/ATS assembly : t2)	engine running	20° C: 2.5 to 3.0 V
44	–		
45	shield return	ignition on/engine running	0.25 V (max)

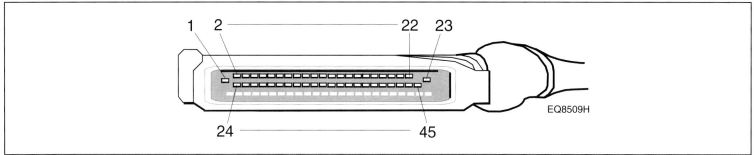

45 pin ECM multi-plug, Bosch Motronic MP 9.0

Pin Table – Simos 4S

Pin	Connection	Test condition	Measurements
1	earth	ignition on/engine running	0.25 V (max)
2	injector driver (cylinder 1) : t1	engine running	3.8 ms
3-6	–		
7	amplifier control signal : t2	engine cranking/running	0 to 12 V (switching)
8	supply from ignition switch : t15 (via main relay : t5)	ignition on/engine running	nbv
9	knock sensor shield : t3	ignition on/engine running	0.25 V (max)
10	–		
11	instrument panel		data not available
12	CTS signal : t3	ignition on/engine running	20° C: 2.5 to 3.0 V
			80° C: 0.30 to 0.60 V
13	air conditioning		data not available
14	MAF sensor signal : t1	ignition on	1.2 V
		engine running	1.7 V
15	–		
16	CAS (Hall Effect earth) : t3	engine cranking/running	0.25 V (max)
17	OS signal : t3	ignition on	1.3 to 1.4 V
		engine running	0.80 to 1.80 V (switching)
		open circuit	1.50 to 1.60 V
		short circuit to other wire	0.50 V (approx)
		short circuit to earth	0.15 to 0.25 V (approx)
		short circuit to positive	2.51 V (approx)
18	idle switch (TCA : t3)	ignition on/engine running:	
		idle contacts closed	0.25 V (max)
		idle contacts open	nbv
19	instrument panel		data not available
20	OS heater driver: t2	engine running:	
		OS heater inactive	nbv
		OS heater active	1.25 V (max)

Pin	Connection	Test condition	Measurements
21	OS screen	ignition on/engine running	0.25 (max)
22	–		
23	supply from main relay : t6	ignition on/engine running	nbv
24	–		
25	ISSM (TCA : t2)	idle speed, active	0 to 5.0 V (switching)
26	MAF sensor return : t2	engine running	0.25 V (max)
27	–		
28	TVPS signal (TCA : t8)	idle speed	0.5 to 4.0 V
29	ATS return : t1	ignition on/engine running	0.25 V (max)
30	ISSM (TCA : t1)	idle speed, active	0 to 5.0 V (switching)
31	fuel pump relay driver	ignition on	nbv
		engine cranking/running	1.25 V (max)
32	ignition switch : t50	engine cranking	nbv
33	CFSV driver : t1	ignition on	nbv
		engine running, above idle, operating temperature:	
		CFSV inactive	nbv
		CFSV active	0 to 12 V (switching)
		duty cycle	0 to 99%
34	KS signal : t2	engine running, KS active	1.0 V AC (peak to peak)
35	sensor return (HES (-), CTS : t1,TCA : t7)	ignition on/engine running	0.25 V (max)
36	KS return : t1	engine running, KS active	0.25 V (max)
37	ATS signal : t1	ignition on/engine running	10 ° C: 2.0 V
38	supply from ignition switch : t15	ignition on/engine running	nbv
39	A/C		data not available
40	TPS signal (TCA : t5)	ignition on/engine running:	
		throttle closed	4.0 V
		throttle fully open	0.75 V
41	TPS/TVPS supply (TCA : t4)	ignition on/engine running	5.0 V ± 0.1
42	OS signal return : t4	engine running	0.25 V (max)
43	–		
44	HES (CID) signal : t2	engine running	5.0 to 7.0 V (average)
45	HES (CID) supply : t3	ignition on/engine running	9.0 V (min)
46	injector driver (cylinder 2) : t1	engine running	3.8 ms
47	injector driver (cylinder 3) : t1	engine running	3.8 ms
48	injector driver (cylinder 4) : t1	engine running	3.8 ms
49-66	–		
67	CAS signal (Hall Effect) : t2	engine cranking/running	0 to 12 V (switching)
68	CAS supply (Hall Effect) : t1	ignition on/engine running	9.0 V (min)

68 pin ECM multi-plug, Simos 4S

Pin Table – VAG Digifant (45 pin)

Pin	Connection	Test condition	Measurements
1	earth	ignition on/engine running	0.25 V (max)
2	injector driver : t1	ignition on	nbv briefly, then 0 V
		engine running, cold	3.0 to 3.5 ms
		engine running, hot	2.0 to 2.5 ms
		snap acceleration	6.0 ms
3-6	–		
7	amplifier control signal : t2	engine cranking/running	0 to 12 V (switching)

Pin Table – VAG Digifant (45 pin) (continued)

Pin	Connection	Test condition	Measurements
8	supply from ignition switch : t15 (via main relay : t5)	ignition on/engine running	nbv
9	KS return : t3	engine running, KS active	0.25 V (max)
10	–		
11	VSS signal	vehicle in motion	0 to 5 V (switching)
12	CTS signal : t2	ignition on/engine running	0° C: 1.8 to 2.5 V
			20° C: 0.95 to 1.25 V
			40° C: 0.50 to 0.85 V
			80° C: 0.20 to 0.4 V
13	–		
14	AFS signal : t2	ignition on	0.2 to 0.5 V
		idle speed	0.5 to 1.5 V
		2000 rpm	1.75 to 2.25 V
		3000 rpm	2.0 to 2.7 V
		snap accelerate	3.0 to 4.5 V
		fully open (off load)	4.0 to 4.5 V
15	–		
16	AFS supply : t3	ignition on/engine running	5.0 V ± 0.1
17	OS return : t4	ignition on/engine running	0.25 V (max)
18	–		
19	tachometer		data not available
20	OS heater driver : t1	engine running:	
		OS inactive	nbv
		OS active	1.25 V (max)
21	OS screen	engine running	0.25 V (max)
22	–		
23	supply from main relay : t6	ignition on/engine running	nbv
24-29	–		
30	ISCV driver : t1	ignition on	nbv
		engine running, idle speed:	
		cold	6.0 to 6.5 V
		hot	7.0 to 9.0 V
		duty cycle	30 to 60 %
31	fuel pump relay driver : t85	ignition on	nbv
		engine cranking/running	1.25 V (max)
32	ignition switch : t50 (AT only)	engine cranking	nbv
33	CFSV driver : t1	ignition on	nbv
		engine running, above idle, operating temperature:	
		CFSV inactive	nbv
		CFSV active	0 to 12 V (switching)
		duty cycle	0 to 99%
34	KS signal : t2	engine running, KS active	1.0 V AC
35	sensor return (CTS : t1, TPS: t3)	ignition on/engine running	0.25 V (max)
36	KS return : t1	engine running, KS active	0.25 V (max)
37	ATS signal (AFS : t1)	ignition on/engine running	20° C: 0.95 to 2.25 V
			80° C: 0.2 to 0.4 V
38	–		
39	A/C		data not available
40	TPS signal : t2	ignition on	
		throttle closed	0.3 to 0.7 V
		throttle fully open	> 4.25 V
41	TPS supply : t1	ignition on/engine running	5.0 V ± 0.1
42	OS signal : t3	ignition on, OS multiplug disconnected	0.4 to 0.5 V
		engine running, hot	200 to 1000 mV (switching)
		throttle fully open	0.5 to 1.0 V
		deceleration (fuel cut-off)	0 to 0.5 V
		switching frequency	1 sec intervals (approx)
43	SD connector		data not available

Pin	Connection	Test condition	Measurements
44	HES signal : t2	ignition on:	
		trigger vane cut out in air gap	< 700 mV
		trigger vane diverting hall voltage	5.0 to 10.0 V
		engine running:	
		idle	5.0 to 7.0 V (mean)
45	HES supply : t2	ignition on/engine running	9.0 V (min)

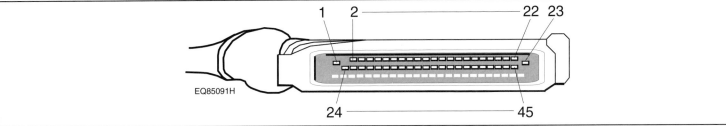

EQ85091H

45 pin ECM multi-plug, VAG Digifant

Pin Table – VAG Digifant (68 pin)

Pin	Connection	Test condition	Measurements
1	earth	ignition on/engine running	0.25 V (max)
2	injector driver (cylinder 4) : t1	ignition on	nbv
		engine running, cold	> 3.5 ms
		engine running, hot	3.5 ms
		snap acceleration	20 ms (approx)
		deceleration	0 ms (approx)
3	TPS signal : t2	ignition on/engine running:	
		throttle closed	0.5 to 1.5 V
		throttle fully open	3.0 to 5.0 V
4	TPS supply : t1	ignition on/engine running	5.0 V ± 0.1
5	–		
6	fuel pump relay driver : t85	ignition on	nbv
		engine cranking/running	1.25 V (max)
7	–		
8	amplifier control signal : t2	engine cranking/running	0 to 5.0 V (switching)
9	supply from ignition switch through main relay : t15	ignition on/engine running	nbv
10	KS shield : t3	engine running, KS active	0.25 V (max)
11-13	–		
14	CTS signal : t2	ignition on/engine running	10° C: 1.00 V
			80° C: 0.20 V
15-19	–		
20	OS signal : t3	ignition on, OS multiplug disconnected	0.4 to 0.5 V
		engine running, hot	200 to 1000 mV (switching)
		throttle fully-open	0.5 to 1.0 V
		deceleration (fuel cut-off)	0 to 0.5 V
		switching frequency	1 sec intervals (approx)
21	idle switch signal : t2	ignition on/engine running:	
		throttle closed	0 V
		throttle open	nbv
22	–		
23	supply from main relay : t87	ignition on/engine running	nbv
24	injector driver (cylinder 1) : t1	engine running, cold	> 3.5 ms
		engine running, hot	3.5 ms
		snap acceleration	20 ms (approx)
		deceleration (fuel cut off)	0 ms (approx)
25	injector driver (cylinder 2) : t1	engine running, cold	> 3.5 ms
		engine running, hot	3.5 ms
		snap acceleration	20 ms (approx)
		deceleration (fuel cut off)	0 ms (approx)

Pin Table – VAG Digifant (68 pin) (continued)

Pin	Connection	Test condition	Measurements
26	injector driver (cylinder 3) : t1	engine running, cold	> 3.5 ms
		engine running, hot	3.5 ms
		snap acceleration	20 ms (approx)
		deceleration (fuel cut off)	0 ms (approx)
27	ISCV driver : t1	ignition on	nbv
		engine running, idle speed:	
		cold	6.0 to 6.5 V
		hot	7.0 to 9.0 V
		duty cycle	30 to 60%
28	OS relay driver : t86	engine running:	
		OS heater inactive	nbv
		OS heater active	1.25 V (max)
29-30	–		
31	CFSV driver : t1	ignition on	nbv
		engine running, above idle, operating temperature:	
		CFSV inactive	nbv
		CFSV active	0 to 12 V (switching)
		duty cycle	0 to 99%
32	KS signal : t2	engine running, KS active	1.0 to 2.0 V AC (peak to peak)
33	earth	ignition on/engine running	0.25 V (max)
34	KS return : t1	engine running, KS active	0.25 V (max)
35	–		
36	ATS signal : t2	ignition on/engine running	10° C: 1.5 V
37	–		
38	supply from ignition switch : t15	ignition on/engine running	nbv
39	A/C		data not available
40	HES supply : t+	ignition on/engine running	9.0 V (min)
41	–		
42	OS return : t4	ignition on/engine running	0.25 V (max)
43	SD connector		data not available
44	HES (CID) signal : t0	ignition on:	
		multiplug disconnected	5.0 to 10.0 V
		trigger vane cut out space in air gap	< 700 mV.
		trigger vane diverting hall voltage	5.0 to 10.0 V
		engine running	0 to 12.0 V (switching)
		duty cycle	50%
45-50	–		
51	trip computer		data not available
52-54	–		
55	KS shield : t3	engine running, KS active	0.25 V (max)
56	KS signal : t2	engine running, KS active	1.0 to 2.0 V AC (peak to peak)
57	KS return : t1	engine running, KS active	0.25 V (max)
58-64	–		
65	OS shield : t3	OS active	0.25 V (max)
66	–		
67	HES (ignition) signal : t2	engine cranking/running	0 to 5.0 V (switching)
		duty cycle	50%
68	HES supply : t1	ignition on/engine running	5.0 V

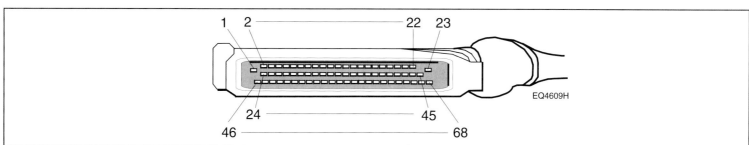

68 pin ECM multi-plug, VAG Digifant

Wiring Diagrams

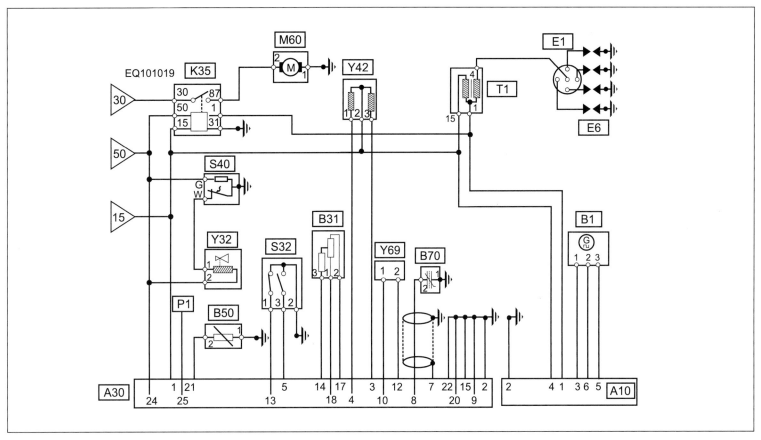

System wiring diagram, Bosch KE-Jetronic.

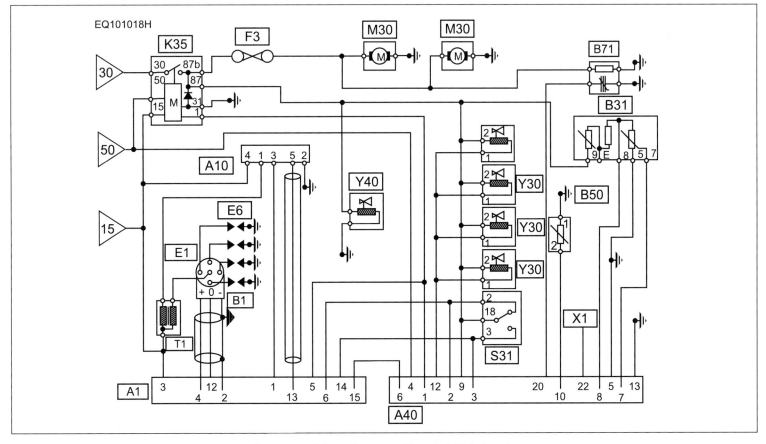

System wiring diagram, Bosch LE Jetronic

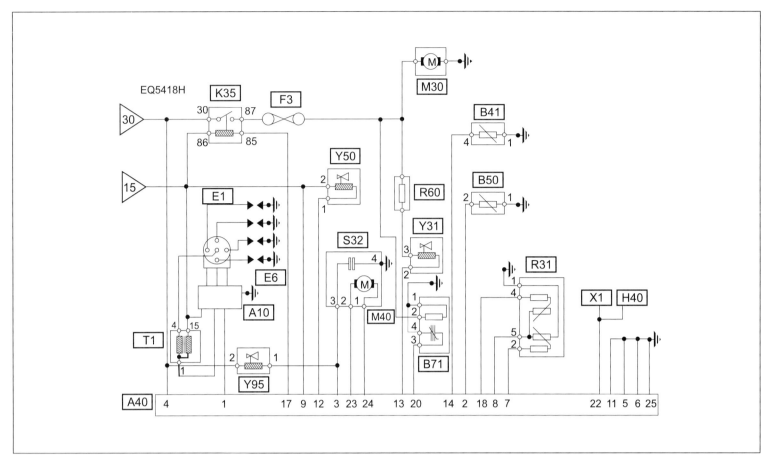

System wiring diagram, Bosch Mono-Jetronic

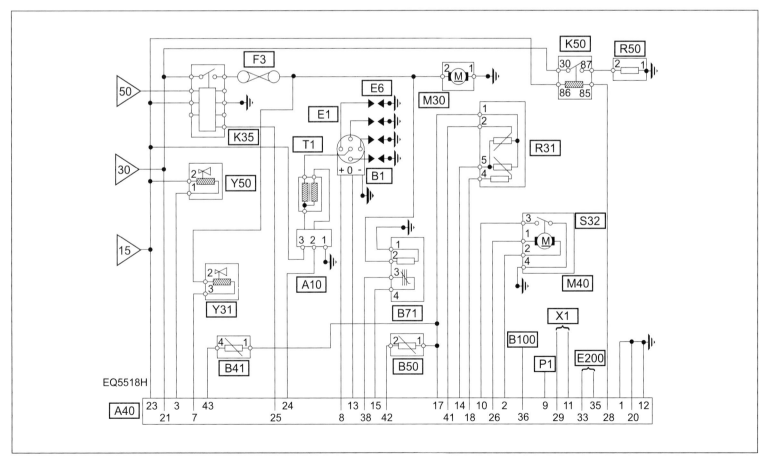

System wiring diagram, Bosch Mono-Motronic 1.2.3

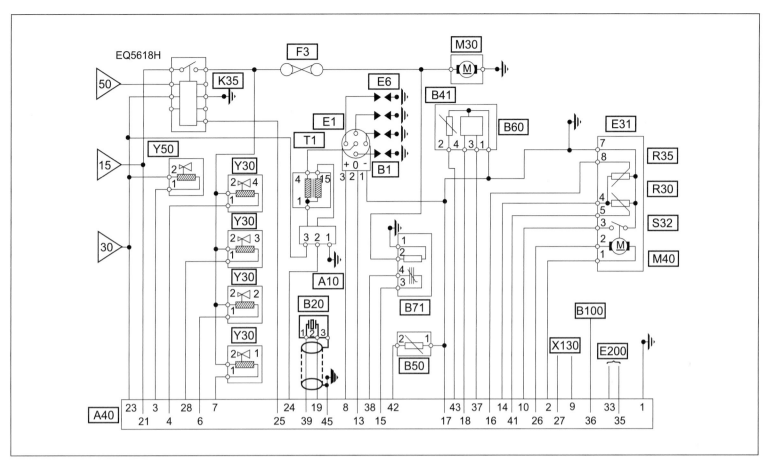

System wiring diagram, Bosch Motronic MP 9.0

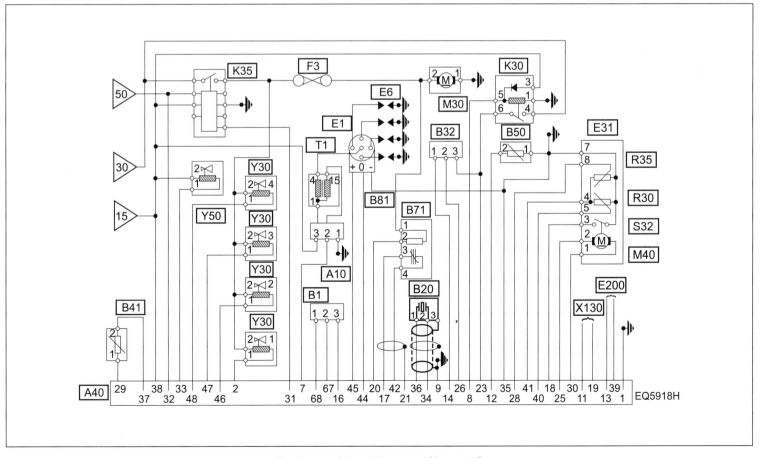

System wiring diagram, Simos 4S

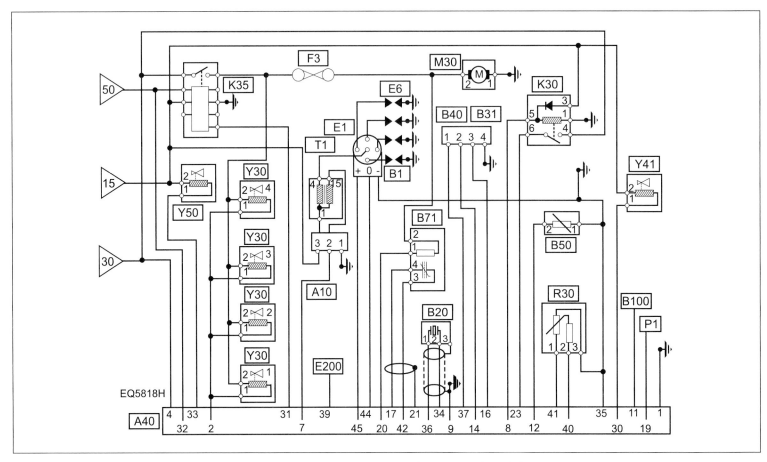

System wiring diagram, VAG Digifant (45 pin)

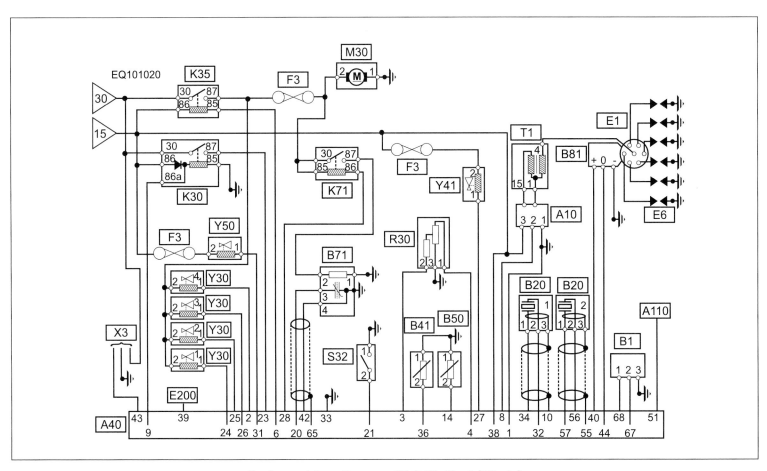

System wiring diagram, VAG Digifant (68 pin)

Chapter 27
Skoda

Contents

Index of Skoda vehicles/systems

Model	Engine code	Year	System
Favorit/Forman (Pickup)	781/135B	1993 to 1996	Bosch Mono-Motronic 1.2.3
Favorit/Forman (Pickup)	781/136B	1994 to 1996	Bosch Mono-Motronic 1.2.3
Felicia 1.3i	**135B**	**1995 to 1998**	**Bosch Mono-Motronic 1.2.3**
Felicia 1.3i	136B	1995 to 1998	Bosch Mono-Motronic 1.2.3
Felicia 1.6	**AEE**	**1995 to 1998**	**Magneti-Marelli 1AV**

Note: *The vehicles accentuated in bold type are the actual vehicles upon which the ECM pin tables and wiring diagrams are based. Other vehicle with the same system may be similar; but are also likely to contain some differences.*

Pin Table – Bosch Mono-Motronic 1.2.3

Pin	Item	Test Condition	Measurements
1	earth	ignition on/engine running	0.25 V (max)
2	stepper motor : t2	idle speed, active	0 to 5.0 V (switching)
3	CFSV driver : t1	ignition on	nbv
		engine running, above idle, operating temperature:	
		CFSV inactive	nbv
		CFSV active	0 to 12 V (switching)
		duty cycle	0 to 99%
4-6	–		
7	injector driver : t1	engine running, cold	3.0 to 4.5 ms
		engine running, hot:	
		idle	2.0 ms
		2000 rpm	2.0 ms
		snap acceleration	10 to 15 ms
8	HES supply voltage : t+	ignition on/engine running	9.0 V (min)
9	tachometer		data not available
10	idle switch : t3	ignition on/engine running:	
		throttle closed	0 V
		throttle open	nbv
11-12	–		
13	HES signal : t0	engine cranking/running	0 to 12.0 V (switching)
		duty cycle	35%
14	TPS supply : t5	ignition on/engine running	5.0 V ± 0.1
15	OS return : t4	engine running	0.25 V (max)
16			
17	sensor return (ATS : t1, CTS : t1, TPS : t1)	ignition on/engine running	0.25 V (max)
18	TPS signal : t4	ignition on/engine running:	
		throttle closed	0 V
		throttle fully open	4.0 V
19	–		
20	earth	ignition on/engine running	0.25 V (max)
21	supply from battery : t30	ignition off/on/engine running	nbv
22			
23	supply from ignition switch : t15	ignition on/engine running	nbv
24	amplifier control signal : t2	engine cranking/running	0 to 12.0 V (switching)
25	fuel pump relay driver : t86	ignition on	nbv
		engine cranking/running	1.25 V (max)
26	stepper motor : t1	idle speed, active	0 to 5.0 V (switching)
27-28	–		
29	SD connector		data not available
30-37	–		
38	oxygen sensor signal : t3	ignition on, OS multiplug disconnected	0.4 to 0.5 V
		engine running, hot, 2000 rpm	200 to 1000 mV (switching)
		throttle fully-open	0.5 to 1.0 V
		deceleration (fuel cut-off)	0 V to 0.5 V
		switching frequency	1 sec intervals (approx)
39-40	–		
41	TPS signal : t2	ignition on/engine running:	
		throttle closed	1.9 V
		throttle fully open	4.9 V
42	CTS signal : t2	ignition on/engine running	20° C: 2.00 V
			80° C: 0.20 V
43	ATS signal : t4	ignition on/engine running	20° C: 2.30 V
44	shield return	ignition on/engine running	0.25 V (max)
45	–		

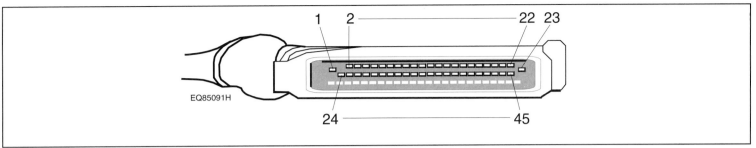

45 pin ECM multi-plug, Bosch Mono-Motronic 1.2.3

Pin Table – Magneti-Marelli 1AV

Pin	Item	Test Condition	Measurement
1	earth	ignition on/engine running	0.25 V (max)
2	stepper motor (TCA : t1)	idle speed, active	0 to 5.0 V (switching)
3	CFSV driver : t1	ignition off/on	nbv
		engine running, above idle, operating temperature:	
		CFSV inactive	nbv
		CFSV active	0 to 12 V (switching)
		duty cycle	0 to 99%
4	injector driver (cylinder 4) : t1	engine running, cold	> 4.0 ms
		engine running, hot	4.0 ms
		snap acceleration	> 6.0 ms
6	injector driver (cylinder 2) : t1	engine running, cold	> 4.0 ms
		engine running, hot	4.0 ms
		snap acceleration	> 6.0 ms
7	injector driver (cylinder 1) : t1	engine running, cold	> 4.0 ms
		engine running, hot	4.0 ms
		snap acceleration	> 6.0 ms
8	HES supply voltage: t+	ignition on/engine running	9.0 V (min)
9	instrument panel connection		data not available
10	idle switch (TCA : t3)	ignition on/engine running:	
		throttle closed	0 V
		throttle open	nbv
11-12	–		
13	HES signal : t0	engine running	0 to 12.0 V (switching)
		duty cycle	35%
14	TPS supply (TCA : t4)	ignition on/engine running	5.0 V ± 0.1
15	oxygen sensor signal : t3	ignition on, OS multiplug disconnected	0.4 to 0.5 V
		engine running, hot, 2000 rpm	200 to 1000 mV (switching)
		throttle fully-open	0.5 to 1.0 V
		deceleration (fuel cut-off)	0 V to 0.5 V
		switching frequency	1 sec intervals (approx)
16	TVPS signal (TCA : t8)	ignition on/engine running	0.5 V to 4.9 V
		idle speed, engine hot	3.0 V
17	sensor return (CTS : t1, HES : t-, MAP : t1, TCA : t7)	ignition on, engine running	0.25 V (max)
18	MAP sensor signal : t4	ignition on	4.5 V
		engine running, idle, hot	1.25 to 1.30 V
		engine running, WOT	4.0 to 4.5 V
19	KS signal : t2	engine running, KS active	1.0 V AC (peak to peak)
20	–		
21	supply from ignition switch : t15	ignition on/engine running	nbv
22	–		
23	supply from battery : t30	ignition off/on/engine running	nbv
24	amplifier control signal : t2	engine cranking/running	0 to 12.0 V (switching)
25	fuel pump relay driver : t86	ignition on	nbv
		engine cranking/running	1.25 V (max)
26	stepper motor (TCA : t2)	idle speed, active	0 to 5.0 V (switching)

Pin Table – Magneti-Marelli 1AV (continued)

Pin	Item	Test Condition	Measurement
27	instrument panel connection		data not available
28	injector driver (cyl 2) : t1	engine running, cold	> 4.0 ms
		engine running, hot	4.0 ms
		snap acceleration	> 6.0 ms
29-32	–		
33	air conditioning	data not available	
34	–		
35	air conditioning		data not available
36	VSS signal : t3	vehicle in motion/drive wheels rotating	0 to 12 V (switching)
37	MAP sensor supply : t3	ignition on/engine running	5.0 V ± 0.1
38	OS return : t4	ignition on/engine running	0.25 V (max)
39	KS return : t1	engine running	0.25 V (max)
40	–		
41	TPS signal (TCA : t5)	ignition on/engine running:	
		throttle closed	4.0 V
		throttle open	0.6 to 0.8 V
42	CTS signal : t2	ignition on/engine running	20° C: 2.50 to 3.00 V
			80° C: 0.30 to 0.60 V
43	ATS signal : t2	ignition on/engine running	30° C: 2.00 to 3.00 V
44	–		
45	KS shield return : t3	engine running	0.25 V (max)

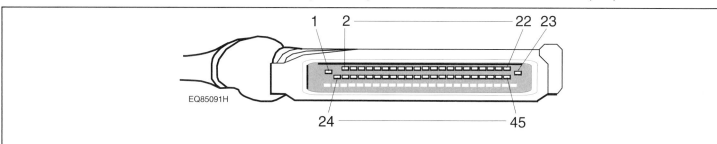

45 pin ECM multi-plug, Magneti-Marelli 1AV

Wiring Diagrams

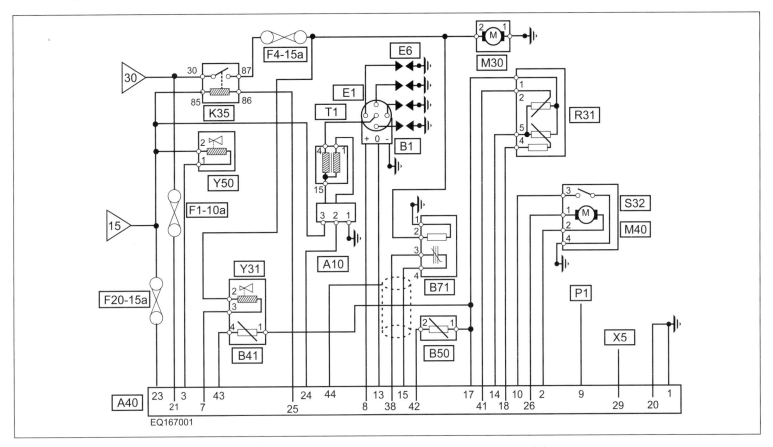

System wiring diagram, Bosch Mono-Motronic 1.2.3

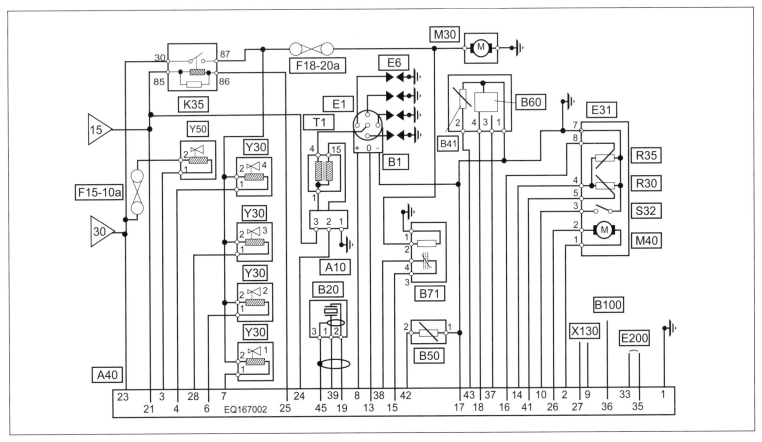

System wiring diagram, Magneti-Marelli 1AV

Notes

Chapter 28
Subaru

Contents

Index of Subaru vehicles/systems

Model	Engine code	Year	System
Impreza 1.6i SOHC 16V		1993 to 1997	Subaru MPFi
Impreza 1.8i SOHC 16V		1993 to 1997	Subaru MPFi
Impreza 2.0 Turbo DOHC 16V		1994 to 1997	Subaru MPFi
Impreza 2.0i 16v		1996 to 1997	Subaru MPFi
Justy (J12) 1.2i cat		1992 to 1997	Subaru MPFi
Legacy 1.8i SOHC 16V	AY/EJ18	1991 to 1993	Subaru MPFi
Legacy 2.0 cat SOHC 16V	**AY/EJ20EN**	**1991 to 1996**	**Subaru MPFi**
Legacy 2.0 4 Cam Turbo DOHC 16V	AY/EJ20-GN	1991 to 1994	Subaru MPFi
Legacy 2.2 & Cat	EJ22	1989 to 1997	Subaru MPFi
L-Series Coupe 1.8	EA82	1988 to 1990	Subaru MPFi
L-Series Turbo 4x4	EA82	1985 to 1988	Subaru MPFi
SVX DOHC 24V		1992 to 1997	Subaru MPFi
Vivio SOHC 8V		1992 to 1996	Subaru MPFi
XT Turbo Coupe	EA82	1985 to 1989	Subaru MPFi
XT Turbo Coupe	EA82	1989 to 1991	Subaru MPFi
1.8 Turbo Coupe 4x4	EA82	1986 to 1989	Subaru MPFi

Note: *The vehicles accentuated in bold type are the actual vehicles upon which the ECM pin tables and wiring diagrams are based. Other vehicle with the same system may be similar; but are also likely to contain some differences.*

Pin Table – Subaru MPFi

Pin	Item	Test Condition	Measurements
B1	ISCV driver : t3	ignition on/engine running	6.0 to 7.0 V
B2	ISCV driver : t1	ignition on	8.0 to 9.0 V
		engine running	9.0 to 10 V
B3-B4	–		
B5	supply to main relay : t2	ignition on/engine running	nbv
B6	CFSV driver : t1	ignition on	nbv
		engine running, above idle, operating temperature:	
		CFSV inactive	nbv
		CFSV active	0 to 12 V (switching)
		duty cycle	0 to 99%
B7-B8	–		
B9	amplifier control (cyls 3 and 4)	engine cranking/running	0 to 5.0 V (switching)
B10	amplifier control (cyls 1 and 2)	engine cranking/running	0 to 5.0 V (switching)
B11	injector driver (cylinder 3) : t1	ignition off/on	nbv
		engine running, cold	> 3.5 ms
		hot idle	3.5 ms
		3000 rpm	3.4 ms
		snap acceleration	20 ms (approx)
		deceleration	1 ms (approx)
B12	injector driver (cylinder 2) : t1	ignition off/on	nbv
		engine running, cold	> 3.5 ms
		hot idle	3.5 ms
		3000 rpm	3.4 ms
		snap acceleration	20 ms (approx)
		deceleration	1 ms (approx)
B13	injector driver (cylinder 1) : t1	ignition off/on	nbv
		engine running, cold	> 3.5 ms
		hot idle	3.5 ms
		3000 rpm	3.4 ms
		snap acceleration	20 ms (approx)
		deceleration	1 ms (approx)
B14	earth (supply)	ignition on/engine running	0.25 V (max)
B15	earth (ignition system)	ignition on/engine running	0.25 V (max)
B16	–		
B17	radiator fan control	ignition on/engine running:	
		fan control active	0 V
		fan control inactive	nbv
B18	SD connector	ignition on/engine running	nbv
B19	SD warning lamp	ignition on, lamp on	< 1.0 V
		engine running:	
		lamp illuminated	< 1.0 V
		lamp off	nbv
B20-B21	–		
B22	air conditioning, relay cut-off	Ignition on/engine running:	
		A/C on	0 V
		A/C off	nbv
		when connected	0 V
B23	fuel pump relay driver : t3	ignition on	nbv
		engine cranking/running	1.25 V (max)
B24	earth (injectors)	ignition on/engine running	0.25 V (max)
B25	earth (injectors)	ignition on/engine running	0.25 V (max)
B26	injector driver (cylinder 4) : t1	ignition off/on	nbv
		engine running, cold	> 3.5 ms
		hot idle	3.5 ms
		3000 rpm	3.4 ms
		snap acceleration	20 ms (approx)
		deceleration	1 ms (approx)

Pin	Item	Test Condition	Measurements
C1	CAS signal : t1	engine cranking (VM specified):	0.1 V RMS (min)
		values not stated by VM, expect:	
		engine cranking	> 4.0 V AC (peak to peak)
		idle:	> 8.0 V AC (peak to peak)
		cruise:	> 14.0 V AC (peak to peak)
C2	CAS return : t2	engine running	0.25 V (max)
C3	CAS shield return	ignition on/engine running	0.25 V (max)
C4	KS shield return	ignition on/engine running	0.25 V (max)
C5	KS signal : t2	engine running, KS active	3.0 to 4.0 V
C6	TS, idle contact : t1	ignition on/engine running:	
		throttle closed	0 V
		throttle part/fully open	5.0 V ± 0.1
C7	SD connection		data not available
C8	SD connection		data not available
C9	air conditioning		data not available
C10	starter switch	engine cranking	nbv
C11	economy switch (AT)	ignition on/engine running:	
		switch active	0 V
		switch inactive	nbv
C12	SD connector, test mode : t3	ignition on/engine running	7 V
		when connected	0 V
C13	SD connector, read memory : t2	ignition on/engine running	7 V
		when connected	0 V
C14	–		
C15	SD connector : t8		data not available
C16	tachometer		data not available
D1	TPS earth : t2	ignition on/engine running	0.25 V (max)
D2	TPS signal : t4	ignition on/engine running:	
		throttle closed	4.7 V
		throttle open	0.9 V
D3	TPS supply : t3	ignition on/engine running	5.0 V ± 0.1
D4	camshaft sensor signal : t1	engine cranking (VM specified):	0.1 V RMS (min)
		values not stated by VM, expect:	
		idle speed	8.0 V AC (peak to peak)
D5	camshaft sensor return : t2	ignition on/engine running	0.25 V (max)
D6	camshaft sensor shield : t3	ignition on/engine running	0.25 V (max)
D7	–		
D8	AFS : t5		data not available
D9	automatic transmission	ignition on/engine running:	
		P range	0 V
		other positions	nbv
D10	neutral switch (AT and MT)	ignition on/engine running:	
		AT: N range	0 V
		AT: other position	nbv
		MT: Neutral position	7 V
		MT: other position	nbv
D11	VSS signal : t2	vehicle in motion	0 or 5 V (switching)
D12	ignition switch supply: t15	ignition on/engine running	nbv
A1	–		
A2	supply from main relay: t3	ignition on/engine running	nbv
A3-A5	–		
A6	oxygen sensor : t3	ignition key on:	
		AT	0.1 to 0.9 V
		MT	0.6 V
		engine running, hot	200 to 1000 mV (switching)
		throttle fully-open, rich mixture	0.7 to 1.0 V
		deceleration (lean mixture)	0 to 0.2 V
		switching frequency	1 sec intervals (approx)
A7	CTS signal : t1	ignition on/engine running	20° C: 2.00 to 2.50 V
			80° C: 0.7 to 1.50 V

Pin Table – Subaru MPFi (continued)

Pin	Item	Test Condition	Measurements
A8	AFS supply : t1	ignition on/engine running	nbv
A9	AFS signal : t4	ignition on	0 to 0.30 V
		idle	0.80 to 1.20 V
A10	AFS return : t2	ignition on/engine running	0.25 V (max)
A11	earth (control system)	ignition on/engine running	0.25 V (max)
A12	–		
A13	supply from main relay : t3	ignition on/engine running	nbv
A14	–		
A15	supply from battery : t30	ignition off/on/engine running	nbv
A16	–		
A17	OS shield	ignition on/engine running	0.25 V (max)
A18-A19	–		
A20	AT/MT identification	ignition on/engine running:	
		AT	0 V
		MT	7.0 V
A21	AFS shield, CTS return : t1, TPS shield	ignition on/engine running	0.25 V (max)
A22	earth (control system)	ignition on/engine running	0.25 V (max)

Eq120007

76 pin ECM multi-plug, Subaru MPFi

Wiring Diagram

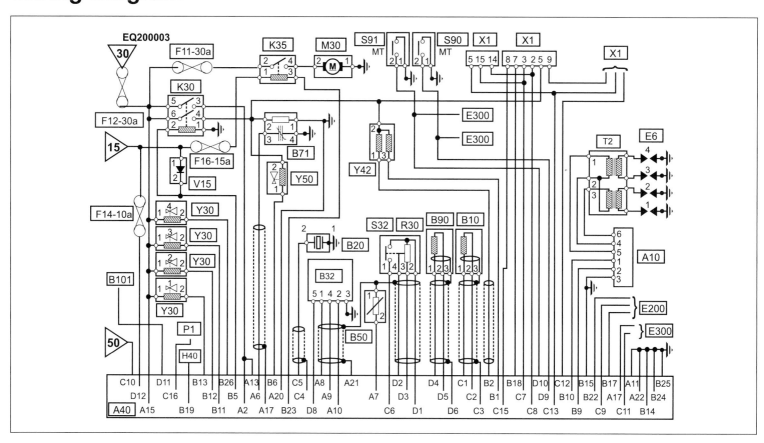

System wiring diagram, Subaru MPFi

Chapter 29
Suzuki

Contents

Index of Suzuki vehicles/systems

Model	Engine code	Year	System
Alto 1.0	G10B	1997	Suzuki EPi-MPi
Baleno 1.3	G13BB	1995 to 1997	Suzuki EPi-MPi
Baleno 1.6	G16B	1995 to 1997	Suzuki EPi-MPi
Baleno 1.8	J18A	1996 to 1997	Suzuki EPi-MPi
Cappuccino DOHC 12V	F6A	1993 to 1996	Suzuki EPi-MPi
Samurai 1.3l	G13BA	1995 to 1996	Suzuki EPi-SPi
Swift 1.0i cat SOHC 6V	G10A	1991 to 1997	Suzuki EPi-MPi
Swift 1.0l cat SOHC 6V	G10A	1991 to 1998	Suzuki EPi-SPi
Swift 1.3l cat SOHC 8V	G13BA	1992 to 1997	Suzuki EPi-MPi
Swift 1.3l DOHC 16V	**G13B**	**1992 to 1995**	**Suzuki EPi-MPi**
Swift 1.3l cat SOHC 8V	G13BA	1992 to 1998	Suzuki EPi-SPi
Swift Cabrio DOHC cat	**G13B**	**1992 to 1995**	**Suzuki EPi-MPi**
Swift Gti DOHC 16V		**1986 to 1989**	**Suzuki EPi-MPi**
Swift SF 416l SOHC 16V	G16B	1989 to 1992	Suzuki EPi-SPi
Swift SF 416l 4x4 cat SOHC 16V	G16B	1989 to 1992	Suzuki EPi-SPi
Swift SF 413 Gti DOHC	**G13B**	**1988 to 1992**	**Suzuki EPi-MPi**
Swift SF 413 DOHC cat	**G13B**	**1988 to 1992**	**Suzuki EPi-MPi**
Swift SF 416l SOHC 16V	G16B	1989 to 1992	Suzuki EPi-MPi
Swift SF 416l 4x4 SOHC	G16B	1989 to 1992	Suzuki EPi-MPi
Swift SF 416l 4x4 cat	G16B	1989 to 1992	Suzuki EPi-MPi
Swift SF 416l 4x4 SOHC	**G16B**	**1989 to 1992**	**Suzuki EPi-SPi**
Vitara EFi SOHC 16V	G16B	1991 to 1997	Suzuki EPi-MPi
Vitara Sport SPi SOHC	G16A	1994 to 1997	Suzuki EPi-MPi
Vitara 2.0 V6	H20A	1995 to 1997	Suzuki EPi-MPi
X-90 1.6	G16B	1996 to 1997	Suzuki EPi-MPi

Note: *The vehicles accentuated in bold type are the actual vehicles upon which the ECM pin tables and wiring diagrams are based. Other vehicles with the same system may be similar; but are also likely to contain some differences.*

Pin Table – Suzuki EPi-MPi

Connector A

Pin	Item	Test Condition	Measurements
A1	supply from relay : t87	ignition on/engine running	nbv
A2	supply from relay : t87	ignition on/engine running	nbv
A3	AFS supply : t2	ignition on/engine running	nbv
A4	sensor supply (TPS : t1, CO adjuster : t2)	ignition on/engine running	5.0 V ± 0.1
A5	sensor return (AFS : t1, TPS : t3, CO adjuster : t1)	ignition on/engine running	0.25 V (max)
A6	MAF sensor signal : t3	ignition on	0.2 to 0.8 V
A7	CTS signal : t2	ignition on/engine running	20° C: 3.00 to 3.50 V
			80° C: 1.00 to 1.30 V
A8	OS signal : t3	ignition on	0.4 to 0.5 V
		engine running, hot	200 to 1000 mV (switching)
		throttle fully open	0.5 to 1.0 V
		deceleration (fuel cut off)	0 to 0.5 V
		switching frequency	1 sec intervals (approx)
A9	TPS signal : t2	ignition on/engine running:	
		throttle closed	0 to 1.0 V
		throttle open	3.0 to 5.0 V
A10	VSS signal : t2	vehicle in motion	0 to 5 V (switching)
A11	–		
A12	ignition primary signal via suppresser		data not available
A13-A15	–		
A16	supply from battery : t30	ignition off/on/engine running	nbv
A17	–		
A18	A/C		data not available
A19	SD connector : tD		data not available
A20	–		
A21	TS, idle contact : t4	ignition on	5 V
		idle speed	0.25 V (max)
A22	SD connector : tB		data not available
A23-A24	–		

Connector B

Pin	Item	Test Condition	Measurements
B1	CAS signal : t2	engine cranking:	> 4.0 V AC (peak to peak)
		idle:	> 8.0 V AC (peak to peak)
		cruise:	> 14.0 V AC (peak to peak)
B2	SD warning lamp : t1	ignition on, lamp on	1.25 V (max)
		engine running:	
		no faults present	nbv
		faults present, lamp on	1.25 V (max)
B3-B4	–		
B5	CFSV driver : t1	ignition on	nbv
		engine running, above idle, operating temperature:	
		CFSV inactive	nbv
		CFSV active	0 to 12 V (switching)
		duty cycle	0 to 99%
B6-B7	–		
B8	main relay driver : t85	ignition on	nbv briefly, then 0 V
		engine running	1.25 V (max)
B9	earth	ignition on/engine running	0.25 V (max)
B10	CAS return : t1	engine running	0.25 V (max)
B11-B12	–		
B13	fuel pump relay driver: t85	ignition on for first 3 seconds	0 to 4 V
		ignition on	nbv
		engine cranking/running	1.25 V (max)
B14			

Pin	Item	Test Condition	Measurements
B15	CO pot signal : t3	ignition on/engine running: voltage range	0.1 to 4.9 V
B16	–		
B17	earth	ignition on/engine running	0.25 V (max)
B18	ISCV driver : t1	ignition on	nbv
		engine running, idle speed:	
		cold	6.0 to 6.5 V
		hot	7.0 to 9.0 V
		duty cycle	30 to 60%

Connector C

Pin	Item	Test Condition	Measurements
C1	engine start signal	ignition on/engine running	0 to 1 V
		engine cranking	nbv
C2	supply from main relay : t87	ignition on/engine running	nbv
C3	injector supply : t2		data not available
C4	injector supply : t2		data not available
C5	–		
C6	amplifier control signal : t3	engine cranking/running	0 to 3.0 V (switching)
C7	supply from main relay : t87	ignition on/engine running	nbv
C8	injector driver : t1		data not available
C9	injector driver : t1		data not available
C10	–		

EQ120003

52 pin ECM multi-plug, Suzuki EPI-MPI

Pin Table – Suzuki EPi-SPi

Connector A

Pin	Item	Test Condition	Measurement
A1	cranking signal : t50	engine cranking	nbv
A2	park/neutral switch (AT only)	ignition on/engine running:	
		lever in P or N	0 V
		lever in R, D, 2 or L	5.0 V
A3	idle switch signal (TCA : t3)	ignition on/engine running:	
		throttle closed	0 V
		throttle open	5.0 V
A4	sensor supply (MAP sensor : t2, TPS : t1)	ignition on/engine running	5.0 V ± 0.1
A5	MAP sensor signal : t1	ignition on	5.0 V
		760 mm Hg	3.5 to 4.1 V
A6	OS signal : t1	ignition on, OS multiplug disconnected	0.4 to 0.5 V
		engine running, hot	200 to 1000 mV (switching)
		throttle fully-open	0.5 to 1.0 V
		deceleration (fuel cut-off)	0 to 0.5 V
		switching frequency	1 sec intervals (approx)
A7	shield	ignition on/engine running	0.25 V (max)
A8	CAS signal : t2	engine cranking	> 4.0 V AC (peak to peak)
		Idle	> 8.0 V AC (peak to peak)
		cruise	> 14.0 V AC (peak to peak)
A9	–		
A10	air conditioning (if fitted)		data not available
A11	VSS signal : t3	vehicle in motion	0 to 5 V (switching)

Pin Table – Suzuki EPi-SPi (continued)

Connector A (continued)

Pin	Item	Test Condition	Measurement
A12	SD connector : tB		data not available
A13	ATS signal : t2	ignition on/engine running	20° C: 2.00 to 2.50 V
			80° C: 0.45 to 0.80 V
A14	CTS signal : t2	ignition on/engine running	20° C: 2.00 to 2.50 V
			80° C: 0.45 to 0.80 V
A15	TPS signal : t2	ignition on/engine running:	
		throttle closed	0.5 V
		throttle fully open	5.0 V
A16	sensor return (MAP sensor : t2, TPS : t4, CTS : t1, ATS : t1.)	ignition on/engine running	0.25 V (max)
A17	CAS return : t1	engine running	0.25 V (max)
A18	amplifier control signal : tIGt	engine cranking/running	0 to 5.0 V (switching)

Connector B

Pin	Item	Test Condition	Measurement
B1	supply from ignition switch : t15	ignition on/engine running	nbv
B2	–		
B3	EGR solenoid valve driver : t1	ignition on	nbv
		engine running:	
		EGR inactive	nbv
		EGR active	1.25 V (max)
B4	ISCV driver : t1	ignition on	nbv
		engine running, idle speed:	
		cold	6.0 to 6.5 V
		hot	7.0 to 9.0 V
		duty cycle	30 to 60%
B5	injector driver : t1	engine running, hot:	0.7 ms
		deceleration	0 ms
B6	amplifier control signal : tIGf	engine cranking/running	0 to 5.0 V (switching)
B7	supply from battery : t30	ignition off/on/engine running	nbv
B8	SD connector : tD		data not available
B9	SD warning lamp : t1	ignition on, lamp on	1.25 V (max)
		engine running:	
		no faults present	nbv
		faults present, lamp on	1.25 V (max)
B10	fuel pump relay driver: t85	ignition on	nbv
		engine cranking/running	1.25 V (max)
B11	earth	ignition on/engine running	0.25 V (max)
B12	–		

EQ120058

30 pin ECM multi-plug, Suzuki EPI-SPI

Wiring Diagrams

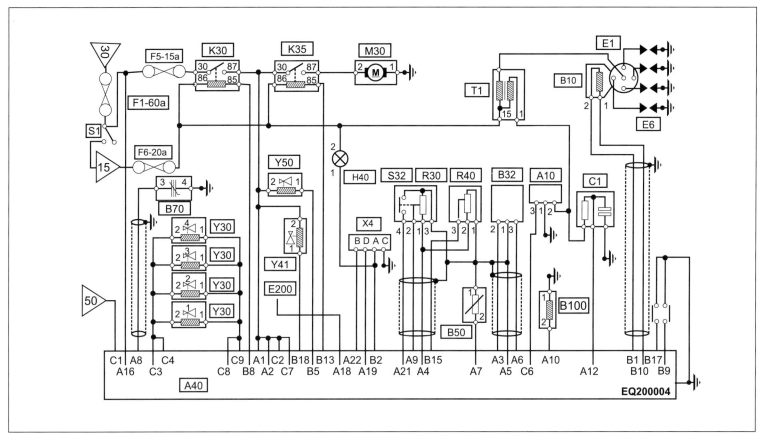

System wiring diagram, Suzuki EPi-MPi

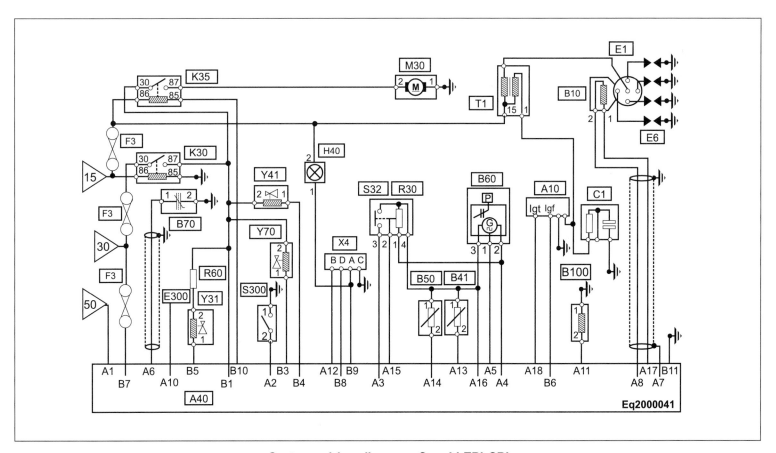

System wiring diagram, Suzuki EPi-SPi

Notes

Notes

Chapter 30
Toyota

Contents

Index of Toyota vehicles/systems

Model	Engine code	Year	System
4 Runner 3.0i 4wd V6	3VZ-E	1991 to 1995	TCCS AFS (6-Cyl)
Avensis 1.6i cat	4A-FE	1998 to 1999	TCCS MAP (4-Cyl)
Avensis 1.8i cat	7A-FE	1998 to 1999	TCCS MAP/AFS (4-Cyl)
Avensis 2.0 cat	3S-FE	1998 to 1999	TCCS MAP (4-Cyl)
Camry 2.0i OHC 4WD	3S-FE	1988 to 1989	TCCS AFS (4-Cyl)
Camry 2.0i OHC	3S-FE	1987 to 1991	TCCS AFS (4-Cyl)
Camry 2.0i OHC	3S-FE	1987 to 1991	TCCS AFS (4-Cyl)
Camry 2.2i 16v DOHC cat	5S-FE	1991 to 1996	TCCS AFS (4-Cyl)
Camry 2.5i V6 OHC cat	2VZ-FE	1988 to 1991	TCCS AFS (6-Cyl)
Camry 3.0i V6 24V DOHC cat	**3VZ-FE**	**1991 to 1996**	**TCCS AFS (6-Cyl)**
Camry 3.0i V6 24V DOHC cat	3VZ-FE	1991 to 1996	TCCS MAP/AFS (4-Cyl)
Carina E 1.6i 16V DOHC cat AT	4A-FE	1992 to 1997	TCCS MAP (4-Cyl)
Carina E 1.6I 16v DOHC cat MT	**4A-FE (AT190)**	**1992 to 1997**	**TCCS MAP (4-Cyl)**
Carina E 1.6I cat	4A-FE	1995 to 1998	TCCS MAP (4-Cyl)
Carina E 1.6I cat	4A-FE	1996 to 1998	TCCS MAP (4-Cyl)
Carina E 1.8 16v DOHC	7A-FE	1995 to 1997	TCCS MAP/AFS (4-Cyl)
Carina E 1.8i cat	7A-FE	1996 to 1998	TCCS MAP/AFS (4-Cyl)
Carina E 2.0 Gti cat	3S-GE	1994 to 1997	TCCS AFS (4-Cyl)
Carina E 2.0i DOHC cat	3S-FE	1992 to 1997	TCCS AFS (4-Cyl)
Carina E 2.0i DOHC cat	3S-GE	1992 to 1994	TCCS AFS (4-Cyl)
Carina II 2.0i OHC cat	3S-FE	1988 to 1993	TCCS AFS (4-Cyl)
Carina II 2.0i OHC	3S-FE	1988 to 1992	TCCS AFS (4-Cyl)

Index of Toyota vehicles/systems (continued)

Model	Engine code	Year	System
Celica 1.8i 16v DOHC	7A-FE	1994 to 1999	TCCS MAP/AFS (4-Cyl)
Celica 2.0 16v DOHC cat	3S-GE	1990 to 1994	TCCS MAP/AFS (4-Cyl)
Celica 2.0 16v DOHC	3S-GEL	1985 to 1990	TCCS AFS (4-Cyl)
Celica 2.0 GT 16v DOHC cat	3S-GE	1990 to 1994	TCCS MAP/AFS (4-Cyl)
Celica 2.0 GT cat	3S-GE	1994 to 1999	TCCS MAP/AFS (4-Cyl)
Celica 2.0 GT	3S-GE	1986 to 1989	TCCS MAP/AFS (4-Cyl)
Celica 2.0 GT	3S-GE	1990 to 1994	TCCS MAP/AFS (4-Cyl)
Celica 2.0 GT-4 cat	3S-GTE	1994 to 1997	TCCS AFS (4-Cyl)
Celica 2.0 GT-4 turbo 16v cat	3S-GTE	1988 to 1990	TCCS AFS (4-Cyl)
Celica 2.0 GT-4 turbo 16v cat	3S-GTE	1990 to 1994	TCCS AFS (4-Cyl)
Celica 2.2i 16v DOHC cat	5S-FE	1991 to 1994	TCCS MAP (4-Cyl)
Corolla (AE92) 1.6 GTi cat	4A-FE (AE101)	1992 to 1996	TCCS MAP (4-Cyl)
Corolla 1.3i OHC cat	2E-E	1990 to 1992	TCCS MAP (4-Cyl)
Corolla 1.3i 16v DOHC cat	4E-FE	1992 to 1997	TCCS MAP (4-Cyl)
Corolla 1.3i cat	4E-FE	1997 to 1999	TCCS MAP (4-Cyl)
Corolla 1.6 GT coupe OHC	4A-GE	1984 to 1987	TCCS MAP (4-Cyl)
Corolla 1.6 GT OHC	4A-GEL	1985 to 1987	TCCS MAP (4-Cyl)
Corolla 1.6 GTi cat	**4A-GE (AE92)**	**1987 to 1989**	**TCCS AFS (4-Cyl)**
Corolla 1.6 GTi OHC cat	4A-GE	1987 to 1989	TCCS MAP (4-Cyl)
Corolla 1.6 GTi OHC cat	4A-GE	1987 to 1992	TCCS MAP (4-Cyl)
Corolla 1.6 GTi OHC cat	4A-GE	1989 to 1992	TCCS MAP (4-Cyl)
Corolla 1.6 GTi OHC cat	4A-GE	1989 to 1992	TCCS MAP (4-Cyl)
Corolla 1.6 GTi OHC	4A-GE	1987 to 1989	TCCS MAP (4-Cyl)
Corolla 1.6 GTi OHC	4A-GE	1987 to 1992	TCCS MAP (4-Cyl)
Corolla 1.6 GTi OHC	4A-GE	1989 to 1992	TCCS MAP (4-Cyl)
Corolla 1.6i & 4x4 OHC cat	4A-FE	1990 to 1992	TCCS MAP (4-Cyl)
Corolla 1.6i & 4x4 OHC cat	4A-FE	1989 to 1992	TCCS MAP (4-Cyl)
Corolla 1.6i 16v DOHC cat	**4A-FE**	**1992 to 1997**	**TCCS MAP (4-Cyl)**
Corolla 1.6i Cat	4A-FE	1997 to 1999	TCCS MAP (4-Cyl)
Corolla 1.8i 16v DOHC cat	7A-FE	1993 to 1995	TCCS MAP/AFS (4-Cyl)
Hi-Ace 2.4i 4x4 OHC	2RZ-E	1989 to 1995	TCCS MAP (4-Cyl)
Hi-Ace 2.4i OHC	2RZ-E	1989 to 1995	TCCS MAP (4-Cyl)
Land Cruiser 4.5	1FZ-FE	1995 to 1998	TCCS AFS (4-Cyl)
Land Cruiser Amazon 4.7i V8	2UZ-FE	1998 to 1999	TCCS AFS (6-Cyl)
Land Cruiser Colorado	5VZ-FE	1996 to 1999	TCCS AFS (4-Cyl)
MR2 1.6 cat	4A-GE	1985 to 1990	TCCS MAP (4-Cyl)
MR2 1.6 OHC	4A-GE	1985 to 1990	TCCS MAP (4-Cyl)
MR2 2.0 16v DOHC cat	3S-FE	1990 to 1994	TCCS AFS (4-Cyl)
MR2 2.0 16v DOHC GT cat	3S-GE	1990 to 1994	TCCS MAP (4-Cyl)
MR2 GT cat	3S-GE	1994 to 1999	TCCS MAP (4-Cyl)
Paseo 1.5	5E-FE	1996 to 1999	TCCS MAP/AFS (4-Cyl)
Picnic 2.0 16v DOHC	3S-FE	1996 to 1999	TCCS MAP (4-Cyl)
Previa 2.4i 16v DOHC cat	2TZ-FE	1990 to 1999	TCCS AFS (4-Cyl)
RAV 4 2.0i 16v DOHC	3S-FE	1994 to 1999	TCCS MAP (4-Cyl)
Starlet 1.3 16v DOHC	4E-FE	1996 to 1999	TCCS MAP (4-Cyl)
Starlet 1.3i 12v SOHC	2E-E	1990 to 1996	TCCS MAP (4-Cyl)
Supra 3.0i 24v DOHC cat	7M-GE	1986 to 1993	TCCS MAP (4-Cyl)
Supra 3.0i 24v DOHC	7M-GE	1986 to 1993	TCCS MAP (4-Cyl)
Supra 3.0i Turbo DOHC DIS cat	2JZ-GTE	1993 to 1997	TCCS AFS (4-Cyl)
Supra 3.0i turbo DOHC DIS cat	7M-GTE	1988 to 1993	TCCS AFS (4-Cyl)
Tarago 2.4i 16v DOHC cat	2TZ-FE	1990 to 1997	TCCS AFS (4-Cyl)

Note: *The vehicles accentuated in bold type are the actual vehicles upon which the ECM pin tables and wiring diagrams are based. Other vehicle with the same system may be similar; but are also likely to contain some differences.*

Pin Table – TCCS MAP (4-cyl)

26 pin connector

Pin	Item	Test Condition	Measurements
O/D	–		
NE+	RPM sensor : t2	engine cranking:	> 2.0 V AC (peak to peak)
		idle:	> 11.0 V AC (peak to peak)
		cruise:	> 14.0 V AC (peak to peak)
RSO	ISCV drivers : t3	ignition on	nbv
		engine running, idle speed:	
		cold	6.0 to 6.5 V
		hot	7.0 to 9.0 V
		duty cycle	30 to 60%
HT	oxygen sensor heater	ignition on	nbv
		engine running, active	1.25 V (max)
G(-)	TDC sensor return : t1	engine cranking:	> 2.0 V AC (peak to peak)
		idle:	> 11.0 V AC (peak to peak)
		cruise:	> 14.0 V AC (peak to peak)
E1	earth	ignition on/engine running	0.25 V (max)
STA	ignition switch : t STA (50)	engine cranking	nbv
G(+)	TDC sensor signal : t2	engine cranking:	> 2.0 V AC (peak to peak)
		idle:	> 11.0 V AC (peak to peak)
		cruise:	> 14.0 V AC (peak to peak)
No.10	injectors driver : t1	ignition on	nbv
		engine running, cold	3.5 ms
		engine running, hot:	
		idle	2.3 ms
		2000 rpm	2.1 ms
		3000 rpm	2.0 ms
		snap acceleration	> 8.0 ms
		deceleration (fuel cut off)	0 ms
NSW	supply from ignition switch : t IG2	engine cranking	nbv
IGT	amplifier	engine cranking/running	0.7 to 1.0 V
No.20	injectors driver : t1	ignition on	nbv
		engine running, cold	3.5 ms
		engine running, hot:	
		idle	2.3 ms
		2000 rpm	2.1 ms
		3000 rpm	2.0 ms
		snap acceleration	> 8.0 ms
IGF	amplifier	engine cranking/running	0.7 to 1.0 V
RSC	ISCV driver : t1	ignition on	nbv
		engine running, idle speed:	
		cold	6.0 to 6.5 V
		hot	7.0 to 9.0 V
		duty cycle	30 to 60%
E01	earth	ignition on/engine running	0.25 V (max)
NE-	RPM sensor return : t1	ignition on/engine running	0.25 V (max)
ISC	A/C idle up VSV	ignition on	nbv
		engine running:	
		active	1.0 to 3.0 V
		non-active	nbv
EO2	earth	ignition on/engine running	0.25 V (max)

Pin Table – TCCS MAP (4-cyl) (continued)

16 pin connector

Pin	Item	Test Condition	Measurements
PIM	MAP signal : t3	ignition on	3.3 to 3.9 V
		engine running:	
		idle speed	1.5 V (approx)
		WOT	3.3 to 3.9 V
OX	OS signal : t3	ignition on, OS multiplug	
		disconnected	0.4 to 0.5 V
		engine running, hot	200 to 1000 mV (switching)
		throttle fully-open	0.5 to 1.0 V
		deceleration (fuel cut-off)	0 to 0.5 V
		switching frequency	1 sec intervals (approx)
E2	sensor return	ignition on/engine running	0.25 V (max)
IDL	TS, idle contact : t2	ignition on/engine running:	
		throttle closed	0.25 V (max)
		throttle fully open	nbv
E21	sensor return	ignition on/engine running	0.25 V (max)
THA	ATS signal : t2	ignition on/engine running	20° C: 2.0 to 2.8 V
			80° C: 0.4 to 0.8 V
TE2	SD connector		data not available
VTA	TPS signal : t3	ignition on/engine running:	
		throttle closed	0.3 to 0.8 V
		throttle fully open	3.2 to 4.9 V
KNK	KS signal : t2	ignition on/engine running	1.0 V AC (peak to peak)
THW	CTS signal : t2	ignition on/engine running	20° C: 2.0 to 2.8 V
			80° C: 0.4 to 0.8 V
VF	SD connector		data not available
VCC	supply voltage (MAP sensor, TPS)	ignition on/engine running	5.0 V ± 0.1
TE1	SD connector	ignition on/engine running:	
		not actuated	nbv
		actuated	0.50 V (max)

12 pin connector

Pin	Item	Test Condition	Measurements
+B1	supply from main relay : t4	ignition on/engine running	nbv
ACT	air conditioning		data not available
ED	ED monitor		data not available
ELS	Tail-light relay demister switch		data not available
BATT	supply from battery : t30	ignition off/on/engine running	nbv
+B	main relay supply : t4	ignition on/engine running	nbv
AC1	A/C amplifier		data not available
FC	fuel pump relay : t1	ignition on	nbv
		engine running	1.25 V (max)
W	SD warning lamp : t1	ignition on/engine running:	
		no faults present	nbv
		faults present, lamp on	0 V
SPD	VSS	vehicle in motion	0 to 12 V (switching)

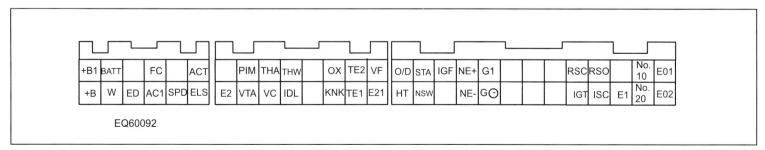

54 pin ECM multi-plug, TCCS MAP (4-Cyl)

Pin Table – TCCS AFS (4-cyl, 4A-GE)

14 pin connector

Pin	Item	Test Condition	Measurements
+B1	supply from main relay : t87	ignition on/engine running	nbv
BATT	supply from battery : t30	ignition off/on/engine running	nbv
THA	ATS sensor (AFS : tTHA)	ignition on/engine running	20° C: 2.0 to 2.8 V
VS	AFS signal : tVS	ignition on:	
		throttle closed	2.5 to 5.4 V
		throttle fully open	6.2 to 8.8 V
		engine idling	3.9 to 5.8 V
VC	AFS reference voltage : t4	ignition on/engine running	5.1 to 10.8 V
+B	main relay supply : t87	ignition on/engine running	nbv
SPD	VSS signal	vehicle in motion	0 to 12 V (switching)
STP	stop light switch		data not available
E21	sensor return	ignition on/engine running	0.25 V (max)

18 pin connector

Pin	Item	Test Condition	Measurements
NE	RPM sensor signal : t2	engine cranking:	> 2.0 V AC (peak to peak)
		idle:	> 11.0 V AC (peak to peak)
		cruise:	> 14.0 V AC (peak to peak)
G	TDC sensor signal : t2	engine cranking:	> 2.0 V AC (peak to peak)
		idle:	> 11.0 V AC (peak to peak)
		cruise:	> 14.0 V AC (peak to peak)
G -	sensor return (TDC : t1, RPM : t1)	engine running	0.25 V (max)
IGF	amplifier	engine running	0.7 to 1.0 V
IDL	idle contact (TPS : t2)	ignition on/engine running:	
		throttle closed	0 V
		throttle fully open	4.50 to 5.50 V (approx)
T	SD connector		data not available
W	SD warning lamp	ignition on, lamp on	1.25 V (max)
		engine running:	
		no faults present	nbv
		faults present, lamp on	0 V
FPU	fuel pressure solenoid	ignition on/engine cold	nbv
		fuel temperature, hot	1.25 V (max)
THW	CTS signal : t2	ignition on/engine running	20° C: 2.0 to 2.8 V
			80° C: 0.4 to 0.8 V
VTA	TPS signal : t3	ignition on/engine running:	
		throttle closed	0.5 V
		throttle fully open	4.50 to 5.40 V (approx)
VCC	TPS supply : t5	ignition on/engine running	5.0 V ± 0.1
OX	oxygen sensor signal : t3	engine running	200 to 1000 mV (switching)
		throttle fully open	0.5 to 1.0 V
		fuel cut-off	0 to 0.5 V
		switching frequency	8 in 10 secs (approx)
E2	TPS return : t3	ignition on/engine running	0.25 V (max)
A/C	A/C magnetic switch		data not available
R/P	fuel control switch		data not available
HT	OS heater driver : t4	ignition on	nbv
		engine running:	
		cold	1.25 V (max)
		hot	nbv
V-ISC	Idle-up VSV : t2	engine running:	
		actuated	nbv
		not actuated	0 V

Pin Table – TCCS AFS (4-cyl, 4A-GE) (continued)

10 pin connector

Pin	Item	Test Condition	Measurements
VF	SD connector		data not available
STA	ignition switch : tSTA (50)	engine cranking	nbv
No.10	injectors driver : t1	ignition on	nbv
		engine running, cold	3.5 ms
		engine running, hot:	
		idle	2.3 ms
		2000 rpm	2.1 ms
		3000 rpm	2.0 ms
		snap acceleration	> 8.0 ms
		deceleration	0 ms
E01	earth	ignition on/engine running	0.25 V (max)
STH	ICOV driver : t1	ignition on	nbv
		engine running:	
		ICOV inactive	nbv
		ICOV active	1.25 V (max)
E1	earth	ignition on/engine running	0.25 V (max)
IGT	amplifier control signal	ignition on/engine running	0.7 to 1.0 V
No.20	injectors driver : t1	ignition on	nbv
		engine running, cold	3.5 ms
		engine running, hot:	
		idle	2.3 ms
		2000 rpm	2.1 ms
		3000 rpm	2.0 ms
		snap acceleration	> 8.0 ms
		deceleration	0 ms
EO2	earth	ignition on/engine running	0.25 V (max)

+B1	BATT	THA	VS	VC		
+B		SPD	STP	E21		

EQ60091

NE		G	G⊖	IGF	IDL	T	W	FPU
THW	VTA	VCC		E2	A/C	R/P	HT	V-ISC

	VF	STA	No.10	E01
STH	E1	IGT	No.20	E02

42 pin ECM multi-plug, TCCS AFS (4-Cyl)

Pin Table – TCCS AFS (6-cyl)

26 pin connector

Pin	Connection	Test condition	Measurements
E01	earth	ignition on/engine running	0.25 V (max)
E02	earth	ignition on/engine running	0.25 V (max)
No.10	injector driver (cylinder 1) : t1	ignition on	nbv
		engine running, cold	> 3.5 ms
		engine running, hot	3.5 ms
		snap acceleration	20 ms (approx)
		deceleration	0 ms (approx)
STJ	CSV driver : t1	engine cranking:	
		valve inactive, above 15° C	nbv
		valve active, below 15° C	1.25 V (max)

Pin	Connection	Test condition	Measurements
No.20	injector driver (cylinder 2) : t1	ignition on	nbv
		engine running, cold	> 3.5 ms
		engine running, hot	3.5 ms
		snap acceleration	20 ms (approx)
		deceleration	0 ms (approx)
E1	earth	ignition on/engine running	0.25 V (max)
S1	AT		data not available
No.30	injector driver (cylinder 3) : t1	ignition on	nbv
		engine running, cold	> 3.5 ms
		engine running, hot	3.5 ms
		snap acceleration	20 ms (approx)
		deceleration	0 ms (approx)
S2	AT		data not available
No.40	injector driver (cylinder 4) : t1	ignition on	nbv
		engine running, cold	> 3.5 ms
		engine running, hot	3.5 ms
		snap acceleration	20 ms (approx)
		deceleration	0 ms (approx)
SL	AT		data not available
No.50	injector driver (cylinder 5) : t1	ignition on	nbv
		engine running, cold	> 3.5 ms
		engine running, hot	3.5 ms
		snap acceleration	20 ms (approx)
		deceleration	0 ms (approx)
ISC1	stepper motor : t1	ignition on	nbv
		idle speed, active	0 to nbv (switching)
No.60	injector driver (cylinder 6) : t1	ignition on	nbv
		engine running, cold	> 3.5 ms
		engine running, hot	3.5 ms
		snap acceleration	20 ms (approx)
		deceleration	0 ms (approx)
ISC2	stepper motor : t2	ignition on	nbv
		idle speed, active	0 to nbv (switching)
FPR	fuel pump relay driver: t85	ignition on	nbv
		engine cranking/running	1.25 V (max)
ISC3	stepper motor : t3	ignition on	nbv
		idle speed, active	0 to nbv (switching)
IGT	amplifier control signal : tIGt	cranking/engine running	0.7 to 1.0 V (switching)
		idle speed, active	0 to nbv (switching)
ISC4	stepper motor : t4	ignition on	nbv
		idle speed, active	0 to nbv (switching)
IGF	amplifier control signal : tIGf	engine cranking/running	0.7 to 1.0 V (switching)
L	AT		data not available
–			
2	AT		data not available
VF1	SD connector : tVF1		data not available
–			
VF2	SD connector : tVF2		data not available

16 pin connector

Pin	Connection	Test condition	Measurements
DG	SD connector : tDG		data not available
SP2	VSS No 2 signal	drive wheels rotating or vehicle in motion	0 to 12 V (switching)
TE1	SD connector : tTE1		data not available
TE2	SD connector : tTE2		data not available
KNK1	KS1 signal : t2	engine running, KS active	1.0 to 2.0 V AC (peak to peak)
KNK2	KS2 signal : t2	engine running, KS active	1.0 to 2.0 V AC (peak to peak)
OY1	OS1 signal : t3	ignition on, OS multiplug disconnected	0.4 to 0.5 V
		engine running, hot	200 to 1000 mV (switching)
		throttle fully-open	0.5 to 1.0 V
		deceleration (fuel cut-off)	0 to 0.5 V
		switching frequency	1 sec intervals (approx)

Pin Table – TCCS AFS (6-cyl) (continued)

16 pin connector (continued)

Pin	Connection	Test condition	Measurements
OY2	OS2 signal : t3	ignition on, OS multiplug disconnected	0.4 to 0.5 V
		engine running, hot	200 to 1000 mV (switching)
		throttle fully-open	0.5 to 1.0 V
		deceleration (fuel cut-off)	0 to 0.5 V
		switching frequency	1 sec intervals (approx)
THW	CTS signal : t2	ignition on/engine running	20° C: 2.00 to 3.00 V
			80° C: 0.10 to 1.00 V
THA	ATS signal (AFS : tTHA)	ignition on/engine running	20° C: 1.00 to 3.00 V
IDL	idle switch (TPS : t3)	ignition on/engine running:	
		throttle closed	0 V
		throttle open	nbv
VS	AFS signal : tVS	ignition on/engine running:	
		flap fully closed	3.70 to 4.30 V
		flap fully open	0.20 to 0.50 V
		Idle speed	1.60 to 4.10 V
		3000 rpm	1.00 to 2.00 V
VTA	TPS signal : t2	ignition on/engine running:	
		throttle closed	0.3 to 0.8 V
		throttle fully open	2.7 to 5.2 V
VC	sensor supply (AFS : tVC, TPS : t1)	ignition on/engine running	4. 0 to 6.0 V
E2	sensor return (AFS,CTS, TPS : t4)	ignition on/engine running	0.25 V (max)

12 pin connector

Pin	Connection	Test condition	Measurements
G-	sensor return (CID, TDC, RPM sensor)	ignition on/engine running	0.25 V (max)
NE	RPM sensor	engine cranking	> 4.0 V AC (peak to peak)
		idle	> 8.0 V AC (peak to peak)
		cruise	>14.0 V AC (peak to peak)
	–		
G1	TDC signal	engine cranking	> 4.0 V AC (peak to peak)
		idle	> 8.0 V AC (peak to peak)
		cruise	>14.0 V AC (peak to peak)
	–		
G2	CID signal	engine cranking	> 4.0 V AC (peak to peak)
		idle	> 8.0 V AC (peak to peak)
		cruise	>14.0 V AC (peak to peak)
IACV	AAV driver	engine running:	
		valve inactive	nbv
		valve active	1.25 V (max)
FPU	fuel pressure solenoid driver : t1	ignition on	nbv
		engine running:	
		valve inactive	nbv
		valve active	1.25 V (max)
KWS	kick down switch AT		data not available

22 pin connector

Pin	Connection	Test condition	Measurements
STA	cranking signal : t50	engine cranking	nbv
NSW	AT		data not available
	–		
	–		
OD2	cruise control		data not available
P	AT		data not available
SP1	VSS No 1 signal	drive wheels rotating	
		or vehicle in motion	0 to 12 V (switching)
R	AT		data not available
A/C	air conditioning		data not available
OD1	cruise control		data not available
ACT	air conditioning		data not available

Pin	Connection	Test condition	Measurements
W	SD warning lamp	ignition on, lamp on	1.25 V (max)
		engine running:	
		no faults present	nbv
		faults present, lamp on	1.25 V (max)
M-REL	main relay driver : t86	ignition off	0 V
		ignition on/engine running	nbv
BK	AT		data not available
BATT	supply from battery : t30	ignition off/on/engine running	nbv
IGSW	supply from ignition switch : t15	ignition on/engine running	nbv
+B1	supply from main relay : t87	ignition on/engine running	nbv
+B	supply from main relay : t87	ignition on/engine running	nbv

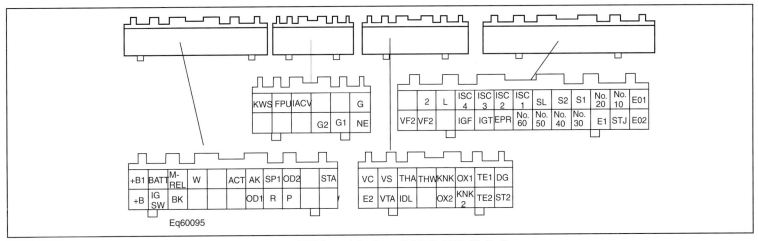

76 pin ECM multi-plug, TCCS AFS (6-Cyl)

Wiring Diagrams

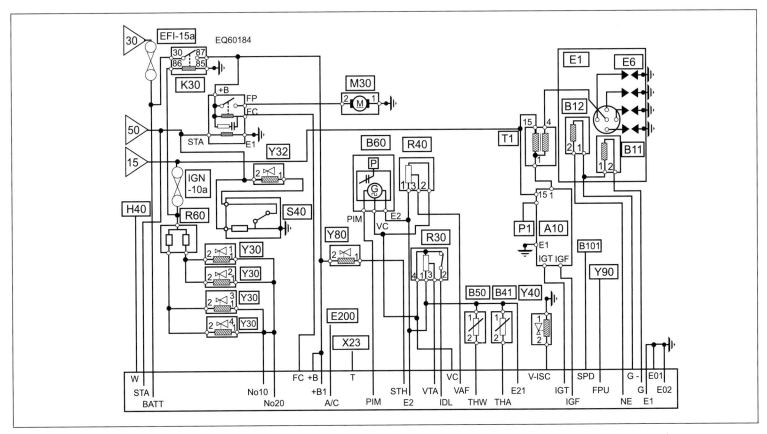

System wiring diagram, TCCS MAP (4-Cyl)

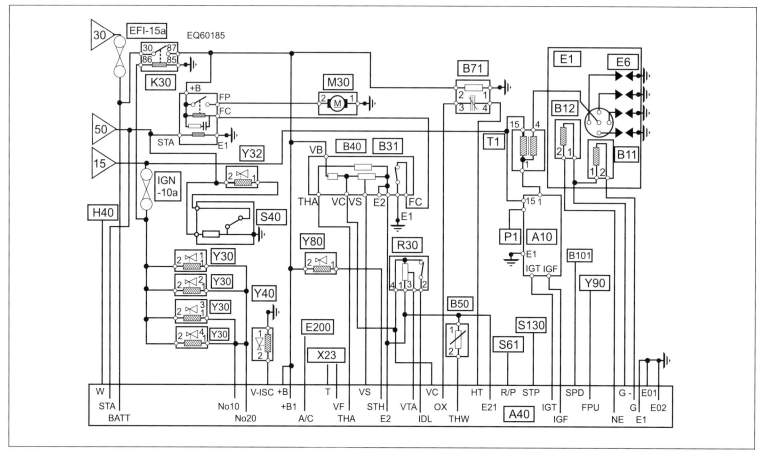

System wiring diagram, TCCS AFS (4-Cyl)

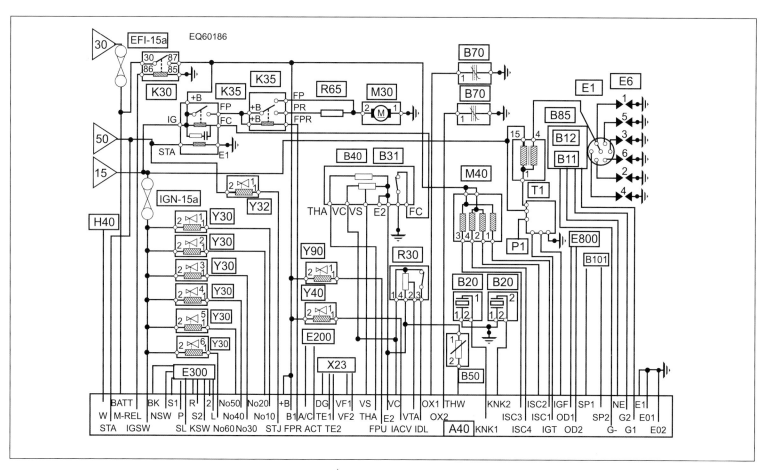

System wiring diagram, TCCS AFS (6-Cyl)

Chapter 31
Vauxhall

Contents

Index of Vauxhall vehicles/systems

Model	Engine code	Year	System
Ascona C 1.8E	18E	1983 to 1986	LE2 Jetronic (4-cyl)
Ascona-C 1.8 SOHC 82kW	18SE	1986 to 1988	LE3 Jetronic
Astra 1.6i SOHC (74kW) Cat	C16SE	1991 to 1992	Bosch Motronic 1.5 (4-cyl)
Astra 1.8 GTE	18E	1983 to 1984	LE2 Jetronic (4-cyl)
Astra 1.8i DOHC 16v	**C18XE**	**1993 to 1995**	**Simtec 56**
Astra 1.8i GTE	18E	1984 to 1987	LE2 Jetronic (4-cyl)
Astra 1.8i SOHC 82kW 15.04	18SE	1987 to 1991	LE3 Jetronic
Astra 2.0i 16v DOHC	**C20XE**	**1993 to 1997**	**Bosch Motronic 2.8**
Astra 2.0i 16v DOHC (110kW) 15.04	20XEJ	1988 to 1991	Bosch Motronic 2.5
Astra 2.0i 16v DOHC (110kW) US83 Cat	C20XE	1990 to 1994	Bosch Motronic 2.5
Astra 2.0i cat	**C20NE**	**1991 to 1995**	**Bosch Motronic 1.5.2**
Astra 2.0i SOHC (85kW) Cat US83	C20NE	1990 to 1992	Bosch Motronic 1.5 (4-cyl)
Astra 2.0i SOHC (95/91kW)15.04	20SEH	1990 to 19930	Bosch Motronic 1.5 (4-cyl)
Astra F 1.4i 16v cat (DIS)	X14XE	1996 to 1997	GM-Multec-S MPi
Astra F 1.4i 8v cat (w/distributor)	C14SE	1991 to 1992	GM-Multec-M MPi
Astra F 1.4i 8v cat (DIS)	C14SE	1993 to 1997	GM-Multec-M MPi
Astra F 1.4i cat	C14NZ	1990 to 1996	GM-Multec CFi-HE
Astra F 1.6 cat	C16NZ	1990 to 1993	GM-Multec CFi
Astra F 1.6i 16v cat (DIS)	X16XEL	1995 to 1997	GM-Multec-S MPi
Astra F 1.6i 8v cat (DIS)	C16SE	1992 to 1993	GM-Multec-M MPi
Astra F 1.6i 8v cat (DIS)	C16SE	1993 to 1997	GM-Multec-M MPi
Astra F 1.6i cat SPi DIS	X16SZ	1993 to 1996	GM-Multec CFi-DIS
Astra F 1.8i cat	C18NZ	1991 to 1995	GM-Multec CFi
Astra GTE 2.0	20NE	1987 to 1990	Bosch Motronic ML4.1
Astra GTE 2.0	20SEH	1987 to 1990	Bosch Motronic ML4.1
Astra-F 1.6i cat SPi DIS	X16SZR	1996 to 1997	GM-Multec CFi-DIS
Astravan 1.6i cat	C16NZ	1991 to 1992	GM-Multec CFi

Index of Vauxhall vehicles/systems (continued)

Model	Engine code	Year	System
Belmont 1.4i cat	C14NZ	1990 to 1993	GM-Multec CFi-HE
Belmont 1.6 cat	**C16NZ**	**1990 to 1992**	**GM-Multec CFi**
Belmont 1.8i cat	C18NZ	1990 to 1991	GM-Multec CFi
Belmont 1.8i SOHC 82kW 15.04	18SE	1988 to 1991	LE3 Jetronic
Belmont 1.8i	18E	1984 to 1987	LE2 Jetronic (4-cyl)
Calibra 2.0i SOHC & 4x4 (85kW) Cat US83	C20NE	1990 to 1994	Bosch Motronic 1.5 (4-cyl)
Calibra 2.0 16v& 4x4	C20XE	1993 to 1996	Bosch Motronic 2.8
Calibra 2.0i 16v DOHC (110kW) & 4x4 Cat	C20XE	1990 to 1995	Bosch Motronic 2.5
Calibra 2.0i DOHC 16v	X20XEV	1995 to 1996	Simtec 56.1
Calibra 2.0i Turbo	**C20 LET**	**1992 to 1997**	**Bosch Motronic 2.7**
Carlton 1.8i SOHC 85kW 15.04	18SEH	1988 to 1989	LE3 Jetronic
Carlton 1.8i SOHC 85kW 15.04	18SEH	1989 to 1992	LE3 Jetronic
Carlton 2.0i SOHC (73kW) Cat US83	C20NEJ	1990 to 1993	Bosch Motronic 1.5 (4-cyl)
Carlton 2.0i SOHC (85kW) Cat US83	C20NE	1990 to 1993	Bosch Motronic 1.5 (4-cyl)
Carlton 2.0i SOHC (90kW) 15.04	20SE	1990 to 1993	Bosch Motronic 1.5 (4-cyl)
Carlton 2.0i	20SE	1987 to 1990	Bosch Motronic ML4.1
Carlton 2.4i CIH (92kW) Cat US83	C24NE	1990 to 1993	Bosch Motronic 1.5 (6-cyl)
Carlton 2.6i CIH (110kW) Cat US83	C26NE	1990 to 1993	Bosch Motronic 1.5 (6-cyl)
Carlton 3.0 (CIH)	30NE	1987 to 1990	LE2 Jetronic (6-cyl)
Carlton 3.0 (CIH)	30NE	1987 to 1990	LE2 Jetronic (6-cyl)
Carlton 3.0i CIH (130kW) Cat US83	C30NE	1990 to 1993	Bosch Motronic 1.5 (6-cyl)
Carlton DOHC 24v (150kW) Cat US83	C30SE	1989 to 1994	Bosch Motronic 1.5 (6-cyl)
Carlton DOHC 24v (147kW) estate Cat US83	C30SEJ	1990 to 1994	Bosch Motronic 1.5 (6-cyl)
Cavalier 1.6i cat SPi DIS	X16SZ	1993 to 1995	GM-Multec CFi-DIS
Cavalier 1.6i cat	C16NZ	1990 to 1995	GM-Multec CFi
Cavalier 1.6i cat	C16NZ2	1993 to 1994	GM-Multec CFi
Cavalier 1.8i cat	C18NZ	1990 to 1995	GM-Multec CFi
Cavalier 1800 SOHC 82kW	**18SE**	**1986 to 1988**	**LE3 Jetronic**
Cavalier 1800	**18E**	**1982 to 1986**	**LE2 Jetronic (4-cyl)**
Cavalier 2.0 16v	C20XE	1993 on	Bosch Motronic 2.8
Cavalier 2.0 16v DOHC (110kW) & 4x4 Cat	C20XE	1989 to 1995	Bosch Motronic 2.5
Cavalier 2.0 SOHC (85kW) 15.04	**20NE**	**1990 to 1993**	**Bosch Motronic 1.5 (4-cyl)**
Cavalier 2.0	**20NE**	**1987 to 1990**	**Bosch Motronic ML4.1**
Cavalier 2.0	20SEH	1987 to 1990	Bosch Motronic ML4.1
Cavalier 2.0i 16v DOHC (110kW) 15.04	**20XEJ**	**1989 to 1991**	**Bosch Motronic 2.5**
Cavalier 2.0i DOHC 16v	X20XEV	1995	Simtec 56.1
Cavalier 2.0i SOHC & 4x4 (95kW) 15.04	20SEH	1990 to 1993	Bosch Motronic 1.5 (4-cyl)
Cavalier 2.0i SOHC (85kW) Cat US83	C20NE	1990 to 1994	Bosch Motronic 1.5 (4-cyl)
Cavalier SRi 130	20SEH	1987 to 1990	Bosch Motronic ML4.1
Corsa 1.6 MPI SOHC (72kW) Cat US83	C16SE	1990 to 1992	Bosch Motronic 1.5 (4-cyl)
Corsa B 1.4i cat	C14NZ	1993 to 1997	GM-Multec CFi-HE
Corsa-A 1.2i cat	C12NZ	1990 to 1993	GM-Multec CFi-HE
Corsa-A 1.4i 8v cat (DIS)	C14SE	1993	GM-Multec MPi
Corsa-A 1.4i 8v cat (w/distributor)	**C14SE**	**1992 to 1993**	**GM-Multec-M MPi**
Corsa-A 1.4i cat	C14NZ	1990 to 1993	GM-Multec CFi-HE
Corsa-A 1.6i 8v cat (DIS)	**C16SE**	**1992 to 1993**	**GM-Multec-M MPi**
Corsa-A 1.6i cat	C16NZ	1990 to 1992	GM-Multec CFi
Corsa-B 1.2i cat	C12NZ	1993 to 1997	GM-Multec CFi-HE
Corsa-B 1.2i DIS cat	**X12SZ**	**1993 to 1997**	**GM-Multec CFi-DIS**
Corsa-B 1.4i 16v cat (DIS)	**X14XE**	**1995 to 1997**	**GM-Multec-XS MPi**
Corsa-B 1.4i 8v cat (DIS)	C14SE	1993 to 1994	GM-Multec-M MPi
Corsa-B 1.6i 16v cat (DIS)	X16XE	1995 to 1997	GM-Multec-XS MPi
Corsa-B GSi 1.6i,16v DOHC cat (DIS)	C16XE	1993 to 1995	GM-Multec-S MPi
Frontera 2.0i SOHC (85kW) Cat US83	C20NE	1991 to 1995	Bosch Motronic 1.5 (4-cyl)
Frontera 2.4i CIH (92kW) Cat US83	C24NE	1991 to 1994	Bosch Motronic 1.5 (6-cyl)
Kadett 2.0i 16v DOHC (110kW) 15.04	20XEJ	1988 to 1991	Bosch Motronic 2.5
Kadett 2.0i 16v DOHC (110kW) US83 Cat	C20XE	1990 to 1992	Bosch Motronic 2.5
Kadett 2.0i SOHC (85kW) Cat US83	C20NE	1990 to 1993	Bosch Motronic 1.5 (4-cyl)
Kadett 2.0i	20NE	1987 to 1990	Bosch Motronic ML4.1

Model	Engine code	Year	System
Kadett 2.0i	20SEH	1987 to 1990	Bosch Motronic ML4.1
Kadett D 1.8 GTE	18E	1983 to 1984	LE2 Jetronic (4-cyl)
Kadett E 1.8 GTE	18E	1984 to 1986	LE2 Jetronic (4-cyl)
Kadett GSi 2.0i SOHC (95/91kW) 15.04	20SEH	1990 to 1993	Bosch Motronic 1.5 (4-cyl)
Kadett-E 1.4i cat	C14NZ	1990 to 1993	GM-Multec CFi
Kadett-E 1.8i cat	C18NZ	1990 to 1991	GM-Multec CFi
Kadett-E 1.8i SOHC 82kW 15.04	18SE	1987 to 1991	LE3 Jetronic
Monza 2.5E (CIH)	25NE	1987 to 1990	LE2 Jetronic (6-cyl)
Nova 1.2i cat	**C12NZ**	**1990 to 1994**	**GM-Multec CFi-HE**
Nova 1.4i 8v cat (DIS)	C14SE	1993	GM-Multec MPi
Nova 1.4i 8v cat (w/distributor)	**C14SE**	**1992 to 1993**	**GM-Multec-M MPi**
Nova 1.4i cat	C14NZ	1990 to 1993	GM-Multec CFi-HE
Nova 1.6 MPI SOHC (72kW) Cat US83	C16SEI	1990 to 1992	Bosch Motronic 1.5 (4-cyl)
Nova 1.6i 8v cat (DIS)	**C16SE**	**1992 to 1993**	**GM-Multec-M MPi**
Nova 1.6i cat	C16NZ	1990 to 1992	GM-Multec CFi
Omega 1.8i SOHC 85kW 15.04	18SEH	1988 to 1989	LE3 Jetronic
Omega 1.8i SOHC 85kW 15.04	18SEH	1989 to 1992	LE3 Jetronic
Omega 2.0i (not UK)	20SE	1987 to 1990	Bosch Motronic ML4.1
Omega 2.0i SOHC (73kW) Cat US83	C20NEJ	1990 to 1993	Bosch Motronic 1.5 (4-cyl)
Omega 2.0i SOHC (85kW) Cat US83	C20NE	1990 to 1993	Bosch Motronic 1.5 (4-cyl)
Omega 2.0i SOHC (90kW) 15.04	20SE	1990 to 1993	Bosch Motronic 1.5 (4-cyl)
Omega-B 2.0i 16v cat	**X20XEV**	**1994 to 1997**	**Simtec 56.1**
Omega-B cat 2.0i	**X20SE**	**1994 to 1997**	**Bosch Motronic 1.5.4**
Omega 2.4i CIH (92kW) Cat US83	C24NE	1990 to 1993	Bosch Motronic 1.5 (6-cyl)
Omega 2.5 V6 cat	X25XE	1994 to 1997	Bosch Motronic 2.8.1
Omega 2.6i CIH (110kW) Cat US83	C26NE	1990 to 1993	Bosch Motronic 1.5 (6-cyl)
Omega 3.0 V6 cat	**X30XE**	**1994 to 1997**	**Bosch Motronic 2.8.1**
Omega 3.0(CIH)	30NE	1987 to 1990	LE2 Jetronic (6-cyl)
Omega 3.0(CIH)	30NE	1987 to 1990	LE2 Jetronic (6-cyl)
Omega 3.0i CIH (130kW) Cat US83	C30NE	1990 to 1993	Bosch Motronic 1.5 (6-cyl)
Omega DOHC 24v (150kW) Cat US83	**C30SE**	**1989 to 1994**	**Bosch Motronic 1.5 (6-cyl)**
Omega DOHC 24v (147kW) estate Cat US83	C30SEJ	1990 to 1992	Bosch Motronic 1.5 (6-cyl)
Senator 2.5E CIH	25NE	1987 to 1990	LE2 Jetronic (6-cyl)
Senator 3.0 (CIH)	**30NE**	**1987 to 1990**	**LE2 Jetronic (6-cyl)**
Senator-B 2.6i CIH (110kW) Cat US83	C26NE	1990 to 1993	Bosch Motronic 1.5 (6-cyl)
Senator-B 3.0i CIH (130kW) Cat US83	C30NE	1990 to 1993	Bosch Motronic 1.5 (6-cyl)
Senator-B DOHC 24v (150kW) Cat US83	C30SE	1989 to 1994	Bosch Motronic 1.5 (6-cyl)
Senator-B DOHC 24v (147kW) estate Cat US83	C30SEJ	1990 to 1994	Bosch Motronic 1.5 (6-cyl)
Tigra 1.4i 16v cat (DIS)	X14XE	1994 to 1997	GM-Multec-S MPi
Tigra 1.6i 16v cat (DIS)	X16XE	1994 to 1997	GM-Multec-S MPi
Vectra 2.0 16v DOHC (110kW) 4x4 Cat	C20XE	1989 to 1992	Bosch Motronic 2.5
Vectra 2.0 SOHC (85kW) 15.04	20NE	1990 to 1993	Bosch Motronic 1.5 (4-cyl)
Vectra 2.0i (not UK)	20SEH	1987 to 1990	Bosch Motronic ML4.1
Vectra 2.0i SOHC & 4x4 (95kW) 15.04	20SEH	1990 to 1993	Bosch Motronic 1.5 (4-cyl)
Vectra 2.0i SOHC (85kW) Cat US83	C20NE	1990 to 1994	Bosch Motronic 1.5 (4-cyl)
Vectra 2.5 V6 cat	**X25XE**	**1994 to 1997**	**Bosch Motronic 2.8.3**
Vectra GSi 2000 16v DOHC (110kW) 15.04	20XEJ	1989 to 1992	Bosch Motronic 2.5
Vectra-A 2.0i DOHC 16v	X20XEV	1995	Simtec 56.1
Vectra-A 1.6i cat SPi DIS	X16SZ	1993 to 1995	GM-Multec CFi-DIS
Vectra-A 1.6i cat	C16NZ	1990 to 1995	GM-Multec CFi
Vectra-A 1.6i cat	C16NZ2	1993 to 1994	GM-Multec CFi
Vectra-A 1.8i cat	C18NZ	1990 to 1995	GM-Multec CFi
Vectra-B 1.8i DOHC 16v	**X18XE**	**1995 to 1997**	**Simtec 56.5**
Vectra-B 2.0i DOHC 16v	X20XEV	1995 to 1997	Simtec 56.5
Vectra-B 1.6l 16v DOHC cat (DIS)	**X16XEL**	**1995 to 1997**	**GM-Multec-S MPi**
Vectra-B 1.6i cat SPi DIS	X16SZR	1995 to 1997	GM-Multec CFi-DIS

Note: *The vehicles accentuated in bold type are the actual vehicles upon which the ECM pin tables and wiring diagrams are based. Other vehicle with the same system may be similar; but are also likely to contain some differences.*

Pin Table – Bosch LE2 Jetronic (4-cyl)

Pin	Item	Test Condition	Measurements
1	amplifier speed signal : t1	ignition on	nbv
		engine cranking/running	200 V (min)
		dynamic volt drop	2.0 V (max)
2	TS, idle contact : t2	engine cranking/running:	
		throttle closed	0 V
		throttle open	nbv
3	TS, full-load contact : t3	engine cranking/running:	
		throttle fully open	0 V
		throttle open/closed	nbv
4	cranking signal : t50	engine cranking	nbv
		AT inhibitor switch (AT only)	
5	earth (AFS return : t5)	engine running	0.25 V (max)
7	AFS signal : t7	engine cranking	less than 3 V
		idle	4.50 to 5.00 V
		snap accelerate	7.00 to 8.00 V
		2000 rpm	5.50 to 6.00 V
		3000 rpm	6.00 to 7.00 V
8	ATS signal (AFS : t8)	engine running	20° C: 9.00 to 9.50 V
9	supply from main relay : t87	engine cranking/running	nbv
10	CTS signal : t2	engine running	80° C: 5.30 to 6.00 V
			20° C: 1.25 to 1.75 V
12	injector driver : t1	engine running, hot	2.5 ms
		engine running, cold	3.5 to 4.0 ms
		snap acceleration	> 6.0 ms
13	earth	ignition on/engine running	0.25 V (max)
14-25	–		

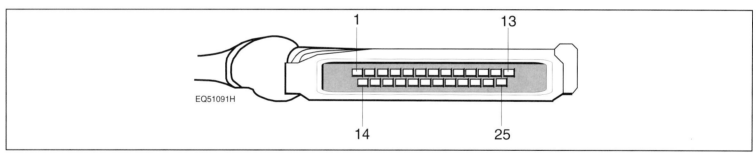

EQ51091H

25 pin ECM multi-plug, Bosch LE2 Jetronic (4-cyl)

Pin Table – Bosch LE2 Jetronic (6-cyl)

Pin	Item	Test Condition	Measurements
1	amplifier speed signal : t1	ignition on	nbv
		engine cranking/running	200 V (min)
		dynamic volt drop	2.0 V (max)
2	TS, idle contact : t2	engine cranking/running:	
		throttle closed	0 V
		throttle open	nbv
3	TS, full-load contact : t3	engine cranking/running	
		throttle fully open	0 V
		throttle open/closed	nbv
4	cranking signal : t50	engine cranking	nbv
5	earth (AFS return : t5)	engine cranking/running	0.25 V (max)
6	–		
7	AFS signal : t7	engine cranking	< 3 V
		idle	4.50 to 5.00 V
		2000 rpm	5.50 to 6.00 V
		3000 rpm	6.00 to 7.00 V
		snap accelerate	7.00 to 8.00 V
8	ATS signal (AFS : t8)	engine running	20° C: 9.00 to 9.50 V

Pin	Item	Test Condition	Measurements
9	supply from main relay : t87	engine cranking/running	nbv
10	CTS signal : t2	engine running	20° C: 7.00 to 8.00 V
			80° C: 1.50 to 2.50 V
12	injector driver (cyls 1, 2, 3) : t1	engine cranking, cold	3.5 to 4.0 ms
		engine running, cold	3.5 to 4.0 ms
		engine cranking, hot	2.5 ms
		engine running, hot	2.5 ms
		snap acceleration	> 6.0 ms
13	earth	engine cranking/running	0.25 V (max)
24	injector driver (cyls 4, 5, 6) : t1	engine cranking, cold	3.5 to 4.0 ms
		engine running, cold	3.5 to 4.0 ms
		engine cranking, hot	2.5 ms
		engine running, hot	2.5 ms
		snap acceleration	> 6.0 ms
25	earth	engine cranking/running	0.25 V (max)

25 pin ECM multi-plug, Bosch LE2 Jetronic (6-cyl)

Pin Table – Bosch LE3 Jetronic

Pin	Item	Test Condition	Measurements
1	engine speed signal from ignition ECM : t5	engine cranking/running	0 to nbv (switching)
2	supply from main relay : t87	ignition on/engine running	nbv
3	injector driver : t1	engine cranking, cold	3.5 to 4.0 ms (min)
		engine running, cold	3.5 to 4.0 ms (min)
		engine cranking, hot	2.5 ms (min)
		engine running, hot	2.5 ms
		snap acceleration	6.0 ms (min)
4	earth	ignition on/engine running	0.25 V (max)
5	earth	ignition on/engine running	0.25 V (max)
6	service connection**		
7	–		
8	CTS signal : t2	ignition on/engine running	20° C: 1.5 to 2.0 V
			80° C: 0.4 to 0.8 V
9	–		
10	engine load signal to ignition ECM : t15	engine cranking/running	0 to nbv (switching)
11	AFS signal output (internal connection)	ignition on	0.20 to 0.30 V
		idle	0.75 to 1.00 V
		2000 rpm	1.25 to 2.25 V
		3000 rpm	2.00 to 2.50 V
		snap accelerate	3.00 to 4.50 V
12	main relay driver : t85b	ignition on	nbv
		engine cranking/running	1.25 V (max)
13	ignition ECM : t7 (E16ES 88/89 only)	engine cranking/running	0 to nbv (switching)
14	TS, full load contact : t3	ignition on/engine running:	
		throttle closed/part open	5.0 V ± 0.1
		throttle fully open	0 V
15	TS, idle contact : t2	ignition on/engine running:	
		throttle closed	0 V
		throttle part/fully open	5.0 V ± 0.1

** when this pin is connected to earth, the ECM will enrich the AFR in the mid speed range.

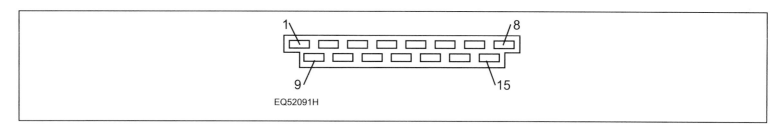

EQ52091H

15 pin ECM multi-plug, Bosch LE3 Jetronic

Pin Table – Bosch Motronic 1.5 (4-cyl)

Pin	Item	Test Condition	Measurements
1	ignition coil driver : t1	ignition on	nbv
		engine cranking/running	200 V (min)
		dynamic volt drop	2.0 V (max)
2	earth	ignition on/engine running	0.25 V (max)
3	fuel pump relay driver : t85b	ignition on	nbv
		engine cranking/running	1.25 V (max)
4	ISCV driver : t1	ignition on	nbv
		engine running, idle speed:	
		cold:	6.0 to 6.5 V
		duty cycle:	56 to 58%
		hot:	7.0 to 9.0 V
		duty cycle:	40 to 44%
5	FTVV/CFSV driver : t1	ignition on	nbv
		snap accelerate	1 to 99%, 15 Hz (approx)
6	4 WD unit : t2/AT control unit		data not available
7	AFS signal : t2	ignition on	0.20 to 0.30 V
		idle	0.50 to 1.50 V
		2000 rpm	1.75 to 2.25 V
		3000 rpm	2.00 to 2.50 V
		snap accelerate	3.00 to 4.50 V
		fully open (off load)	> 4.50 V
8	–		
9	VSS signal		data not available
10	OS return	ignition on/engine running	0.25 V (max)
11	–		
12	sensor supply (AFS : t3, TPS : t2)	ignition on/engine running	5.0 V ± 0.1
13	SD connector : tB	open circuit	10 V (approx.)
		A & B bridged in SD plug	0.25 V (max)
14	earth	ignition on/engine running	0.25 V max
15	–		
16	injector driver (bank 1) : t1	ignition on	nbv
		engine running, cold	11.0 to 12.0 ms
		engine running, hot	2.0 to 3.0 ms
		snap acceleration	> 6.0 ms
17	injector driver (bank 2) : t1	ignition on	nbv
		engine running, cold	11.0 to 12.0 ms
		engine running, hot	2.0 to 3.0 ms
		snap acceleration	> 6.0 ms
18	supply from battery : t30	ignition off/on/engine running	nbv
19	earth (main ECM)	ignition on/engine running	0.25 V (max)
20	coding earth (non-cat)	ignition on/engine running	0.25 V (max)
	(cat)	ignition on/engine running	5.0 V ± 0.1
21	coding earth (AT)	ignition on/engine running	0.25 V (max)
	(MT)	ignition on/engine running	5.0 V ± 0.1
22	SD warning lamp	ignition on, lamp on	1.25 V (max)
		engine running:	
		no faults present	nbv
		faults present, lamp on	1.25 V (max)
23	–		

Pin	Item	Test Condition	Measurements
24	earth	ignition on/engine running	0.25 V (max)
25	–		
26	sensor return (AFS : t4, CTS : t1, OA : tB, TPS : t1)	ignition on/engine running	0.25 V (max)
27	supply from ignition switch : t15	ignition on/engine running	nbv
28	OS signal : t3	ignition on, OS multiplug disconnected	0.4 to 0.5 V
		engine running, hot	200 to 1000 mV (switching)
		throttle fully-open	0.5 to 1.0 V
		deceleration (fuel cut-off)	0 to 0.5 V
		switching frequency	1 sec intervals (approx)
29-31	–		
32	on board computer : t24	engine running	0 to 10 V (switching)
33	–		
34	engine load signal	engine running:	
		MT	1.6 to 2.4 ms
		AT	1.8 to 2.5 ms
35	–		
36	main relay driver : t85	ignition off	nbv
		ignition on/engine running	1.25 V (max)
37	supply from relay : t87	ignition on/engine running	nbv
38-39	–		
40	A/C cut-off switch	ignition on, inactive	0.25 V (max)
		engine at idle speed and operating temperature: inactive	0.25 V (max)
		vehicle interior warm, actuate A/C switch, switch thermostat to cold and then briefly accelerate the engine active	nbv
41	A/C pressure switch		data not available
42	earth coding connection (MT) or P/N switch (AT)	connected	0.25 V (max)
		AT in P/N	0.25 V (max)
		AT engaged (R, D, 2, 1)	nbv
43	CO – non-Cat (AFS: t1)	ignition on/engine running	2.5 V ± 0.5 V
44	ATS (AFS: t5)	ignition on/engine running	20° C: 3.50 to 3.75 V
			80° C: 1.25 to 1.50 V
45	CTS signal : t2	ignition on/engine running	20° C: 3.00 to 3.75 V
			80° C: 1.00 to 1.30 V
46	octane adjuster : tA	ignition on/engine running	
		95 octane (brown)	0.9 V
		98 octane (brown)	1.6 V
47	earth (4x4 only)	ignition on/engine running	0.25 V (max)
48	CAS return : t2	engine running	0.25 V (max)
49	CAS signal : t1	idle speed	> 8.0 V AC (peak to peak)
50	–		
51	AT control unit : t13 (torque control)	MT	inactive
		AT, idle	inactive
		AT, driving & automatically shifting	active
52	–		
53	TPS signal : t3	ignition on/engine running:	
		throttle closed	0.35 to 0.87 V
		range	0.12 to 1.22 V
		throttle fully open	> 4.25 V
		range	3.90 to 4.95 V
54	oil temperature switch (transmission)	ignition on/engine running:	
		inactive	nbv
		idle speed, inactive	nbv
		4 x 4 vehicles, active	0.25 V (max)
55	SD connector : tG		data not available

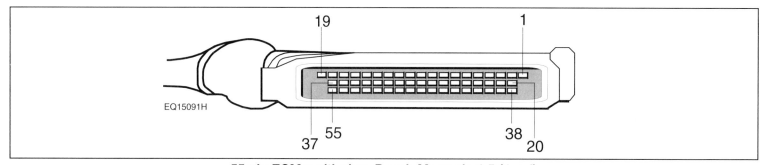

55 pin ECM multi-plug, Bosch Motronic 1.5 (4-cyl)

Pin Table – Bosch Motronic 1.5 (6-cyl)

Pin	Item	Test Condition	Measurements
1	ignition coil driver : t1	ignition on	nbv
		engine cranking/running	200 V (min)
		dynamic volt drop	2.0 V (max)
2	earth	ignition on/engine running	0.25 V (max)
3	fuel pump relay driver : t85b	ignition on	nbv
		engine cranking/running	1.25 V (max)
4	ISCV driver : t1	ignition on	nbv
		engine running, idle speed:	
		cold	6.0 to 6.5 V
		duty cycle	56 to 58%
		hot	7.0 to 9.0 V
		duty cycle	40 to 44%
5	FTVV/CFSV driver : t1	ignition on	nbv
		snap accelerate	1 to 99%, 15 Hz (approx.)
6	4 WD unit : t2/AT control unit		data not available
7	AFS signal : t2	ignition on	0.20 to 0.30 V
		idle	0.50 to 1.50 V
		2000 rpm	1.75 to 2.25 V
		3000 rpm	2.00 to 2.50 V
		snap accelerate	3.00 to 4.50 V
		fully open (off load)	> 4.50
8	HES signal : t2	engine running	2.50 V (average)
9	VSS		data not available
10	OS return	ignition on/engine running	0.25 V (max)
11	KS signal : t2	engine running, KS active	1.0 V AC (peak to peak)
12	sensor supply (AFS : t3, TPS : t2)	ignition on/engine running	5.0 V ± 0.1
13	SD connector : tB		data not available
14	earth	ignition on/engine running	0.25 V (max)
15	–		
16	injector driver (bank 1 : t1)	ignition on	nbv
		engine running, cold	11.0 to 12.0 ms
		engine running, hot	2.0 to 3.0 ms
		snap acceleration	> 6.0 ms
17	injector driver (bank 2 : t1)	ignition on	nbv
		engine running, cold	11.0 to 12.0 ms
		engine running, hot	2.0 to 3.0 ms
		snap acceleration	> 6.0 ms
18	supply from battery : t30	ignition off/on/engine running	nbv
19	earth (main ECM)	ignition on/engine running	0.25 V (max)
20	coding earth (non-cat)	ignition on/engine running	0.25 V (max)
	(cat)	ignition on/engine running	5.0 V ± 0.1
21	coding earth (AT)	ignition on/engine running	0.25 V (max)
	(MT)	ignition on/engine running	5.0 V ± 0.1
22	SD warning lamp	ignition on, lamp on	1.25 V (max)
		engine running:	
		no faults present	nbv
		faults present, lamp on	1.25 V (max)

Pin	Item	Test Condition	Measurements
23	A/C cut-off solenoid		data not available
24	earth	ignition on/engine running	0.25 V (max)
25	–		
26	sensor return (AFS : t4, CTS : t1, TPS : t2)	ignition on/engine running	0.25 V (max)
27	supply from ignition switch : t15	ignition on/engine running	nbv
28	OS signal : t3	ignition on, OS multiplug disconnected	0.4 to 0.5 V
		engine running, hot	200 to 1000 mV (switching)
		throttle fully-open	0.5 to 1.0 V
		deceleration (fuel cut-off)	0 to 0.5 V
		switching frequency	1 sec intervals (approx)
29	KS signal : t2	engine running, KS active	1.0 V AC (peak to peak)
30	KS return : t1	engine running, KS active	0.25 V (max)
31	HES supply : t1	ignition on/engine running	5 V
32	on board computer : t24		data not available
33	ICOV driver : t1	idle speed	nbv
		> 4000 rpm (AT : engage parking brake, AT selector in park)	0.25 V (max)
34	AT control unit : t25		data not available
35	–		
36	main relay driver : t85	ignition off	nbv
		ignition on/engine running	1.25 V (max)
37	supply from relay : t87	ignition on/engine running	nbv
38-39	–		
40	A/C cut-off switch		data not available
41	A/C pressure switch		data not available
42	cranking signal : t50 (AT)	engine cranking	nbv
42	coding earth (MT)	ignition on/engine running	0.25 V (max)
43	CO, non-Cat (AFS : t1)	ignition on/engine running	2.5 V ± 0.5
44	ATS (AFS : t5)	ignition on/engine running	20° C: 3.50 to 3.75 V
45	CTS signal : t2	ignition on/engine running	20° C: 3.00 to 3.75 V
			80° C: 1.00 to 1.30 V
46	octane adjuster : tA	ignition on/engine running:	
		95 octane (brown)	0.9 V
		98 octane (brown)	1.6 V
47	earth (4x4)	ignition on/engine running	0.25 V (max)
48	CAS return : t2	engine running	0.25 V (max)
49	CAS signal : t1	idle speed	> 8.0 V AC (peak to peak)
50	–		
51	AT control unit : t13		data not available
52	–		
53	TPS signal : t3	ignition on/engine running:	
		throttle closed	0.35 to 0.87 V
		throttle fully open	> 4.25 V
54	Oil temperature switch (transmission)	ignition on, inactive	nbv
		idle speed, inactive	nbv
		all vehicles, active	0.25 V (max)
55	SD connector : tG		data not available

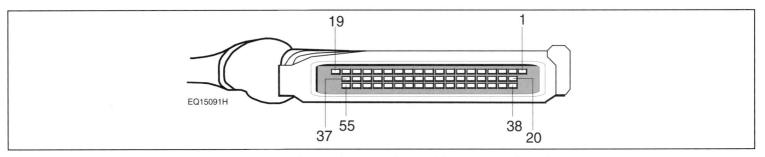

31.5 55 pin ECM multi-plug, Bosch Motronic 1.5 (6-cyl)

Pin Table – Bosch Motronic 1.5.2

Pin	Item	Test Condition	Measurements
1	ignition coil driver : t1	ignition on	nbv
		engine cranking/running	200 V (min)
		dynamic volt drop	2.0 V (max)
2	earth	ignition on/engine running	0.25 V (max)
3	fuel pump relay driver : t85b	ignition on	nbv
		engine cranking/running	1.25 V (max)
4	ISCV driver : t1	ignition on	nbv
		engine running, idle speed:	
		cold	6.0 to 6.5 V
		duty cycle	56 to 58%
		hot	7.0 to 9.0 V
		duty cycle	40 to 44%
5	CFSV driver : t1	ignition on	nbv
		engine running, above idle, operating temperature:	
		CFSV inactive	nbv
		CFSV active	0 to 12 V (switching)
		duty cycle	0 to 99%
6	–		
7	MAF sensor signal : t4	ignition on	1.40 V
		idle	1.90 to 2.25 V
		snap accelerate	> 3.00 V
8	–		
9	VSS (if fitted)	vehicle in motion	0 to 12 V (switching)
10	earth	engine running	0.25 V (max)
11	octane adjuster : tA	ignition on/engine running:	
		95 octane (brown)	0.9 V
		98 octane (brown)	1.6 V
12	TPS supply : t2	ignition on/engine running	5.0 V ± 0.1
13	SD connector : tB	open circuit	10.0 V (approx)
		A & B connected in SD plug	0.25 V (max)
14	earth	ignition on/engine running	0.25 V (max)
15	–		
16	injector driver : t1	ignition on	nbv
		engine running, cold	3.0 to 3.5 ms
		engine running, hot	2.0 to 2.5 ms
		snap acceleration	6.0 ms
17	–		
18	supply from battery : t30	ignition off/on/engine running	nbv
19	earth (main ECM)	ignition on/engine running	0.25 V (max)
20-21	–		
22	SD warning lamp	ignition on, lamp on	1.25 V (max)
		engine running:	
		no faults present	nbv
		faults present, lamp on	1.25 V (max)
23	A/C		data not available
24	earth	ignition on/engine running	0.25 V (max)
25-26	–		
27	supply from ignition switch : t15	ignition on/engine running	nbv
28	OS signal : t3	ignition on, OS multiplug disconnected	0.4 to 0.5 V
		engine running, hot	200 to 1000 mV (switching)
		throttle fully-open	0.5 to 1.0 V
		deceleration (fuel cut-off)	0 to 0.5 V
		switching frequency	1 sec intervals (approx)
29	–		
30	sensor return (AFS : t2, ATS : t1, CTS : t1, Octane plug : tB, TPS : t1)	ignition on/engine running	0.25 V (max)
31-36	–		

Pin	Item	Test Condition	Measurements
37	supply from relay : t87	ignition on/engine running	nbv
38-39	–		
40	A/C cut-off switch	ignition on, inactive	0.25 V (max.)
		engine at idle speed and operating temperature: inactive	0.25 V (max.)
		vehicle interior hot, actuate A/C switch, switch thermostat to cold and then briefly accelerate the engine active	nbv
41	A/C pressure switch	no data available	
42	earth connection (MT)	MT	0.25 V (max)
	or P/N switch (AT)	AT in P/N	0.25 V (max)
		AT engaged (R, D, 2, 1)	nbv
43	–		
44	ATS signal : t2	ignition on/engine running	20° C: 3.00 to 3.50 V
			80° C: 1.00 to 1.30 V
45	CTS signal : t2	ignition on/engine running	20° C: 3.00 to 3.75 V
			80° C: 1.00 to 1.30 V
46	main relay driver : t85	ignition off	nbv
		ignition on/engine running	1.25 V (max)
47	–		
48	CAS return : t2	engine running	0.25 V (max)
49	CAS signal : t1	idle speed	> 8.0 V AC (peak to peak)
50	–		
51	AT control unit : t13 (torque control)	MT	inactive
		AT at idle	inactive
		AT driving & automatically shifting	active
52	–		
53	TPS signal : t3	ignition on/engine running:	
		throttle closed	0.1 to 0.9 V
		throttle fully open	3.9 to 4.8 V
54	–		
55	SD connector : tG		data not available

55 pin ECM multi-plug, Bosch Motronic 1.5.2

Pin Table – Bosch Motronic 1.5.4

Pin	Connection	Test condition	Measurements
1	amplifier control signal : t1	engine cranking/running	0 to 5.0 V (switching)
2	earth	ignition on/engine running	0.25 V (max)
3	fuel pump relay driver : t85	ignition on	nbv
		engine cranking/running	1.25 V (max)
4	ISCV driver: t1	ignition on	nbv
		engine running, idle speed:	
		cold	6.0 to 6.5 V
		hot	7.0 to 9.0 V
		duty cycle, engine hot	44%

Pin Table – Bosch Motronic 1.5.4 (continued)

Pin	Connection	Test condition	Measurements
5	CFSV driver: t1	ignition on	nbv
		engine running, above idle, operating temperature:	
		CFSV inactive	nbv
		CFSV active	0 to 12 V (switching)
		duty cycle	0 to 99%
6	–		
7	MAF sensor signal : t4	ignition on	1.40 V
		idle	1.90 to 2.25 V
		snap accelerate	> 3.00 V
8	–		
9	VSS (if fitted)	vehicle in motion	0 to 12 V (switching)
10	earth	ignition on/engine running	0.25 V (max)
11	KS signal : t1	engine running, KS active	> 1.0 V AC (peak to peak)
12	TPS supply : t2	ignition on/engine running	5.0 V ± 0.1
13	SD connector : t6	open circuit	10 V (approx.)
		A & B bridged in SD connector	0.25 V (max)
14	earth	ignition on/engine running	0.25 V (max)
15			
16	injector driver (cylinder 2) : t1	ignition on	nbv
		engine running, cold	> 4.5 ms
		engine running, hot	3.0 to 3.5 ms
		snap acceleration	> 6.0 ms
17	injector driver (cylinder 1) : t1	ignition on	nbv
		engine cranking, cold	11.0 to 12.0 ms
		engine running, cold	> 4.5 ms
		engine running, hot	3.0 to 3.5 ms
		snap acceleration	> 6.0 ms
18	supply from battery : t30	ignition off/on/engine running	nbv
19	earth (main ECM)	ignition on/engine running	0.25 V (max)
20	amplifier control signal : t3	engine cranking/running	0 to 5.0 V (switching)
21	–		
22	SD warning lamp	ignition on, lamp on	1.25 V (max)
		engine running:	
		no faults present	nbv
		faults present, lamp on	1.25 V (max)
23	EGR solenoid valve driver : t1	ignition on	nbv
		engine running:	
		EGR inactive	nbv
		EGR active	1.25 V (max)
24	earth	ignition on/engine running	0.25 V (max)
25	A/C		data not available
26	ISCV return	ignition on/engine running	0.25 V (max)
27	supply from ignition switch : t15	ignition on/engine running	nbv
28	OS signal : t3	ignition on, OS multiplug disconnected	0.4 to 0.5 V
		engine running, hot	200 to 1000 mV (switching)
		throttle fully-open	0.5 to 1.0 V
		deceleration (fuel cut-off)	0 to 0.5 V
		switching frequency	1 sec intervals (approx)
29	–		
30	sensor return (AFS : t2, ATS : t1, CTS : t1, TPS : t1)	ignition on/engine running	0.25 V (max)
31-33	–		
34	injector driver (cylinder 4) : t1	ignition on	nbv
		engine running, cold	> 4.5 ms
		engine running, hot	3.0 to 3.5 ms
		snap acceleration	> 6.0 ms

Pin	Connection	Test condition	Measurements
35	injector driver (cylinder 3) : t1	ignition on	nbv
		engine running, cold	> 4.5 ms
		engine running, hot	3.0 to 3.5 ms
		snap acceleration	> 6.0 ms
36	–		
37	supply from main relay : t87	ignition on/engine running	nbv
38	AT		data not available
39	–		
40	A/C cut-off switch	ignition on, inactive	0.25 V (max)
		engine at idle speed and operating temperature: inactive	0.25 V (max)
		vehicle interior warm, actuate A/C switch, switch thermostat to cold and then briefly accelerate the engine, active	nbv
41	A/C pressure switch		data not available
42	earth connection (MT)	MT	0.25 V (max)
	or P/N switch (AT)	AT in P/N	0.25 V (max)
		AT engaged (R,D,2,1)	nbv
43	tachometer		data not available
44	ATS signal : t2	ignition on/engine running	0° C: 4.0 to 4.5 V
			20° C: 3.0 to 3.5 V
			80° C: 1.0 to 1.3 V
45	CTS signal : t2	ignition on/engine running	0° C: 4.0 to 4.5 V
			20° C: 3.00 to 3.75 V
			80° C: 1.00 to 1.30 V
46	supply from main relay driver : t85	ignition off	nbv
		ignition on/engine running	1.25 V (max)
47	–		
48	CAS return : t2	engine running	0.25 V (max)
49	CAS signal : t1	idle speed	> 8.0 V AC (peak to peak)
50	–		
51	AT control unit: t13 (torque control)	MT	inactive
		AT, idle speed	inactive
		AT driving & automatically shifting	active
52	–		
53	TPS signal : t3	ignition on/engine running:	
		throttle closed	0.1 to 0.9 V
		throttle fully-open	3.9 to 4.8 V
54	AT		data not available
55	SD connector : t7		data not availalbe

EQ15091H

55 pin ECM multi-plug, Bosch Motronic 1.5.4

Pin Table – Bosch Motronic 2.5

Pin	Item	Test Condition	Measurements
1	amplifier control signal : t4	engine cranking/running	0 to nbv (switching)
2	earth (for ignition driver)	engine running	0.25 V (max)

Pin Table – Bosch Motronic 2.5 (continued)

Pin	Item	Test Condition	Measurements
3	fuel pump relay driver : t85b	ignition on	nbv
		engine cranking/running	1.25 V (max)
4	ISCV driver : t1	ignition on	nbv
		engine running, cold	6.0 to 6.5 V
		frequency	100 to 110
		duty cycle	56 to 58%
		engine running, hot	7.0 to 9.0 V
		duty cycle, no load	40 to 44%
		duty cycle, under load	44 to 50%
5	FTVV/CFSV driver : t1	ignition on	nbv
		engine running, snap accelerate	0 V
6	tachometer		data not available
7	MAF sensor signal : t3	ignition on	1.40 V
		idle	1.90 to 2.25 V
		snap accelerate	> 3.00
8	CID (Hall sensor) signal : t2	engine running	2.50 V (average)
9	VSS signal	vehicle in motion	0 to 12 V (switching)
10	OS earth	engine running	0.25 V (max)
11	KS signal : t1	engine running, KS active	1.0 V AC (peak to peak)
12	–		
13	SD connector : tB		data not available
14	earth (injectors driver)	engine running	0.25 V (max)
16	injector driver (cylinder 3) : t1	ignition on	nbv
		engine cranking, cold	11.0 to 12.0 ms
		engine cranking, hot	> 3.1 ms
		cold idle	> 4.5ms
		hot idle	3.1 to 3.3 ms
17	injector driver (cylinder 1) : t1	ignition on	nbv
		engine cranking, cold	11.0 to 12.0 ms
		engine cranking, hot	> 3.1 ms
		cold idle	> 4.5 ms
		hot idle	3.1 to 3.3 ms
18	supply from battery : t30	ignition off/on/engine running	nbv
19	earth (main ECU earth)	ignition on/engine running	0.25 V (max)
20	earth coding (non-cat)	ignition on/engine running	0.25 V (max)
	(cat)	ignition on/engine running	5.0 V
21	earth coding (AT)	ignition on/engine running	0.25 V (max)
	(MT)	ignition on/engine running	5.0 V ± 0.1
22	SD warning lamp	ignition on, lamp on	1.25 V (max)
		engine running:	
		no faults present	nbv
		faults present, lamp on	1.25 V (max)
24	earth (FTVV & SD connector)	ignition on/engine running	0.25 V (max)
25	MAF sensor (hot wire burn-off) : t4	coolant above 31° C, rpm above 1000, switch off engine	hot wire glows for 1.5 seconds
26	MAF sensor return : t2	ignition on/engine running	0.25 V (max)
27	supply from ignition switch : t15	ignition on/engine running	nbv
28	OS signal : t1	ignition on, OS multiplug disconnected	0.4 to 0.5 V
		engine running, hot	200 to 1000 mV (switching)
		throttle fully-open	0.5 to 1.0 V
		deceleration (fuel cut-off)	0 to 0.5 V
		switching frequency	1 sec intervals (approx)
30	KS return : t2	engine running, KS active	0.25 V (max)
31	CID supply (HES) : t1	ignition on/engine running	11.0 to 13.0 V
32	on board computer : t24		data not available

Pin	Item	Test Condition	Measurements
34	injector driver (cylinder 2) : t1	ignition on	nbv
		engine cranking, cold	11.0 to 12.0 ms
		engine cranking, hot	> 3.1 ms
		cold idle	> 4.5 ms
		hot idle	3.1 to 3.3 ms
35	injector driver (cylinder 4) : t1	ignition on	nbv
		engine cranking, cold	11.0 to 12.0 ms
		engine cranking, hot	> 3.1 ms
		cold idle	> 4.5 ms
		hot idle	3.1 to 3.3 ms
36	main relay driver : t85	ignition off	nbv
		ignition on/engine running	1.25 V (max)
37	supply from relay : t87	ignition on/engine running	nbv
40	A/C compressor switch		data not available
41	A/C high pressure switch		data not available
42	P/N earth	ignition on:	
		gear selected	nbv
		P/N selected	1.25 V (max)
43	CO pot, non-cat (AFS : t6)	ignition on/idle speed	0.9 to 1.4 V (idle)
45	CTS signal : t2	ignition on/engine running	20° C: 3.00 to 3.50 V
			80° C: 1.00 to 1.30 V
46	octane adjuster : tA	ignition on/engine running:	
		brown plug, 95 to 98 octane	1.6 V
47	CAS signal : t1	engine cranking:	> 4.0 V AC (peak to peak)
		idle:	> 11.0 V AC (peak to peak)
		cruise:	> 14.0 V AC (peak to peak)
48	CAS earth : t2	engine running	0.25 V (max)
51	–		
52	TS, idle contact : t2	ignition on/engine running:	
		throttle closed	0.25 V (max)
		throttle open	5.0 V ± 0.1
53	TS, full load contact : t3	ignition on/engine running:	
		throttle fully open	0.25 V (max)
		throttle open/closed	5.0 V ± 0.1
55	SD connector : tG		data not available

55 pin ECM multi-plug, Bosch Motronic 2.5

Pin Table – Bosch Motronic 2.7

Pin	Item	Test Condition	Measurements
1	amplifier control signal : t4	engine cranking/running	0 to nbv (switching)
2	1st gear recognition switch : t2	engine running:	
		1st gear selected	5.0 V
		1st gear not selected	0.25 V (max)
3	fuel pump relay driver : t85b	ignition on	nbv
		engine cranking/running	1.25 V (max)

Pin Table – Bosch Motronic 2.7 (continued)

Pin	Item	Test Condition	Measurements
4	ISCV driver : t1	ignition on	nbv
		engine running, frequency	100 to 110 Hz
		engine running, cold	6.0 to 6.5 V
		duty cycle	56 to 58%
		engine running, hot	7.0 to 9.0 V
		duty cycle, no load	40 to 44%
		duty cycle, under load	44 to 50%
5	CFSV driver : t1	ignition on	nbv
		engine running, above idle, operating temperature:	
		CFSV inactive	nbv
		CFSV active	0 to 12 V (switching)
		duty cycle	0 to 99%
6	–		
7	MAF sensor signal : t3	ignition on	1.40 V
		idle	1.90 to 2.25 V
		snap accelerate	> 3.00 V
8	CID signal (HES) : t2	engine running	2.50 V (switching)
9	VSS signal	vehicle in motion	0 to 12 V (switching)
10	earth	ignition on/engine running	0.25 V (max)
11	KS signal : t1	engine running, KS active	1.0 V AC (peak to peak)
12	sensor supply (TPS: t1, CID: t3)	engine running	4.7 to 5.2 V
13	SD connector : tB		data not available
14	earth (injectors driver)	engine running	0.25 V (max)
15	–		
16	injector driver (cyl 3) : t1	ignition on	nbv
		engine cranking, cold	11.0 to 12.0 ms
		engine cranking, hot	> 3.1 ms
		cold idle	> 4.5 ms
		hot idle	2.0 to 2.8 ms
17	injector driver (cyl 1) : t1	ignition on	nbv
		engine cranking, cold	11.0 to 12.0 ms
		engine cranking, hot	> 3.1 ms
		cold idle	>4.5 ms
		hot idle	2.0 to 2.8 ms
18	supply from battery : t30	ignition off/on/engine running	nbv
19	earth (main ECM earth)	ignition on/engine running	0.25 V (max)
20	–		
21	TBCV driver : t1	engine running:	
		TBCV inactive	nbv
		TBCV active	0 to nbv (switching)
22	SD warning lamp	ignition on, lamp on	1.25 V (max)
		engine running:	
		no faults present	nbv
		faults present, lamp on	1.25 V (max)
24	earth (CFSV & SD connector)	ignition on/engine running	0.25 V (max)
25	MAF sensor (hot wire burn-off) : t4	coolant above 31° C, rpm above 1000, switch off engine	hot wire glows for 1.5 seconds
26	MAF sensor return : t2	ignition on/engine running	0.25 V (max)
27	supply from ignition switch : t15	ignition on/engine running	nbv
28	OS signal : t3	ignition on, OS multiplug disconnected	0.4 to 0.5 V
		engine running, hot	200 to 1000 mV (switching)
		throttle fully-open	0.5 to 1.0 V
		deceleration (fuel cut-off)	0 to 0.5 V
		switching frequency	1 sec intervals (approx)

Pin	Item	Test Condition	Measurements
29	–		
30	KS return : t2	engine running, KS active	0.25 V (max)
31	hot start valve driver : t1	engine running:	
		hot start valve inactive	nbv
		hot start valve active (coolant temperature greater than 100.8° C when engine is started)	1.25 V (max)
32	on board computer : t24		data not available
34	injector driver (cyl 2 : t1)	ignition on	nbv
		engine cranking, cold	11.0 to 12.0 ms
		engine cranking, hot	> 3.1 ms
		cold idle	> 4.5 ms
		hot idle	2.0 to 2.8 ms
35	injector driver (cyl 4) : t1	ignition on	nbv
		engine cranking, cold	11.0 to 12.0 ms
		engine cranking, hot	> 3.1 ms
		cold idle	> 4.5 ms
		hot idle	2.0 to 2.8 ms
36	main relay driver : t85	ignition off	nbv
		ignition on/engine running	1.25 V (max)
37	supply from relay : t87	ignition on/engine running	nbv
38	–		
39	–		
40	A/C compressor switch		data not available
41	A/C high pressure switch		data not available
42	earth	ignition on/engine running	0.25 V (max)
43	tachometer		data not available
44	ATS signal : t2	ignition on/engine running	80° C: 1.00 to 1.30 V 20° C: 3.00 to 3.50 V
45	CTS signal : t2	ignition on/engine running	80° C: 1.00 to 1.30 V 20° C: 3.00 to 3.50 V
46	–		
47	–		
48	CAS earth : t2	engine running	0.25 V (max)
49	CAS signal : t1	engine cranking:	> 4.0 V AC (peak to peak)
		idle:	> 8.0 V AC (peak to peak)
		cruise:	> 14.0 V AC (peak to peak)
50	–		
51	–		
52	reverse gear recognition		data not available
53	TPS signal : t3	ignition on/engine running:	
		throttle closed	0.1 to 0.7 V
		throttle fully-open	3.5 to 4.7 V
54	–		
55	SD connector : tG		data not available

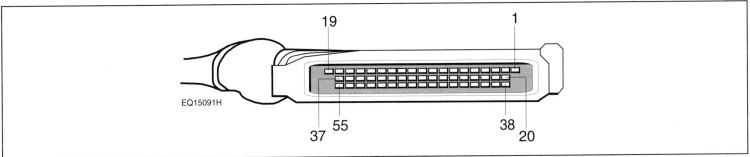

EQ15091H

55 pin ECM multi-plug, Bosch Motronic 2.7

Pin Table – Bosch Motronic 2.8

Pin	Connection	Test condition	Measurements
1	amplifier control signal : t2	engine cranking/running	0 to 5.0 V (switching)
2	–		
3	fuel pump relay driver : t85b	ignition on	nbv
		engine cranking/running	1.25 V (max)
4	ISCV driver : t1	ignition on	nbv
		engine running, frequency	100 to 110 Hz
		engine running, cold	6.0 to 6.5 V
		duty cycle	56 to 58%
		engine running, hot	7.0 to 9.0 V
		duty cycle, no load	40 to 44%
		duty cycle, under load	44 to 50%
5	CFSV driver : t1	ignition on	nbv
		engine running, above idle, operating temperature:	
		CFSV inactive	nbv
		CFSV active	0 to 12 V (switching)
		duty cycle	0 to 99%
6	–		
7	MAF sensor signal : t4	ignition on	1.40 V
		idle	1.90 to 2.25 V
		snap accelerate	> 3.00 V
8	CID (HES) signal : t2	engine running	2.50 V (average)
9	VSS signal	vehicle in motion	0 to 12 V (switching)
10	earth (OS driver)	engine running	0.25 V (max)
11	KS signal : t1	engine running, KS active	1.0 V AC (peak to peak)
12	TPS supply : t1	ignition on/engine running	5.0 V ± 0.1
13	SD connector : tB		data not available
14	earth (injector driver)	ignition on/engine running	0.25 V (max)
15	–		
16	injector driver (cylinder 3) : t1	ignition on	nbv
		engine cranking, cold	11.0 to 12.0 ms
		engine cranking, hot	> 3.1 ms
		cold idle	> 4.5 ms
		hot idle	3.1 to 3.3 ms
17	injector driver (cylinder 1) : t1	ignition on	nbv
		engine cranking, cold	11.0 to 12.0 ms
		engine cranking, hot	> 3.1 ms
		cold idle	> 4.5 ms
		hot idle	3.1 to 3.3 ms
18	supply from battery : t30	ignition off/on/engine running	nbv
19	earth (main ECM)	ignition on/engine running	0.25 V (max)
20	amplifier control signal : t7	engine cranking/running	0 to 5.0 V (switching)
21	–		
22	SD warning lamp : H1	ignition on, lamp on	1.25 V (max)
		engine running:	
		no faults present	nbv
		faults present, lamp on	1.25 V (max)
23	–		
24	earth (drivers: CFSV, SD warning lamp, ISCV, fuel pump relay)	ignition on/engine running	0.25 V (max)
25	A/C compressor driver		data not available
26	–		
27	supply from ignition switch : t15	ignition on/engine running	nbv
28	OS signal : t3	ignition on, OS multiplug disconnected	0.4 to 0.5 V
		engine running, hot	200 to 1000 mV (switching)
		throttle fully-open	0.5 to 1.0 V
		deceleration (fuel cut-off)	0 to 0.5 V
		switching frequency	1 sec intervals (approx)

Pin	Connection	Test condition	Measurements
29			
30	sensor return (ATS : t1, CTS : t1, TPS : t1, AFS : t2, KS : t2)	ignition on/engine running	0.25 V (max)
31			
32	–		
33	–		
34	injector driver (cylinder 2) : t1	ignition on	nbv
		engine cranking, cold	11.0 to 12.0 ms
		engine cranking, hot	> 3.1 ms
		cold idle	> 4.5 ms
		hot idle	3.1 to 3.3 ms
35	injector driver (cylinder 4) : t1	ignition on	nbv
		engine cranking, cold	11.0 to 12.0 ms
		engine cranking, hot	> 3.1 ms
		cold idle	> 4.5 ms
		hot idle	3.1 to 3.3 ms
36			
37	supply from relay : t87	ignition on/engine running	nbv
38	traction control (TC) signal		data not available
39	vehicle coding		data not available
40	A/C compressor signal		data not available
41	A/C high pressure switch		data not available
42	earth (MT models only, model coding)	ignition on/engine running	0.25 V (max)
43	tachometer		data not available
44	ATS signal : t2	ignition on/engine running	20° C: 3.00 to 3.50 V
			80° C: 1.00 to 1.30 V
45	CTS signal : t2	ignition on/engine running	20° C: 3.00 to 3.50 V
			80° C: 1.00 to 1.30 V
46	main relay driver : t85	ignition off	nbv
		ignition on	1.25 V (max)
47	–		
48	CAS earth : t2	engine running	0.25 V (max)
49	CAS signal : t1	engine cranking:	> 4.0 V AC (peak to peak)
		idle:	> 8.0 V AC (peak to peak)
		cruise:	> 14.0 V AC (peak to peak)
50	–		
51	input signal, load reduction, ignition retard, transmission control		data not available
52	–		
53	TPS signal : t3	ignition on/engine running:	
		throttle closed	0.1 to 0.7 V
		throttle fully-open	3.9 to 4.8 V
54	traction control (output signal, load signal)		data not available
55	SD connector : tG		data not available

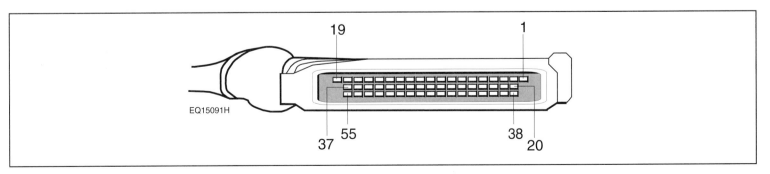

55 pin ECM multi-plug, Bosch Motronic 2.8

Pin Table – Bosch Motronic 2.8.1

Pin	Connection	Test condition	Measurements
1	amplifier control signal : t3	engine cranking/running	0 to 5.0 V (switching)
2	earth (ignition driver)	ignition on/engine running	0.25 V (max)
3	fuel pump relay driver : t86	ignition on	nbv
		engine cranking/running	1.25 V (max)
4	ISCV driver : t1	ignition on	nbv
		engine running, frequency	100 to 110 Hz
		engine running, cold:	
		voltage	6.0 to 6.5 V
		duty cycle	56 to 58%
		engine running, hot:	
		voltage	7.0 to 9.0 V
		duty cycle, no load	40 to 44%
		duty cycle, under load	44 to 50%
5	CFSV driver : t1	ignition on	nbv
		engine running, above idle, operating temperature:	
		CFSV inactive	nbv
		CFSV active	0 to 12 V (switching)
		duty cycle	0 to 99%
6	ICOV driver : t1	ignition on	nbv
		engine running:	
		ICOV inactive	nbv
		ICOV active	1.25 V (max)
7	MAF sensor signal : t4	ignition on	1.40 V
		idle	1.90 to 2.25 V
		snap accelerate	> 3.00 V
8	camshaft sensor signal : t2	engine running	2.50 (average)
9	VSS signal	vehicle in motion	0 to 12 V (switching)
10	earth for oxygen sensor	engine running	0.25 V (max)
11	KS signal : t1	engine running, KS active	1.0 to 2.0 V AC (peak to peak)
12	sensor supply (TPS : t2, EGR sensor : tD)	ignition on/engine running	5.0 V ± 0.1
13	SD connector : t6		data not available
14	earth (injector driver)	ignition on/engine running	0.25 V (max)
15	injector driver (cylinder 5) : t1	ignition on	nbv
		engine cranking, cold	11.0 to 12.0 ms
		engine cranking, hot	> 3.1 ms
		cold idle	> 4.5 ms
		hot idle	3.1 to 3.3 ms
16	injector driver (cylinder 2) : t1	ignition on	nbv
		engine cranking, cold	11.0 to 12.0 ms
		engine cranking, hot	> 3.1 ms
		cold idle	> 4.5 ms
		hot idle	3.1 to 3.3 ms
17	injector driver (cylinder 1) : t1	ignition on	nbv
		engine cranking, cold	11.0 to 12.0 ms
		engine cranking, hot	> 3.1 ms
		cold idle	> 4.5 ms
		hot idle	3.1 to 3.3 ms
18	supply from battery : t30	ignition off/on/engine running	nbv
19	earth (main ECM)	ignition on/engine running	0.25 V (max)
20	amplifier control signal : t1	engine cranking/running	0 to 5.0 V (switching)
21	amplifier control signal : t2	engine cranking/running	0 to 5.0 V (switching)
22	SD warning lamp	ignition on, lamp on	1.25 V (max)
		engine running:	
		no faults present	nbv
		faults present, lamp on	1.25 V (max)
23	EGR driver	ignition on	nbv
		engine running:	
		EGR inactive	nbv
		EGR active	1.25 V (max)

Pin	Connection	Test condition	Measurements
24	earth (drivers CFSV, SD warning lamp, ISCV, fuel pump relay)	ignition on/engine running	0.25 V (max)
25	A/C compressor driver		data not available
26	secondary air pump relay : t85	ignition on:	
		engine running:	
		air pump inactive	nbv
		air pump active	1.25 V (max)
27	supply from ignition switch : t15	ignition on/engine running	nbv
28	OS signal : t3	ignition on, OS multiplug disconnected	0.4 to 0.5 V
		engine running, hot	200 to 1000 mV (switching)
		throttle fully-open	0.5 to 1.0 V
		deceleration (fuel cut-off)	0 to 0.5 V
		switching frequency	1 sec intervals (approx)
29	KS signal : t1	engine running, KS active	1.0 to 2.0 V AC (peak to peak)
30	sensor return (ATS: t1, CTS: t1, TPS: t1, AFS: t2)	ignition on/engine running	0.25 V (max)
31	ICOV driver : t1	ignition on	nbv
		engine running:	
		ICOV inactive	nbv
		ICOV active	1.25 V (max)
32	–		
33	injector driver (cylinder 6) : t1	ignition on	nbv
		engine cranking, cold	11.0 to 12.0 ms
		engine cranking, hot	> 3.1 ms
		cold idle	> 4.5 ms
		hot idle	3.1 to 3.3 ms
34	injector driver (cylinder 4) : t1	ignition on	nbv
		engine cranking, cold	11.0 to 12.0 ms
		engine cranking, hot	> 3.1 ms
		cold idle	> 4.5 ms
		hot idle	3.1 to 3.3 ms
35	injector driver (cylinder 3) : t1	ignition on	nbv
		engine cranking, cold	11.0 to 12.0 ms
		engine cranking, hot	> 3.1 ms
		cold idle	> 4.5 ms
		hot idle	3.1 to 3.3 ms
36	–		
37	voltage supply from relay : t87	ignition on/engine running	nbv
38	input signal (Traction Control, TC)		data not available
39	vehicle coding		data not available
40	A/C compressor signal		data not available
41	A/C high pressure switch		data not available
42	earth (MT models only, model coding)	ignition on/engine running	0.25 V (max)
43	tachometer		data not available
44	ATS signal : t2	ignition on/engine running	80° C: 1.00 to 1.30 V
			20° C: 3.00 to 3.50 V
45	CTS signal : t2	ignition on/engine running	80° C: 1.00 to 1.30 V
			20° C: 3.00 to 3.50 V
46	main relay driver : t85	ignition off	nbv
		ignition on/engine running	1.25 V (max)
47	OS signal : t3	ignition on, OS multiplug disconnected	0.4 to 0.5 V
		engine running, hot	200 to 1000 mV (switching)
		throttle fully-open	0.5 to 1.0 V
		deceleration (fuel cut-off)	0 to 0.5 V
		switching frequency	1 sec intervals (approx)
48	CAS earth : t2	engine running	0.25 V (max)
49	CAS signal : t1	engine cranking:	> 4.0 V AC (peak to peak)
		idle:	> 8.0 V AC (peak to peak)
		cruise:	> 14.0 V AC (peak to peak)
50	EGR sensor signal	engine running:	
		EGR valve closed	1.2 V
		EGR valve fully open	4.3 V

Pin Table – Bosch Motronic 2.8.1 (continued)

Pin	Connection	Test condition	Measurements
51	input signal, load reduction, ignition retard, transmission control		data not available
52	–		
53	TPS signal : t3	ignition on/engine running:	
		throttle closed	0.1 to 0.7 V
		throttle fully-open	3.9 to 4.8 V
54	output signal, load signal, traction control		data not available
55	SD connector : t7		data not available

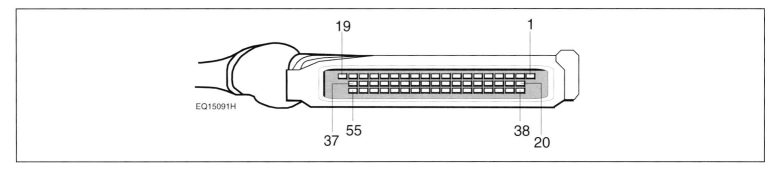

55 pin ECM multi-plug, Bosch Motronic 2.8.1

Pin Table – Bosch Motronic 2.8.3

Pin	Connection	Test condition	Measurements
1	–		
2	ISCV driver : t2	idle speed, engine hot	8 V
		duty cycle	60%
3	injector driver (cylinder 1) : t1	ignition on	nbv
		engine running, hot idle	3 ms
4	injector driver (cylinder 3) : t1	ignition on	nbv
		engine running, hot idle	3 ms
5	injector driver (cylinder 5) : t1	ignition on	nbv
		engine running, hot idle	3 ms
6	earth	ignition on/engine running	0.25 V (max)
7	ICOV driver: t1	ignition on	nbv
		engine running:	
		ICOV non-active	nbv
		ICOV active	1.25 V (max)
8	SD warning lamp : t1	ignition on, lamp on	1.25 V (max)
		engine running:	
		no faults present	nbv
		faults present, lamp on	1.25 V (max)
9-11	–		
12	A/C compressor switch		data not available
13-14	–		
15	EGR sensor signal : tC	engine running:	
		EGR valve closed	1.2 V
		EGR valve fully open	4.3 V
16	ATS signal : t2	ignition on/engine running	80° C: 1.00 to 1.30 V
			20° C: 3.00 to 3.50 V
17	MAF sensor signal : t4	ignition on	0 V
		idle	0.73 V
		2000 rpm	1.14 V
		3000 rpm	1.46 V
		snap accelerate	> 3.00

Pin	Connection	Test condition	Measurements
18	OS signal : t3	ignition on, OS multiplug disconnected	0.4 to 0.5 V
		engine running, hot	200 to 1000 mV (switching)
		throttle fully-open	0.5 to 1.0 V
		deceleration (fuel cut-off)	0 to 0.5 V
		switching frequency	1 sec intervals (approx)
19	OS signal : t3	ignition on, OS multiplug disconnected	0.4 to 0.5 V
		engine running, hot	200 to 1000 mV (switching)
		throttle fully-open	0.5 to 1.0 V
		deceleration (fuel cut-off)	0 to 0.5 V
		switching frequency	1 sec intervals (approx)
20	CAS return : t2	engine running	0.25 V (max)
21-25	–		
26	supply from battery : t30	ignition off/on/engine running	nbv
27	main relay driver : t85	ignition off	nbv
		ignition on/engine running	1.25 V (max)
29	ISCV driver : t1	idle speed, engine hot	8 V
		duty cycle	60%
30	–		
31	injector driver (cylinder 2) : t1	ignition on	nbv
		engine running, hot idle	3 ms
32	injector driver (cylinder 4) : t1	ignition on	nbv
		engine running, hot idle	3 ms
33	injector driver (cylinder 6) : t1	ignition on	nbv
		engine running, hot idle	3 ms
34	earth	ignition on/engine running	0.25 V (max)
35	ICOV driver : t1	ignition on	nbv
		engine running:	
		ICOV non-active	nbv
		ICOV active	1.25 V (max)
36	AC relay		data not available
37	secondary air pump relay driver : t85	ignition on:	
		air pump inactive	nbv
		air pump active	1.25 V (max)
38	CID earth : t2	engine running	0.25 V (max)
39	–		
40	KS 2 signal : t1	engine running, KS active	1.0 V AC (peak to peak)
41-42	–		
43	A/C high/low pressure switch		data not available
44	TPS signal : t3	ignition on/engine running:	
		throttle closed	0.1 to 0.7 V
		throttle fully-open	3.9 to 4.8 V
45	–		
46	earth	ignition on/engine running	0.25 V (max)
47	trip computer		data not available
48	amplifier control signal : t4	engine cranking/running	0 to 5.0 V (switching)
49	–		
50	amplifier control signal : t1	engine cranking/running	0 to 5.0 V (switching)
51	amplifier control signal : t2	engine cranking/running	0 to 5.0 V (switching)
52	–		
53	sensor supply (TPS & EGR)	ignition on/engine running	5.0 V ± 0.1
54	supply from main relay : t87	ignition on/engine running	nbv
55	–		
56	supply from ignition switch : t15	ignition on/engine running	nbv
57-60	–		
61	CFSV driver : t1	ignition on	nbv
		engine running, above idle, operating temperature:	
		CFSV inactive	nbv
		CFSV active	0 to 12 V (switching)
		duty cycle	0 to 99%
62	–		
63	fuel pump relay driver : t86	ignition on	nbv
		engine cranking/running	1.25 V (max)

Pin Table – Bosch Motronic 2.8.3 (continued)

Pin	Connection	Test condition	Measurements
64-65	–		
66	EGR solenoid driver : tA	ignition on	nbv
		engine running:	
		EGR inactive	nbv
		EGR active	0.25 V (max)
67-68	–		
69	AT		data not available
70	KS signal 1 : t1	engine running, KS active	1.0 V AC (peak to peak)
71	sensor return (EGR tB, AFS t2, CTS t1, TPS : t2)	ignition on/engine running	0.25 V (max)
72	–		
73	PSPS signal : t2	idle speed, all accessories off	
		wheels straight	0.45 to 0.70 V
		wheels fully turned to LH or RH	3.50 to 4.20 V
74	CTS signal : t2	ignition on/engine running	20° C: 3.0 to 3.5 V
			80° C: 1.0 to 1.3 V
75-77	–		
78	CAS	engine cranking:	> 4.0 V AC (peak to peak)
		idle:	> 8.0 V AC (peak to peak)
		cruise:	> 14.0 V AC (peak to peak)
79	VSS signal : t2	vehicle in motion	0 to 12 V (switching)
80	tachometer		data not available
81	–		
82	load signal to AT unit		data not available
83-86	–		
87	SD connector		data not available
88	SD connector		data not available

88 pin ECM multi-plug, Bosch Motronic 2.8.3

Pin Table – Bosch Motronic ML4.1 (4-cyl)

Pin	Item	Test Condition	Measurements
1	ignition coil driver : t1	ignition on	nbv
		engine running:	
		dynamic volt drop	2.0 V (max)
		primary switching	200 V (min)
2	TS, idle contact : t2	Ignition on/engine running:	
		throttle closed	0 V
		throttle part/fully open	5.0 ± 0.1 V
3	TS, full-load contact : t3	Ignition on/engine running:	
		throttle closed/part open	5.0 ± 0.1 V
		throttle fully open	0 V
4	SD connector : tB		data not available
5	earth	ignition on/engine running	0.25 V (max)
6	AFS return : t4	ignition on/engine running	0.25 V (max)

Pin	Item	Test Condition	Measurements
7	AFS signal : t2	ignition on	0.20 to 0.30 V
		idle	0.75 to 1.50 V
		2000 rpm	1.75 to 2.25 V
		3000 rpm	2.00 to 2.50 V
		snap accelerate	3.00 to 4.50 V
		WOT (off-load)	> 4.50 V
8	AT control unit (some)		data not available
9	AFS supply : t3		5.0 V ± 0.1
10	earth (auto transmission)	ignition on/engine running	0.25 V (max)
11	–		
12	SD connector : tG		data not available
13	CTS signal : t2	ignition on/engine running	20° C: 3.00 to 3.50 V
			80° C: 1.00 to 1.30 V
14	injector driver : t1	ignition on	nbv
		engine running, cold	3.0 to 3.5 ms
		engine running, hot	2.0 to 2.5 ms
		snap acceleration	6.0 ms
15	octane adjustment : t2	ignition on/engine running:	
		98 octane	0.9 V
		95 octane	1.6 V
16	earth	ignition on/engine running	0.25 V (max)
17	SD warning lamp	ignition on, lamp on	1.25 V (max)
		engine running:	
		no faults present	nbv
		faults present, lamp on	1.25 V (max)
18	supply from battery : t30	ignition off/engine running	nbv
19	earth	ignition on/engine running	0.25 V (max)
20	fuel pump relay driver : t85b	ignition on	nbv
		engine cranking/running	1.25 V (max)
21	AT control unit (some)		data not available
22	ATS signal : (AFS : t5)	ignition on/engine running	20° C: 3.50 to 3.75 V
			80° C: 1.25 to 1.30 V
23	CAS return : t2	engine running	0.25 V (max)
24	OS signal : t3 (catalyst equipped vehicles only)	ignition on, OS multiplug disconnected	0.4 to 0.5 V
		engine running, hot	200 to 1000 mV (switching)
		throttle fully-open	0.5 to 1.0 V
		deceleration (fuel cut-off)	0 to 0.5 V
		switching frequency	1 sec intervals (approx)
25	CAS signal : t1	engine cranking:	> 0.4 V AC(peak to peak)
		idle:	> 8.0 V AC (peak to peak)
		cruise:	> 14.0 V AC (peak to peak)
26	–		
27	earth	ignition on/engine running	0.25 V (max)
28	earth (MT) or starter motor	ignition on	0.25 V (max)
29	air conditioning		data not available
30	CO pot (AFS: t1)	idle	2.45 V ± 0.5
31	FTVV/CFSV driver : t1	ignition on	nbv
		snap accelerate	0 V
32	air conditioning switch		data not available
33	ISCV driver : t1	ignition on	nbv
		engine running, idle speed:	
		cold	6.0 to 6.5 V
		hot	7.0 to 9.0 V
		duty cycle	30 to 60%
34	–		
35	supply from main relay : t87	ignition on	nbv

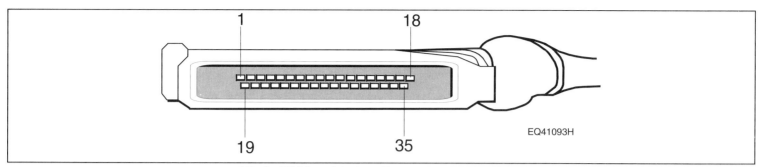

35 pin ECM multi-plug, Bosch Motronic ML4.1

Pin Table – GM-Multec CFI DIS (Corsa, X12SZ)

Section A

Pin	Item	Test Condition	Measurements
A1	KS signal filter	engine running:	
		KS, inactive	9.0 V
		KS, active	0 V
A2	CAS signal : t1	engine cranking	> 2.0 V AC (peak to peak)
		idle:	> 11.0 V AC (peak to peak)
		cruise:	> 14.0 V AC (peak to peak)
A7	MAP sensor signal : tB	ignition on	4.5 to 4.9 V
		idle speed	1.5 V
		engine running, WOT	4.5 to 4.9 V
A8	TPS signal : tC	ignition on/engine running:	
		throttle closed	0.5 to 0.9 V
		throttle fully open	4.5 V (approx.)
A9	EGR amplifier trigger signal	KS active	data not available
A10	CFSV driver : t1	ignition on	nbv
		engine running, above idle, operating temperature:	
		CFSV inactive	nbv
		CFSV active	0 to 12 V (switching)
		duty cycle	0 to 99%
A11	sensor return (CTS : t1, MAP : tC)	ignition on/engine running	0.25 V (max)
A12	earth	ignition on/engine running	0.25 V (max)

Section B

B1	supply from battery : t30	ignition on/off/engine running	nbv
B2	VSS signal : t1	vehicle in motion	0 to 12 V (switching)
B3	CAS signal : t2	cranking	> 4.0 V AC (peak to peak)
		idle	> 8.0 V AC (peak to peak)
		cruise	>14.0 V AC (peak to peak)
B4	on board computer		data not available
B5	AT control unit (auto)		data not available
B6	fuel pump relay driver: t85	ignition on	nbv
		engine cranking/running	1.25 V (max)
B7	SD connector : tG		data not available
B8	sensor supply (MAP: tC, TPS : tA)	ignition on/engine running	5.0 V ± 0.1
B10	earth	ignition on/engine running	0.25 V (max)
B11	OS signal : t2	ignition on, OS multiplug disconnected	0.4 to 0.5 V
		engine running, hot	200 to 1000 mV (switching)
		throttle fully-open	0.5 to 1.0 V
		deceleration (fuel cut-off)	0 to 0.5 V
		switching frequency	1 sec intervals (approx.)
B12	CTS signal : t2	ignition on/engine running	20° C: 2.0 to 2.5 V
			100° C: 0.50 to 0.80 V

Section C

Pin	Item	Test Condition	Measurements
C1	SD warning lamp	ignition on, lamp on	1.25 V (max)
		engine running:	
		no faults present	nbv
		faults present, lamp on	1.25 V (max)
C2	AT control unit : t29, tachometer		data not available
C3	amplifier control signal B	engine cranking/running	0 to 5.0 (switching)
C4	supply from ignition : t15	ignition on/engine running	nbv
C5	stepper motor : tC	idle speed, active	0 V to nbv (switching)
C6	stepper motor : tD	idle speed, active	0 V to nbv (switching)
C8	stepper motor : tB	idle speed, active	0 V to nbv (switching)
C9	stepper motor : tA	idle speed, active	0 V to nbv (switching)
C10	injector driver : t1	engine cranking, cold	> 3.0 ms
		engine running, cold	2.5 to 3.0 ms
		engine running, hot:	
		idle	1.50 to 1.75 ms
		2000 rpm	1.50 to 1.75 ms
		3000 rpm	1.50 to 1.75 ms
		snap acceleration	> 6.0 ms
C13	connected to ECM: tC14		
C14	connected to ECM: tC13		
C16	supply from battery : t30	ignition off/on/engine running	nbv

Section D

Pin	Item	Test Condition	Measurements
D1	earth	ignition on/engine running	0.25 V (max)
D2	sensor return (TPS: tB, EGR valve: tB)	ignition on/engine running	0.25 V (max)
D3	KS signal: t2	engine running, KS active	1.0 V AC (peak to peak)
D7	AT control unit : t13		data not available
D8	SD connector : tB	ignition on/engine running	0.25 V (max)
D9	P/N switch (AT models)		data not available
D10	amplifier control signal : tB	engine cranking/running	0 to 5.0 V (switching)
D11	EGR valve: tC	engine running, EGR active:	
		valve closed	1.20 V
		valve open	4.30 V

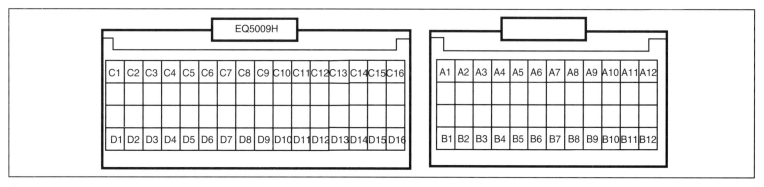

56 pin ECM multi-plug, GM Multec CFI DIS (Corsa, X12SZ)

Pin Table – GM-Multec CFi (Belmont, C16NZ)

Section A

Pin	Item	Test Condition	Measurement
A1	supply from fuel pump relay : t86	engine cranking/running	nbv
A2	trip computer		data not available
A3	–		
A4	AT control unit		data not available

Pin Table – GM-Multec CFi (Belmont, C16NZ) (continued)

Section A (continued)

Pin	Item	Test Condition	Measurement
A5	SD warning lamp	engine running:	
		no faults present	nbv
		faults present	1.25 V (max)
A6	supply from ignition switch : t15	ignition on/engine running	nbv
A7	–		
A8	SD connector : tG		data not available
A9	SD connector : tB		data not available
A10	VSS signal : t3	vehicle in motion	5.0 to 7.0 V
A11	sensor return (CTS : t1,MAP : tA)	ignition on/engine running	0.25 V (max)
A12	earth	ignition on/engine running	0.25 V (max)

Section B

Pin	Item	Test Condition	Measurement
B1	supply from battery	ignition off/on/engine running	nbv
B2	–		
B3	earth	ignition on/engine running	0.25 V (max)
B4	–		
B5	inductive trigger signal : t2	engine cranking:	> 2.0 V AC (peak to peak)
		idle:	> 11.0 V AC (peak to peak)
		cruise:	> 14.0 V AC (peak to peak)
B6	–		
B7	AT transmission		data not available
B8	trip computer		data not available
B9	–		
B10	P/N switch (where fitted)		data not available
B11-B12	–		

Section C

Pin	Item	Test Condition	Measurement
C1	tachometer, AT control unit		data not available
C2	–		
C3	stepper motor : tB	idle speed, active	0 to nbv (switching)
C4	stepper motor : tA	idle speed, active	0 to nbv (switching)
C5	stepper motor : tC	idle speed, active	0 to nbv (switching)
C6	stepper motor : tD	idle speed, active	0 to nbv (switching)
C7-C9	–		
C10	CTS signal : t2	ignition on/engine running	20° C: 2.0 to 2.5 V
			100° C: 0.50 to 0.80 V
C11	MAP sensor signal : tB	ignition on	4.5 to 4.9 V
		idle speed	1.5 V
		engine running, WOT	4.5 to 4.9 V
C12	octane adjuster : tA	ignition on/engine running:	
		multi-plug disconnected	5.0 V ± 0.1
C13	TPS signal : tC	ignition on/engine running:	
		throttle closed	0.5 to 0.9 V
		throttle fully open	4.5 V
C14	sensor supply (TPS : tA, MAP : tC)	ignition on/engine running	5.0 V ± 0.1
C15	–		
C16	supply from battery	ignition off/on/engine running	nbv

Section D

Pin	Item	Test Condition	Measurement
D1	earth	ignition on/engine running	0.25 V (max)
D2	sensor return (TPS : tB, octane adjuster : tB)	ignition on/engine running	0.25 V (max)
D3	–		
D4	amplifier signal : t4	engine cranking/running	2.0 to 3.0 V (switching)
D5	inductive trigger return : t1	ignition on/engine running	0.25 V (max)
D6	earth	ignition on/engine running	0.25 V (max)

Pin	Item	Test Condition	Measurement
D7	OS signal : t2	ignition on	350 to 400 mV
		engine running	200 to 1000 mV (switching)
		throttle fully open	0.5 to 1.0 V
		deceleration (fuel cut off)	0 to 0.5 V
		switching frequency	1 sec intervals
D8	–		
D9	connected to ECM : tD10	wire bridge for injection control	
D10	connected to ECM : tD9	wire bridge for injection control	
D11-D14	–		
D15	injector driver : t1	ignition on	nbv
		engine cranking, cold	> 3.0 ms
		engine running, cold	2.5 to 3.0 ms
		engine running, hot:	
		idle	1.50 to 1.75 ms
		2000 rpm	1.50 to 1.75 ms
		3000 rpm	1.50 to 1.75 ms
		snap accelerate	> 6.0 ms
D16	–		

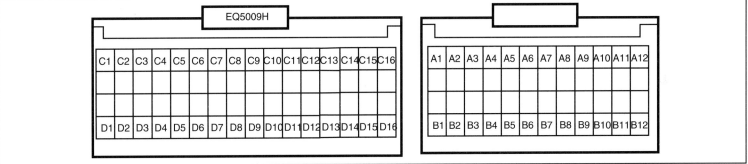

56 pin ECM multi-plug, GM Multec CFi (Belmont, C16NZ)

Pin Table – GM-Multec CFi-HE (Nova 1.2, C12NZ)

Section A

Pin	Item	Test Condition	Measurements
A1	supply from fuel pump relay : t86	engine cranking/running	nbv
A2-A4	–		
A5	SD warning lamp	ignition on, lamp on	1.25 V (max)
		engine running:	
		no faults present	nbv
		faults present, lamp on	1.25 V (max)
A6	supply from ignition switch : t15	ignition on/engine running	nbv
A7	–		
A8	SD connector : tG		data not available
A9	SD connector : tB		data not available
A10	VSS signal : t3	vehicle in motion	0 to 12 V (switching)
A11	sensor return (CTS : t1, MAP: tA)	ignition on/engine running	0.25 V (max)
A12	earth	ignition on/engine running	0.25 V (max)

Section B

Pin	Item	Test Condition	Measurements
B1	supply from battery : t30	ignition off/on/engine running	nbv
B2	–		
B3	earth	ignition on/engine running	0.25 V (max)
B4	–		
B5	hall effect signal : t2	engine running	5.0 to 7.0 V
B6-B12	–		

Pin Table – GM-Multec CFi-HE (Nova 1.2, C12NZ) (continued)

Section C

Pin	Item	Test Condition	Measurements
C1-C2	–		
C3	stepper motor : tB	idle speed, active	0 V to nbv (switching)
C4	stepper motor : tA	engine idle, active	0 V to nbv (switching)
C5	stepper motor : tC	engine idle, active	0 V to nbv (switching)
C6	stepper motor : tD	engine idle, active	0 V to nbv (switching)
C7-C9	–		
C10	CTS signal : t2	ignition on/engine running	20° C: 2.0 to 2.5 V
			100° C: 0.50 to 0.80 V
C11	MAP sensor signal : tB	ignition on	4.5 to 4.9 V
		idle speed	1.5 V
		engine running, WOT	4.5 to 4.9 V
C12	octane adjuster : tA	ignition on/engine running:	
		multiplug disconnected	5.0 V ± 0.1
C13	TPS signal: tC	ignition on/engine running:	
		throttle closed	0.5 to 0.9 V
		throttle fully open	4.5 V
C14	sensor return (TPS : tA, MAP sensor : tC)	ignition on/engine running	5.0 V ± 0.1
C15	–		
C16	supply from battery : t30	ignition off/on/engine running	nbv

Section D

Pin	Item	Test Condition	Measurements
D1	earth	ignition on/engine running	0.25 V (max)
D2	sensor return (TPS : tB, octane adjuster : tB)	ignition on/engine running	0.25 V (max)
D3	–		
D4	amplifier control signal : t4	engine cranking/running	2 to 3 V (switching)
D5	hall effect supply : t1	ignition on/engine running	11.0 to 13.0 V
D6	earth	ignition on/engine running	0.25 V (max)
D7	OS signal: t2	ignition on, OS multiplug disconnected	0.4 to 0.5 V
		engine running, hot	200 to 1000 mV (switching)
		throttle fully-open	0.5 to 1.0 V
		deceleration (fuel cut-off)	0 to 0.5 V
		switching frequency	1 sec intervals (approx.)
D8-D14	–		
D15	injector driver : t1	engine cranking, cold	> 3.0 ms
		engine running, cold	2.5 to 3.0 ms
		engine running, hot	1.50 to 1.75 ms
		2000 rpm	1.50 to 1.75 ms
		3000 rpm	1.50 to 1.75 ms
		snap acceleration	> 6.0 ms
D16	–		

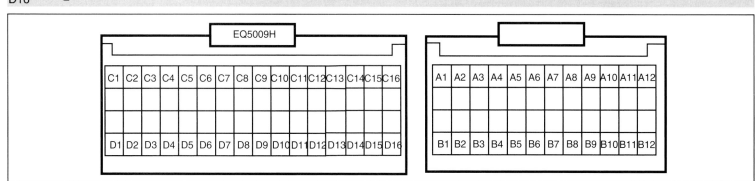

56 pin ECM multi-plug, GM Multec CFi-HE (Nova 1.2, C12NZ)

Pin Table – GM-Multec MPi (Corsa/Nova, C14SE)

Section A

Pin	Item	Test Condition	Measurement
A2	CAS return : t1	engine cranking/running	0.25 V (max)
A7	MAP sensor signal : tB	ignition on	4.5 to 4.9 V
		engine running:	
		idle speed	1.6 V ± 0.6
		WOT	4.5 to 4.9 V
A8	TPS signal : tC	ignition on/engine running:	
		throttle closed	0.3 to 0.9 V
		throttle fully open	4.2 to 4.8 V
A11	sensor return (ATS: t1, CTS : t1, MAP : tA)	ignition on/engine running	0.25 V (max)
A12	main ECM earth	ignition on/engine running	0.25 V (max)

Section B

Pin	Item	Test Condition	Measurement
B1	supply from battery : t30	ignition off/on/engine running	nbv
B2	VSS signal : t1	vehicle in motion	5.0 to 7.0 V (average)
B3	CAS signal : t2	engine cranking:	> 4.0 V AC (peak to peak)
		idle:	> 8.0 V AC (peak to peak)
		cruise:	> 14.0 V AC (peak to peak)
B6	fuel pump relay driver : t87	ignition on	nbv
		engine cranking/running	1.25 V
B7	SD connector : tG		data not available
B8	sensor supply (MAP : tC, TPS : tA)	ignition on/engine running	5.0 V ± 0.1
B10	earth	ignition on/engine running	0.25 V (max)
B11	OS signal : t2	ignition on, OS multiplug disconnected	0.4 to 0.5 V
		engine running, hot	200 to 1000 mV (switching)
		throttle fully-open	0.5 to 1.0 V
		deceleration (fuel cut-off)	0 to 0.5 V
		switching frequency	1 sec intervals (approx.)
B12	CTS signal : t2	ignition on/engine running	20° C: 2.00 to 2.50 V 70° C: 2.75 to 3.00 V

Section C

Pin	Item	Test Condition	Measurement
C1	SD warning lamp	ignition on, lamp on	1.25 V (max)
		engine running:	
		no faults present	nbv
		faults present, lamp on	1.25 V (max)
C2	tachometer		data not available
C4	supply from ignition switch : t15	ignition on/engine running	nbv
C5	stepper motor : tC	idle speed, active	0 to nbv (switching)
C6	stepper motor : tD	idle speed, active	0 to nbv (switching)
C8	stepper motor : tB	idle speed, active	0 to nbv (switching)
C9	stepper motor : tA	idle speed, active	0 to nbv (switching)
C10	injector driver (cyl s 1 & 2) : t1	ignition on	nbv
		engine cranking, cold	11.0 to 12.0 ms
		engine running, cold	3.0 to 4.0 ms
		engine cranking, hot	> 4.0 to 4.5 ms
		engine running, hot:	
		idle	1.0 to 1.6 ms
		2000 rpm	2.0 to 2.5 ms
		3000 rpm	2.0 to 2.5 ms
		snap acceleration	6.0 ms

Pin Table – GM-Multec MPi (Corsa/Nova, C14SE) (continued)

Section C (continued)

Pin	Item	Test Condition	Measurement
C11	injector driver (cyls 3 & 4) : t1	ignition on	nbv
		engine cranking, cold	11.0 to 12.0 ms
		engine running, cold	3.0 to 4.0 ms
		engine cranking, hot	> 4.0 to 4.5 ms
		engine running, hot:	
		idle	1.0 to 1.6 ms
		2000 rpm	2.0 to 2.5 ms
		3000 rpm	2.0 to 2.5 ms
		snap acceleration	6.0 ms
C12	earth (injector 1 & 2)	ignition on/engine running	0.25 V (max)
C13	earth (injector 3 & 4)	ignition on/engine running	0.25 V (max)
C16	supply from battery : t30	ignition off/on/engine running	nbv

Section D

Pin	Item	Test Condition	Measurement
D1	earth (injector driver)	engine running	0.25 V (max)
D2	sensor return (TPS : tB, octane adjuster : tB)	ignition on/engine running	0.25 V (max)
D3	ATS signal : t2	ignition on/engine running	20° C: 2.00 to 2.50 V 60 to 80° C: 3.05 to 2.40 V
D8	SD connector : tB		data not available
D10	amplifier control signal : t4	engine running	0 to 12.0 V (switching)
D11	octane adjuster : tA	ignition on/engine running	5.0 V ± 0.1

56 pin ECM multi-plug, GM Multec MPi (Corsa/Nova, C14SE)

Pin Table – GM-Multec MPi-DIS (Corsa/Nova, C16SE)

Section A

Pin	Item	Test Condition	Measurements
A2	CAS return : t1	engine cranking/running	0.25 V (max)
A7	MAP sensor signal : tB	ignition on	4.5 to 4.9 V
		engine running:	
		WOT	4.5 to 4.9 V
		idle speed	1.6 V ± 0.6
A8	TPS signal : tC	ignition on/engine running:	
		throttle closed	0.3 to 0.9 V
		throttle fully open	4.2 to 4.8 V
A11	sensor return (ATS: t1, CTS : t1, MAP : tA)	ignition on/engine running	0.25 V (max)
A12	main ECM earth	ignition on/engine running	0.25 V (max)

Section B

Pin	Item	Test Condition	Measurements
B1	supply from battery : t30	ignition off/on/engine running	nbv
B2	VSS signal : t1	vehicle in motion	5.0 to 7.0 V (average)

Pin	Item	Test Condition	Measurements
B3	CAS signal : t2	engine cranking:	> 4.0 V AC (peak to peak)
		idle:	> 8.0 V AC (peak to peak)
		cruise:	> 14.0 V AC (peak to peak)
B6	fuel pump relay driver : t87	ignition on	nbv
		engine cranking/running	1.25 V
B7	SD connector : tG		data not available
B8	sensor supply (MAP : tC, TPS : tA)	ignition on/engine running	5.0 V ± 0.1
B10	earth	ignition on/engine running	0.25 V (max)
B11	OS signal : t2	ignition on, OS multiplug disconnected	0.4 to 0.5 V
		engine running, hot	200 to 1000 mV (switching)
		throttle fully-open	0.5 to 1.0 V
		deceleration (fuel cut-off)	0 to 0.5 V
		switching frequency	1 sec intervals (approx)
B12	CTS signal : t2	ignition on/engine running	20° C: 2.00 to 2.50 V
			70° C: 2.75 to 3.00 V

Section C

Pin	Item	Test Condition	Measurements
C1	SD warning lamp	ignition on, lamp on	1.25 V (max)
		engine running:	
		no faults present	nbv
		faults present, lamp on	1.25 V (max)
C2	tachometer		data not available
C4	supply from ignition switch : t15	ignition on/engine running	nbv
C5	stepper motor : tC	idle speed, active	0 to nbv (switching)
C6	stepper motor : tD	idle speed, active	0 to nbv (switching)
C8	stepper motor : tB	idle speed, active	0 to nbv (switching)
C9	stepper motor : tA	idle speed, active	0 to nbv (switching)
C10	injector driver (cyls 1 & 2) : t1	ignition on	nbv
		engine cranking, cold	11.0 to 12.0 ms
		engine running, cold	3.0 to 4.0 ms
		engine cranking, hot	> 4.0 to 4.5 ms
		engine running, hot:	
		idle	1.0 to 1.6 ms
		2000 rpm	2.0 to 2.5 ms
		3000 rpm	2.0 to 2.5 ms
		snap acceleration	6.0 ms
C11	injector driver (cyls 3 & 4) : t1	ignition on	nbv
		engine cranking, cold	11.0 to 12.0 ms
		engine running, cold	3.0 to 4.0 ms
		engine cranking, hot	> 4.0 to 4.5 ms
		engine running, hot:	
		idle	1.0 to 1.6 ms
		2000 rpm	2.0 to 2.5 ms
		3000 rpm	2.0 to 2.5 ms
		snap acceleration	6.0 ms
C12	earth (injector 1 & 2)	ignition on/engine running	0.25 V (max)
C13	earth (injector 3 & 4)	ignition on/engine running	0.25 V (max)
C16	supply from battery : t30	ignition off/on/engine running	nbv

Section D

Pin	Item	Test Condition	Measurements
D1	earth (injector driver)	engine running	0.25 V (max)
D2	sensor return (TPS : tB, octane adjuster : tB)	ignition on/engine running	0.25 V (max)
D3	ATS signal : t2	ignition on/engine running	20° C: 2.00 to 2.50 V
			60 to 80° C: 3.05 to 2.40 V
D8	SD connector : tB		data not available
D10	amplifier control signal : t4	engine running	0 to 12.0 V (switching)
D11	octane adjuster : tA	ignition on/engine running	5.0 V ± 0.1

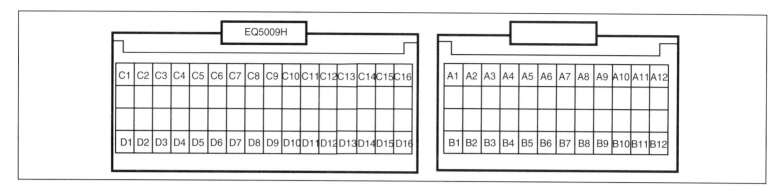

56 pin ECM multi-plug, GM Multec MPi DIS (Corsa/Nova, C16SE)

Pin Table – GM-Multec MPi-S (Corsa 95-97, X14XE)

Section A

Pin	Item	Test Condition	Measurements
A1	stepper motor : tC	idle speed, active	0 to nbv (switching)
A2	stepper motor : tD	idle speed, active	0 to nbv (switching)
A3	stepper motor : tB	idle speed, active	0 to nbv (switching)
A4	stepper motor : tA	idle speed, active	0 to nbv (switching)
A5	CID (camshaft) sensor signal : tB	engine running	0 to nbv (switching)
A6	supply from battery : t30	ignition off/on/engine running	nbv
A7	MAP sensor signal : tB	ignition on	4.5 to 4.9 V
		engine running:	
		WOT	4.5 to 4.9 V
		idle speed	1.6 V ± 0.6
A8	A/C		data not available
A9	AT control unit		data not available
A10	secondary air relay driver : t85	engine running:	
		secondary air inactive	nbv
		engine running, cold (first 3-4 minutes.)	1.25 V (max)
A11	secondary air solenoid valve driver : t1	engine running:	
		secondary air inactive	nbv
		engine running, cold (first 3-4 minutes.)	1.25 V (max)
A12	fuel pump relay driver : t85	ignition on	nbv
		engine cranking/running	1.25 V (max)
A13	CFSV driver : t1	ignition on	nbv
		engine running, above idle,	operating temperature:
		CFSV inactive	nbv
		CFSV active	0 to 12 V (switching)
		duty cycle	0 to 99%
A15	A/C compressor relay driver		data not available
A16	CAS return : t2	engine cranking/running	0.25 V (max)

Section B

Pin	Item	Test Condition	Measurements
B1	main ECM earth	ignition on/engine running	0.25 V (max)
B2	sensor return (CTS : t1,TPS : tB, EGR : tB)	ignition on/engine running	0.25 V (max)
B3	CTS signal : t2	ignition on/engine running	20° C: 2.00 to 2.50 V
			45° C: 1.20 to 3.70 V
			70° C: 2.75 to 3.00 V
			85° C: 2.21 V
			100 to 110° C: 1.43 to 2.00 V
B4	ATS signal : t2	ignition on/engine running	20° C: 2.00 to 2.50 V
			60 to 80° C: 3.05 to 2.40 V
B5	A/C pressure switch		data not available
B8	P/N lever position switch		data not available
B9	SD connector : tB		data not available

Pin	Item	Test Condition	Measurements
B10	SD warning lamp	ignition on, lamp on	1.25 V (max)
		engine running:	
		no faults present	nbv
		faults present, lamp on	1.25 V (max)
B13	tachometer		data not available
B14	CAS signal : t1	engine cranking:	> 4.0 V AC (peak to peak)
		idle:	> 8.0 V AC (peak to peak)
		cruise:	> 14.0 V AC (peak to peak)

Section E

Pin	Item	Test Condition	Measurements
E1	KS signal : t2	engine running:	
		KS non-active	2.5 V (control voltage)
		KS active	1.0 V AC (approx)
E2	injector driver (cyl 3) : t1	ignition on	nbv
		engine cranking, cold	11.0 to 12.0 ms
		engine cranking, hot	> 3.1 ms
		engine running:	
		cold idle	> 4.5 ms
		hot idle	3.1 to 3.3 ms
E3	injector driver (cyl 2) : t1	ignition on	nbv
		engine cranking, cold	11.0 to 12.0 ms
		engine cranking, hot	> 3.1 ms
		engine running:	
		cold idle	> 4.5 ms
		hot idle	3.1 to 3.3 ms
E4	injector driver (cyl 1) : t1	ignition on	nbv
		engine cranking, cold	11.0 to 12.0 ms
		engine cranking, hot	> 3.1 ms
		engine running:	
		cold idle	> 4.5 ms
		hot idle	3.1 to 3.3 ms
E6	injector driver (cyl 4) : t1	ignition on	nbv
		engine cranking, cold	11.0 to 12.0 ms
		engine cranking, hot	> 3.1 ms
		engine running:	
		cold idle	> 4.5 ms
		hot idle	3.1 to 3.3 ms
E7	earth (injectors driver)	ignition on/engine running	0.25 V (max)
E9	earth (OS)	ignition on/engine running	0.25 V (max)
E10	AT torque control signal		data not available
E14	amplifier control signal EST A (cyls 1 & 4)	engine cranking/running	0 to nbv (switching)
E16	supply from ignition switch : t15	ignition on/engine running	nbv

Section F

Pin	Item	Test Condition	Measurements
F1	EGR solenoid valve driver : tA	ignition on	nbv
		engine running:	
		EGR inactive	nbv
		EGR active	1.25 V (max)
F2	EGR valve lift signal : tC	ignition on/engine running:	
		EGR valve closed	1.20 V
		EGR valve fully open	4.30 V
F3	supply from ignition switch : t15	ignition on/engine running	nbv
F5	TPS signal : tC	ignition on/engine running:	
		throttle closed	0.3 to 0.9 V
		throttle fully open	4.2 to 4.8 V
F7	earth (injectors driver)	ignition on/engine running	0.25 V (max)
F8	sensor supply (MAP : tC, TPS: tA, EGR solenoid : tD)	ignition on/engine running	5.0 V ± 0.1

Pin Table – GM-Multec MPi-S (Corsa 95-97, X14XE) (continued)

Section F (continued)

Pin	Item	Test Condition	Measurements
F9	OS signal : t3	ignition on, OS multiplug disconnected	0.4 to 0.5 V
		engine running, hot	200 to 1000 mV (switching)
		throttle fully-open	0.5 to 1.0 V
		deceleration (fuel cut-off)	0 to 0.5 V
		switching frequency	1 sec intervals (approx.)
F10	VSS signal : t1	vehicle in motion	0 to 12 V (switching)
F11	SD connector : tG		data not available
F14	amplifier control signal EST B (cyls 2 & 3)	engine cranking/running	0 to nbv (switching)
F15	sensor return (ATS: t1, MAP: tA)	ignition on/engine running	0.25 V (max)
F16	earth	ignition on/engine running	0.25 V (max)

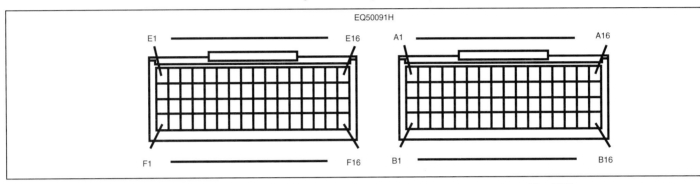

EQ50091H

64 pin ECM multi-plug, GM Multec MPi-S (Corsa 95-97, X14XE)

Pin Table – GM-Multec MPi-S (Vectra, X16XEL)

Section A

Pin	Item	Test Condition	Measurements
A1	stepper motor : tC	idle speed, active	0 to nbv (switching)
A2	stepper motor : tD	idle speed, active	0 to nbv (switching)
A3	stepper motor : tB	idle speed, active	0 to nbv (switching)
A4	stepper motor : tA	idle speed, active	0 to nbv (switching)
A5	CID (camshaft) sensor signal : tB	engine running	0 to nbv (switching)
A6	supply from battery : t30	ignition off/on/engine running	nbv
A7	MAP sensor signal : tB	ignition on	4.5 to 4.9 V
		engine running:	
		WOT	4.5 to 4.9 V
		idle speed	1.6 V ± 0.6
A8	A/C		data not available
A9	AT control unit		data not available
A10	secondary air relay driver : t85	engine running:	
		non-active	nbv
		engine running, cold (first 3-4 minutes.)	1.25 V (max)
A11	secondary air solenoid valve driver : t1	engine running:	
		Secondary air inactive	nbv
		engine running, cold (first 3-4 minutes.)	1.25 V (max)
A12	fuel pump relay driver : t85	ignition on	nbv
		engine cranking/running	1.25 V (max)
A13	CFSV driver : t1	ignition on	nbv
		engine running, above idle, operating temperature:	
		CFSV inactive	nbv
		CFSV active	0 to 12 V (switching)
		duty cycle	0 to 99%
A15	A/C compressor relay driver		data not available
A16	CAS sensor : t2	engine cranking/running	0.25 V (max)

Section B

Pin	Item	Test Condition	Measurements
B1	main ECM earth	ignition on/engine running	0.25 V (max)
B2	sensor return (CTS: t1, TPS : tB, EGR : tB)	ignition on/engine running	0.25 V (max)
B3	CTS signal : t2	ignition on/engine running	20° C: 2.00 to 2.50 V
			45° C: 1.20 and 3.70 V
			70° C: 2.75 to 3.00 V
			85° C: 2.21 V
			100 to 110° C: 1.43 to 2.00 V
B4	ATS signal : t2	ignition on/engine running	20° C: 2.00 to 2.50 V
			60 to 80° C: 3.05 to 2.40 V
B5	A/C pressure switch		data not available
B8	P/N lever position switch		data not available
B9	SD connector : tB		data not available
B10	SD warning lamp	ignition on, lamp on	1.25 V (max)
		engine running:	
		no faults present	nbv
		faults present, lamp on	1.25 V (max)
B13	tachometer		data not available
B14	CAS signal : t1	engine cranking:	> 4.0 V AC (peak to peak)
		idle:	> 8.0 V AC (peak to peak)
		cruise:	> 14.0 V AC (peak to peak)

Section C

Pin	Item	Test Condition	Measurements
C2	injector driver (cyl 3) : t1	ignition on	nbv
		engine cranking, cold	11.0 to 12.0 ms
		engine cranking, hot	> 3.1 ms
		engine running:	
		cold idle	> 4.5 ms
		hot idle	3.1 to 3.3 ms
C3	injector driver (cyl 2) : t1	ignition on	nbv
		engine cranking, cold	11.0 to 12.0 ms
		engine cranking, hot	> 3.1 ms
		engine running:	
		cold idle	> 4.5 ms
		hot idle	3.1 to 3.3 ms
C4	injector driver (cyl 1) : t1	ignition on	nbv
		engine cranking, cold	11.0 to 12.0 ms
		engine cranking, hot	> 3.1 ms
		engine running:	
		cold idle	> 4.5 ms
		hot idle	3.1 to 3.3 ms
C6	injector driver (cyl 4) : t1	ignition on	nbv
		engine cranking, cold	11.0 to 12.0 ms
		engine cranking, hot	> 3.1 ms
		engine running:	
		cold idle	> 4.5 ms
		hot idle	3.1 to 3.3 ms
C7	earth (injectors final stage)	engine running	0.25 V (max)
C9	earth (OS)	engine running	0.25 V (max)
C10	AT torque control signal		data not available
C11	KS signal : t2	engine running, KS active	1.0 V (approx.)
C14	amplifier control signal EST A (cyls 1&4) : t3	engine cranking/running	0 to 5.0 V (switching)
C16	supply from ignition switch : t15	ignition on/engine running	nbv

Section D

Pin	Item	Test Condition	Measurements
D1	EGR solenoid valve driver : tA	ignition on	nbv
		engine running:	
		EGR inactive	nbv
		EGR active	1.25 V (max)

Pin Table – GM-Multec MPi-S (Vectra, X16XEL) (continued)

Section D (continued)

Pin	Item	Test Condition	Measurements
D2	EGR valve lift signal : tC	ignition on/engine running:	
		no vacuum	1.20 V
		200 mm Hg, vacuum	4.30 V
D3	supply from ignition switch : t15	ignition on/engine running	nbv
D5	TPS signal : tC	ignition on/engine running:	
		throttle closed	0.3 to 0.9 V
		throttle fully open	4.2 to 4.8 V
D7	earth (injectors driver)	ignition on/engine running	0.25 V (max)
D8	sensor supply (MAP: tC, TPS : tA, EGR solenoid: tD)	ignition on/engine running	5.0 V ± 0.1
D9	OS signal : t3	ignition on, OS multiplug disconnected	0.4 to 0.5 V
		engine running, hot	200 to 1000 mV (switching)
		throttle fully-open	0.5 to 1.0 V
		deceleration (fuel cut-off)	0 to 0.5 V
		switching frequency	1 sec intervals (approx.)
D10	VSS signal : t1	vehicle in motion	0 to 12 V (switching)
D11	SD connector : tG		data not available
D14	amplifier control signal EST B (cyls 2&3) : t4	engine cranking/running	0 to 5.0 V (switching)
D15	sensor return (ATS: t1, MAP: tA)	ignition on/engine running	0.25 V (max)
D16	earth	ignition on/engine running	0.25 V (max)

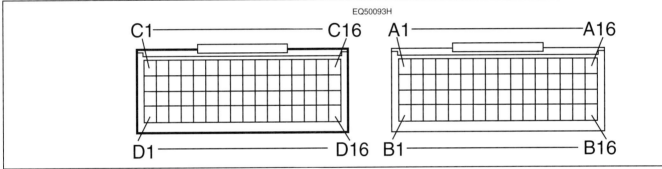

EQ50093H

C1 — C16 A1 — A16
D1 — D16 B1 — B16

64 pin ECM multi-plug, GM Multec MPi-S (Vectra X16XEL)

Pin Table – Simtec 56

Pin	Connection	Test condition	Measurements
1	KS return : t1	engine running, KS active	0.25 V (max)
2	sensor return (CAS : t3, camshaft sensor : t3)	ignition on/engine running	0.25 V (max)
3	CAS oscillator signal : t2	ignition on rotate engine by hand	2.0 V AC (peak to peak)
4	Camshaft oscillator signal : t2	ignition on rotate engine by hand	2.0 V AC (peak to peak)
5	CTS signal : t2	ignition on/engine running	20° C: 3.50 V (approx) 85° C: 1.40 V (approx)
6	ATS signal : t2	ignition on/engine running	20° C: 1.75 V (approx)
7	OS signal : tB	ignition on	5.0 V
		engine running, hot	400 to 3850 mV (switching)
		throttle fully-open	> 3.85 V
		deceleration (fuel cut-off)	< 400 mV
		switching frequency	1 Hz
8	MAF sensor return : t4	ignition on/engine running	0.25 V (max)
9	earth	ignition on/engine running	0.25 V (max)
10-11	–		

Pin	Connection	Test condition	Measurements
12	AC compressor switch	engine running at idle, normal operating temperature:	
		A/C active	nbv
		A/C inactive or not fitted	0 V
13	SD connector : t B		data not available
14	trip computer		data not available
15	fuel pump relay driver : t85b	ignition on	nbv
		engine cranking/running	1.25 V (max)
16	main relay driver : t85	ignition off	nbv
		ignition on/engine running	1.25 V (max)
17	CFSV driver : t1	ignition on	nbv
		engine running, above idle, operating temperature:	
		CFSV inactive	nbv
		CFSV active	0 to 12 V (switching)
		duty cycle	0 to 99%
18	supply from battery : t30	ignition off/on/engine running	nbv
19	earth	ignition on/engine running	0.25 V (max)
20	KS signal : t2	engine running, KS active	2.0 V AC (peak to peak)
21	CAS modulator signal : t1	ignition on rotate engine by hand	2.0 V AC (peak to peak)
22	camshaft modulator signal : t1	ignition on rotate engine by hand	2.0 V AC (peak to peak)
23	–		
24	earth	ignition on/engine running	0.25 V (max)
25	OS sensor return: tD	engine running	0.25 V (max)
26	TPS signal : t3	ignition on/engine running	
		throttle closed	0.1 to 0.9 V
		throttle fully open	3.9 to 4.9 V
27	MAF sensor signal: t2	engine running:	
		idle speed, 1.8 models	0.25 to 0.67 V
		idle speed, 2.0 models	0.30 to 0.70 V
		3000 rpm	1.2 V (approx)
28	earth	ignition on/engine running	0.25 V (max)
29	VSS signal	vehicle in motion	0 to 12 V (switching)
30	earth	ignition on/engine running	0.25 V (max)
31	A/C	ignition on/engine running:	
		A/C active	nbv
		A/C inactive/not fitted	0 V
32	tachometer		data not available
33	–		
34	TPS supply : t2	engine running	5.0 V ± 0.1
35	SD warning lamp	ignition on, lamp on	1.25 V (max)
		engine running:	
		no faults present	nbv
		faults present, lamp on	1.25 V (max)
36	OS heater driver : tA	engine running	
		OS heater inactive	nbv
		OS heater active	1.25 V (max)
37	supply from relay : t87	ignition on/engine running	nbv
38	ignition coil driver (cyls 2 & 3) : t2	ignition on	nbv
		engine cranking/running	400 V (min)
		dynamic volt drop	2.0 V (max)
39	–		
40	ignition coil driver (cyls 1 & 4) : t1	ignition on	nbv
		engine cranking/running	400 V (min)
		dynamic volt drop	2.0 V (max)
41	earth (MT models)	ignition on/engine running	0.25 V (max)
42-45	–		
46	supply from relay : t87	ignition on	nbv
47	supply from ignition switch : t15	ignition on/engine running	nbv

Pin Table – Simtec 56 (continued)

Pin	Connection	Test condition	Measurements
48	injector driver (cyl 4) : t1	ignition on	nbv
		engine cranking, cold	10.0 ms
		engine running, hot	3.2 ms
		snap acceleration	15 ms
		deceleration	0 ms
49	injector driver (cyl 2) : t1	ignition on	nbv
		engine cranking, cold	10.0 ms
		engine running, hot	3.2 ms
		snap acceleration	15 ms
		deceleration	0 ms
50	injector driver (cyl 1) : t1	ignition on	nbv
		engine cranking, cold	10.0 ms
		engine running, hot	3.2 ms
		snap acceleration	15 ms
		deceleration	0 ms
51	injector driver (cyl 3) : t1	ignition on	nbv
		engine cranking, cold	10.0 ms
		engine running, hot	3.2 ms
		snap acceleration	15 ms
		deceleration	0 ms
52	ISCV driver : t1	ignition on	nbv
		engine running:	
		cold	6.0 to 6.5 V
		hot	7.0 to 9.0 V
		duty cycle, hot	40% approx.
53	A/C cut-off relay driver : t85	engine running at idle, normal operating temperature	
		A/C active	1.25 V (max)
		A/C inactive	nbv
54	–		
55	SD connector : t G		data not available

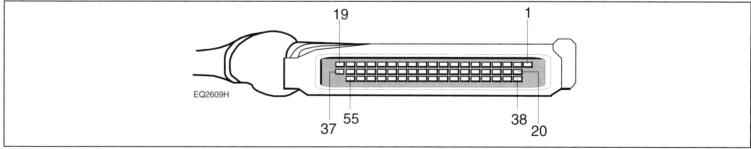

55 pin ECM multi-plug, Simtec 56

Pin Table – Simtec 56.1

Pin	Connection	Test condition	Measurements
1	KS return : t1	engine running, KS active	0.25 V (max)
2	sensor return (CAS : t3, camshaft sensor : t3)	ignition on/engine running	0.25 V (max)
3	CAS oscillator signal : t2	ignition on: rotate engine by hand	2.0 V AC (peak to peak)
4	camshaft oscillator signal : t2	ignition on rotate engine by hand	2.0 V AC (peak to peak)
5	CTS signal : t2	ignition on/engine running	20° C: 3.50 V (approx.) 85° C: 1.40 V (approx.)
6	ATS signal : t2	ignition on/engine running	20° C: 1.75 V (approx.)

Pin	Connection	Test condition	Measurements
7	OS signal : tB	ignition on	5.0 V
		engine running, hot	400 to 3850 mV (switching)
		throttle fully-open	> 3.85 V (constant)
		deceleration (fuel cut-off)	< 400 mV (constant)
		switching frequency	1 Hz
8	MAF sensor return : t4	ignition on/engine running	0.25 V (max)
9	earth	ignition on/engine running	0.25 V (max)
10	torque control (AT models only)	engine hot, idle speed	nbv
		brake depressed, gear selector moved from N to D	0.25 V (max)
11	load signal to AT control unit		data not available
12	A/C compressor switch	engine running at idle, normal operating temperature:	
		A/C active	nbv
		A/C inactive or not fitted	0 V
13	SD connector : tB		data not available
14	trip computer		data not available
15	fuel pump relay driver : t85b	ignition on	nbv
		engine cranking/running	1.25 V (max)
16	main relay driver : t85	ignition off	nbv
		ignition on/engine running	1.25 V (max)
17	CFSV driver : t1	ignition on	nbv
		engine running, above idle, operating temperature:	
		CFSV inactive	nbv
		CFSV active	0 to 12 V (switching)
		duty cycle	0 to 99%
18	supply from battery : t30	ignition off/on/engine running	nbv
19	earth	ignition on/engine running	0.25 V (max)
20	KS signal : t2	engine running, KS active	2.0 V AC (peak to peak)
21	CAS modulator signal : t1	ignition on, rotate engine by hand	2.0 V AC (peak to peak)
22	camshaft modulator signal : t1	ignition on, rotate engine by hand	2.0 V AC (peak to peak)
23	–		
24	earth	ignition on/engine running	0.25 V (max)
25	OS : tD sensor return	engine running	0.25 V (max)
26	TPS signal : t3	ignition on/engine running:	
		throttle closed	0.1 to 0.9 V
		throttle fully open	3.9 to 4.9 V
27	MAF sensor signal : t2	ignition on/engine running:	
		idle speed, 1.8 models	0.25 to 0.67 V
		idle speed, 2.0 models	0.30 to 0.70 V
		3000 rpm	1.2 V
28	earth	ignition on/engine running	0.25 V (max)
29	VSS signal	vehicle in motion	0 to 12 V (switching)
30	MT models (direct earth)	ignition on/engine running	0.25 V (max)
		AT models (earth via P/N switch) ignition on/engine running:	
		gear selector in P or N	0.25 V (max)
		gear selector in R,D,3,2 or 1	nbv
31	A/C	ignition on/engine running:	
		A/C active	nbv
		A/C inactive or not fitted	0 V
32	tachometer		data not available
33	engine compartment relay frame temperature switch		data not available
34	TPS supply : t2	engine running	5.0 V ± 0.1
35	SD warning lamp	ignition on, lamp on	1.25 V (max)
		engine running:	
		no faults present	nbv
		faults present, lamp on	1.25 V (max)
36	OS heater driver : tA	engine running:	
		OS heater inactive	nbv
		OS heater active	1.25 V (max)
37	supply from relay : t87	ignition on/engine running	nbv

Pin Table – Simtec 56.1 (continued)

Pin	Connection	Test condition	Measurements
38	ignition coil driver (cyls 2 & 3)	ignition on	nbv
		engine cranking/running	400 V (min)
		dynamic volt drop	2.0 V (max)
39	programming voltage (not used on vehicle)		
40	ignition coil driver (cyls 1 & 4)	ignition on	nbv
		engine cranking/running	400 V (min)
		dynamic volt drop	2.0 V (max)
41	earth (MT models)	ignition on/engine running	0.25 V (max)
42	EGR control solenoid : t1	ignition on/engine running:	
		EGR non-active	nbv
		EGR active	1.25 V (max)
43	–		
44	secondary air relay driver : t85		
	(also driver for secondary air solenoid).	engine running	nbv
		first 3 to 4 minutes running	
		after cold start	1.25 V (max)
45	–		
46	supply from relay : t87	ignition on/engine running	nbv
47	supply from ignition switch : t15	ignition on/engine running	nbv
48	injector driver (cyl 4) : t1	ignition on	nbv
		engine cranking, cold	10.0 ms
		engine running, hot	3.2 ms
		snap acceleration	15 ms
		deceleration	injector shut off
49	injector driver (cyl 2) : t1	ignition on	nbv
		engine cranking, cold	10.0 ms
		engine running, hot	3.2 ms
		snap acceleration	15 ms
		deceleration	injector shut off
50	injector driver (cyl 1) : t1	ignition on	nbv
		engine cranking, cold	10.0 ms
		engine running, hot	3.2 ms
		snap acceleration	15 ms
		deceleration	injector shut off
51	injector driver (cyl 3) : t1	ignition on	nbv
		engine cranking, cold	10.0 ms
		engine running, hot	3.2 ms
		snap acceleration	15 ms
		deceleration	injector shut off
52	ISCV driver : t1	ignition on	nbv
		engine running:	
		cold	6.0 to 6.5 V
		hot	7.0 to 9.0 V (approx)
		duty cycle, hot	40% (approx.)
53	A/C cut-off relay driver : t85	engine running at idle, normal operating temperature	
		A/C active	1.25 V (max)
		A/C inactive	nbv
54	–		
55	SD connector : tG		data not available

31.22 55 pin ECM multi-plug, Simtec 56.1

Pin Table – Simtec 56.5

Pin	Connection	Test Condition	Measurements
1	SD connector		data not available
2	earth	ignition on/engine running	0.25 V (max)
3	AT load signal to AT control unit		data not available
4	MT models (direct earth)	ignition on/engine running	0.25 V (max)
		AT models (earth via P/N switch)	ignition on/engine running
		gear selector in P or N	0.25 V (max)
		gear selector in R, D, 3, 2 or 1	nbv
5	VSS signal	vehicle in motion	0 to 12 V (switching)
6	torque control (AT models only)	engine hot, idle speed	nbv
		brake depressed, gear selector moved from N to D	0.25 V (max)
7	earth	ignition on/engine running	0.25 V (max)
8	ATS signal : t2	ignition on/engine running	20° C: 1.75 V (approx)
9	A/C compressor switch		data not available
10	OS signal : tD	ignition key on	5.0 V
		engine running, hot	400 to 3850 mV (switching)
		throttle fully-open	> 3.85 V (constant)
		deceleration (fuel cut-off)	< 400 mV constant
		switching frequency	1 Hz
11	earth	ignition on/engine running	0.25 V (max)
12	KS signal : t2	engine running, KS active	2.0 V AC (peak to peak)
13	camshaft modulator signal : t1	ignition on, rotate engine by hand	2.0 V AC (peak to peak)
14	AFS return : t4	ignition on/engine running	0.25 V (max)
15	AFS earth : t1	engine running	0.25 V (max)
16	CAS oscillator signal : t2	ignition on, rotate engine by hand	2.0 V AC (peak to peak)
17	supply from ignition switch : t15	ignition on	nbv
18	TPS supply : t2	engine running	5.0 V ± 0.1
19	earth	ignition on/engine running	0.25 V (max)
20	tachometer		data not available
21	trip computer		data not available
22	SD connector		data not available
23	AC compressor switch		data not available
24	CAS modulator signal : t1	ignition on: rotate engine by hand	2.0 V AC (peak to peak)
25	reduced throttle valve signal (traction control)		data not available
26	TPS signal : t3	ignition on/engine running:	
		throttle closed	0.1 to 0.9 V
		throttle fully-open	3.9 to 4.9 V
27	CTS signal : t2	ignition on/engine running	20° C: 3.50 V
			85° C: 1.40 V
28	–		
29	earth	ignition on/engine running	0.25 V (max)
30	KS earth : t1	engine running, KS active	0.25 V (max)
31	camshaft oscillator signal : t2	ignition on, rotate engine by hand	2.0 V AC (peak to peak)
32	camshaft sensor return : t3	ignition on/engine running	0.25 V (max)
33	MAF sensor signal : t2	engine running:	
		idle speed, 1.8 models	0.25 to 0.67 V
		idle speed, 2.0 models	0.30 to 0.70 V
		3000 rpm	1.2 V (approx)
34	A/C relay		data not available
35	supply from relay : t87	ignition on/engine running	nbv
36	OS return : tB	engine running	0.25 V (max)
37	–		
38	ignition coil driver (cyls 2 & 3)	ignition on	nbv
		engine cranking/running	400 V (min)
		dynamic volt drop	2.0 V (max)
39	ignition coil driver (cyls 1 & 4)	ignition on	nbv
		engine cranking/running	400 V (min)
		dynamic volt drop	2.0 V (max)

Pin Table – Simtec 56.5 (continued)

Pin	Connection	Test Condition	Measurements
40	injector driver (cyl 4) : t1	ignition on	nbv
		engine cranking, cold	10.0 ms
		engine running, hot	3.2 ms
		snap acceleration	15 ms
		deceleration	0 ms
41	injector driver (cyl 2) : t1	ignition on	nbv
		engine cranking, cold	10.0 ms
		engine running, hot	3.2 ms
		snap acceleration	15 ms
		deceleration	0 ms
42	injector driver (cyl 1) : t1	ignition on	nbv
		engine cranking, cold	10.0 ms
		engine running, hot	3.2 ms
		snap acceleration	15 ms
		deceleration	0 ms
43	injector driver (cyl 3) : t1	ignition on	nbv
		engine cranking, cold	10.0 ms
		engine running, hot	3.2 ms
		snap acceleration	15 ms
		deceleration	0 ms
44	supply from relay : t87	ignition on/engine running	nbv
45	EGR control solenoid : t1	ignition on/engine running:	
		inactive	nbv
		active	1.25 V (max)
46	ISCV driver : t1	engine running, idle speed:	
		cold:	6.0 to 6.5 V
		duty cycle	56 to 58%
		hot	7.0 to 9.0 V
		duty cycle	40 to 44%
47	CFSV driver : t1	ignition on	nbv
		engine running:	
		snap accelerate	0 to 8.0 V (switching)
48	OS heater driver : tA	engine running:	
		OS heater inactive	nbv
		OS heater active	1.25 V (max)
49	main relay driver : t85	ignition off	nbv
		ignition on/engine running	1.25 V (max)
50	secondary air relay driver : t85	engine running, hot	nbv
		first 3 to 4 minutes running	
		after cold start	1.25 V (max)
51	–		
52	SD warning lamp	ignition on/engine running:	
		no faults present	nbv
		faults present	0.25 V (max)
53	ICOV driver	ignition on	nbv
		engine running:	
		ICOV inactive	nbv
		ICOV active	1.25 V (max)
54	fuel pump relay driver : t85b	ignition on	nbv
		engine cranking/running	1.25 V (max)
55	supply from battery : t30	ignition off/on/engine running	nbv

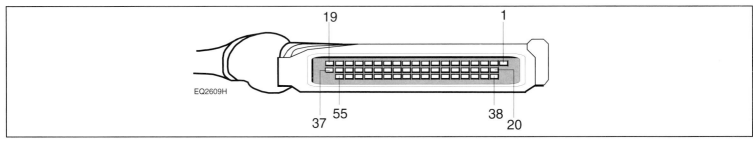

31.23 55 pin ECM multi-plug, Simtec 56.5

Wiring Diagrams

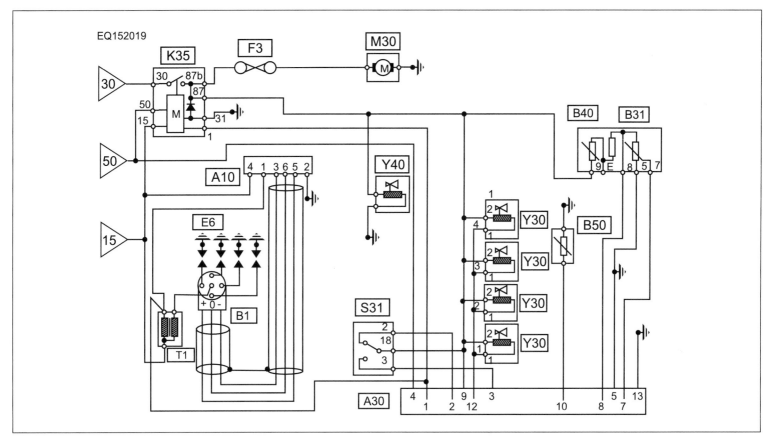

System wiring diagram, Bosch LE2 Jetronic (4-cyl)

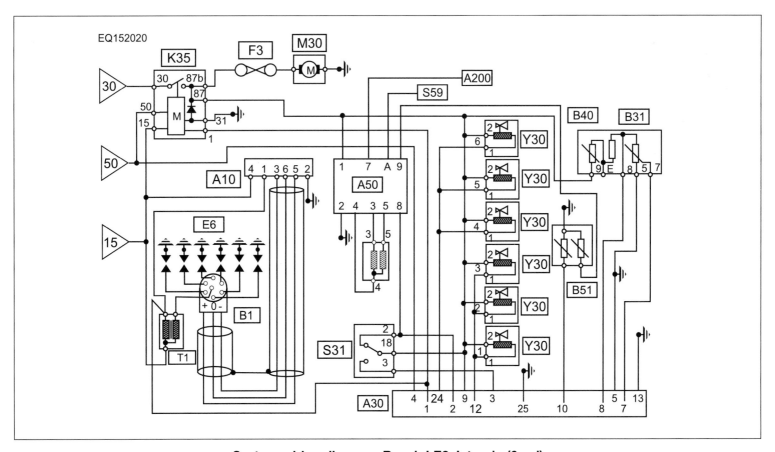

System wiring diagram, Bosch LE2 Jetronic (6-cyl)

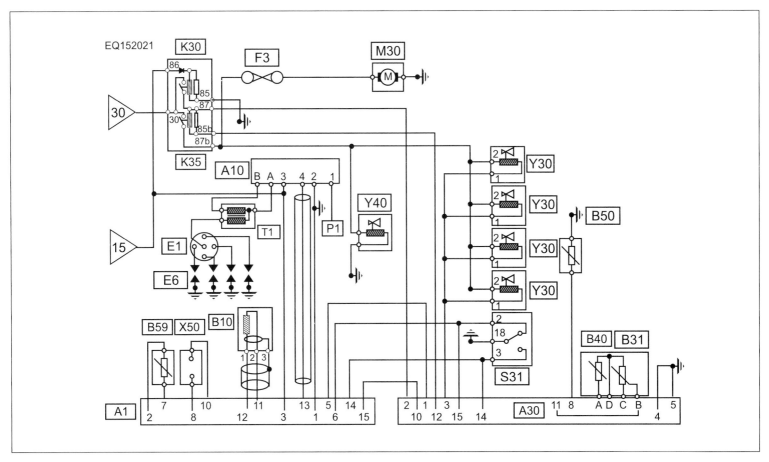

System wiring diagram, Bosch LE3 Jetronic

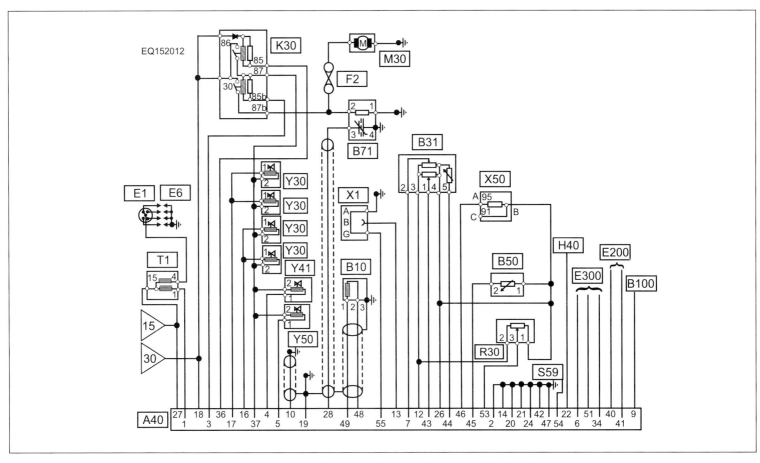

System wiring diagram, Bosch Motronic 1.5 (4-cyl)

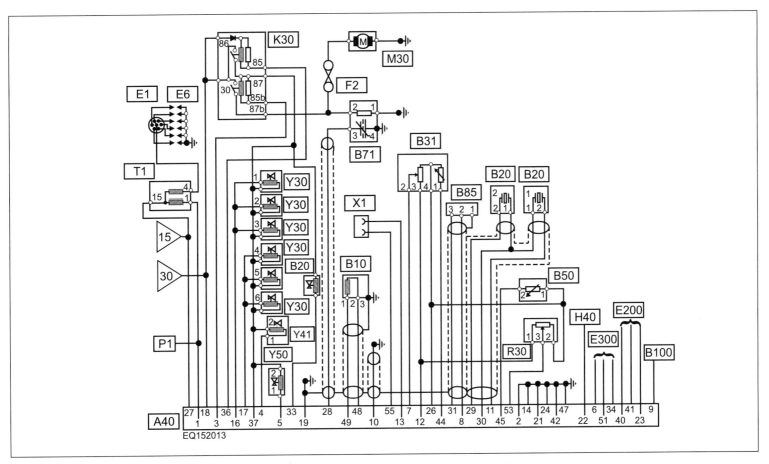

System wiring diagram, Bosch Motronic 1.5 (6-cyl)

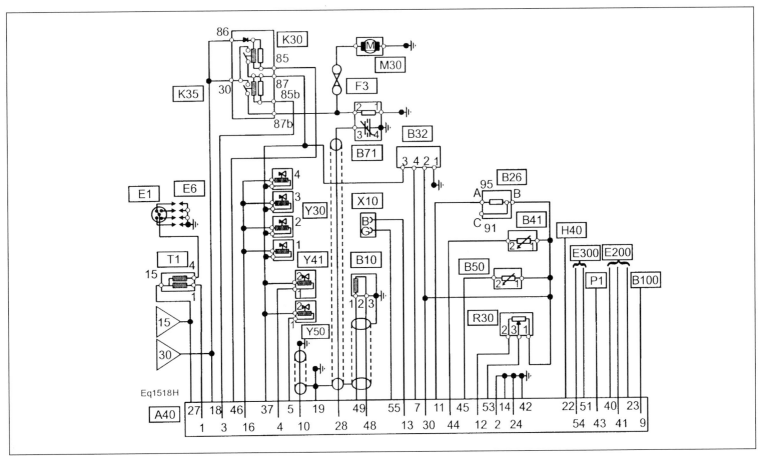

System wiring diagram, Bosch Motronic 1.5.2

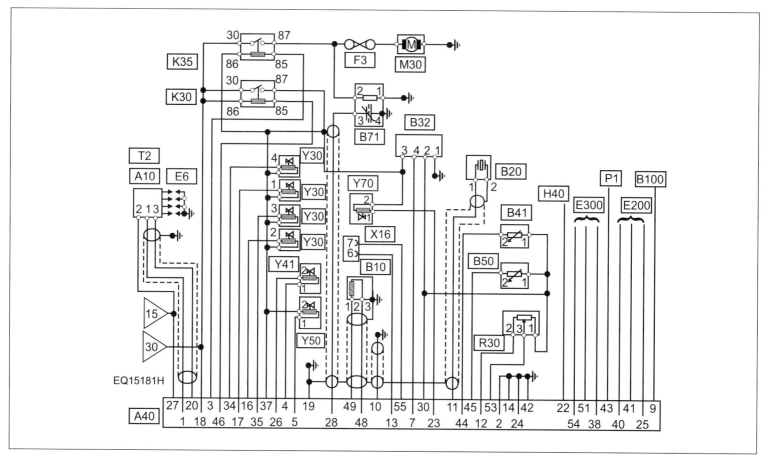

System wiring diagram, Bosch Motronic 1.5.4

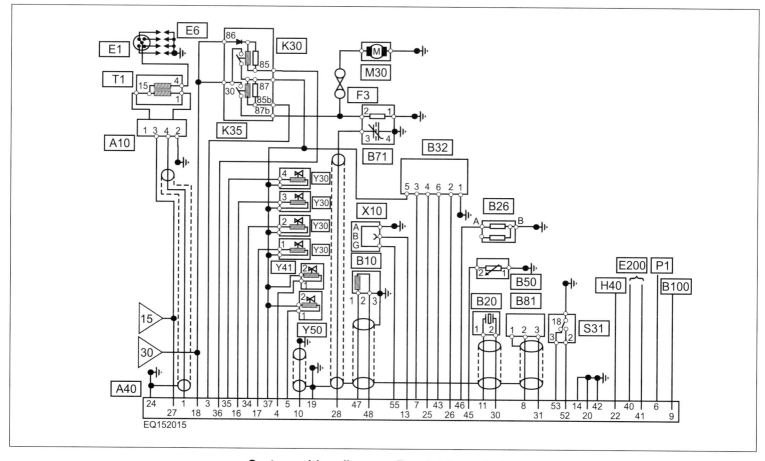

System wiring diagram, Bosch Motronic 2.5

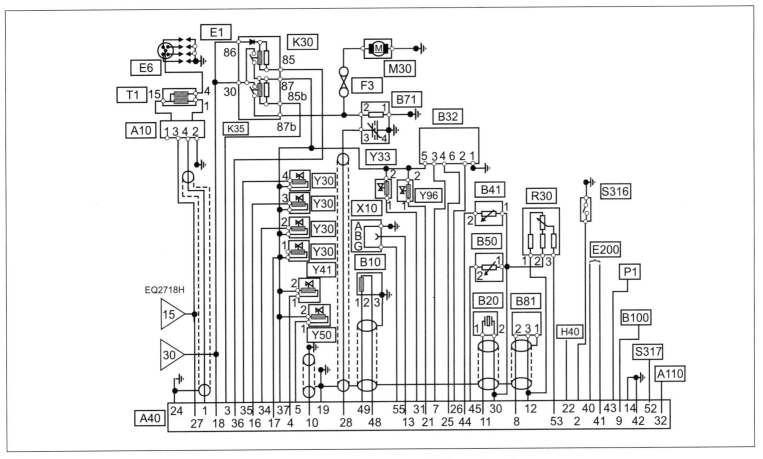

System wiring diagram, Bosch Motronic 2.7

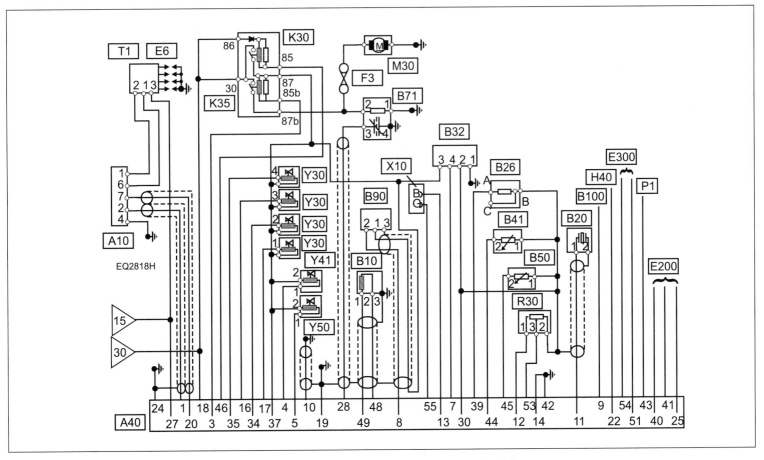

System wiring diagram, Bosch Motronic 2.8

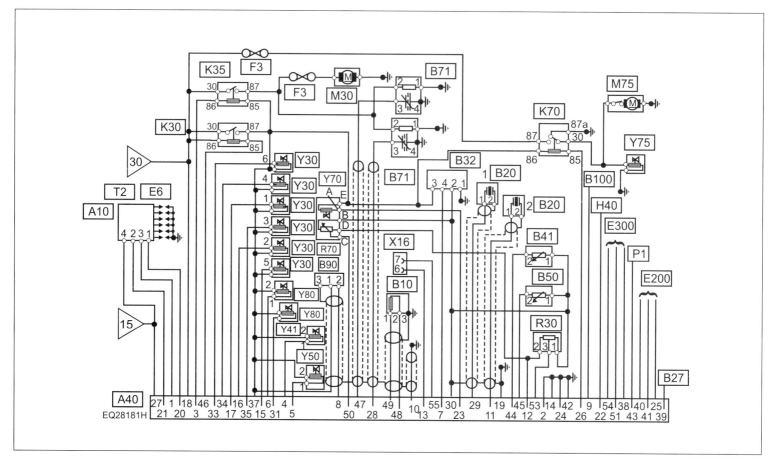

System wiring diagram, Bosch Motronic 2.8.1

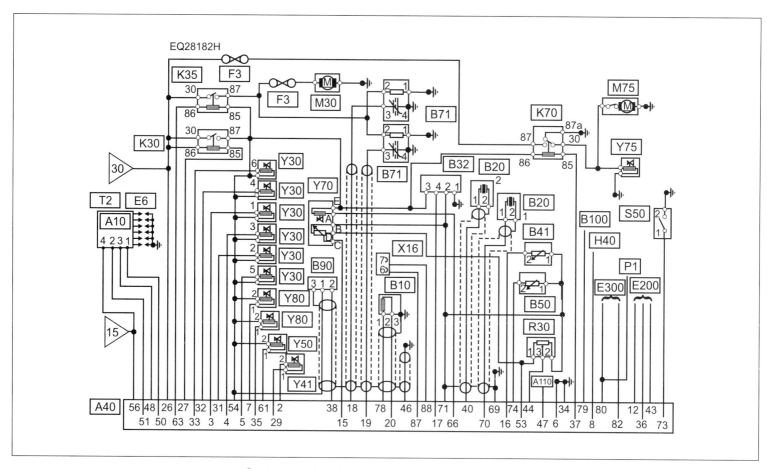

System wiring diagram, Bosch Motronic 2.8.3

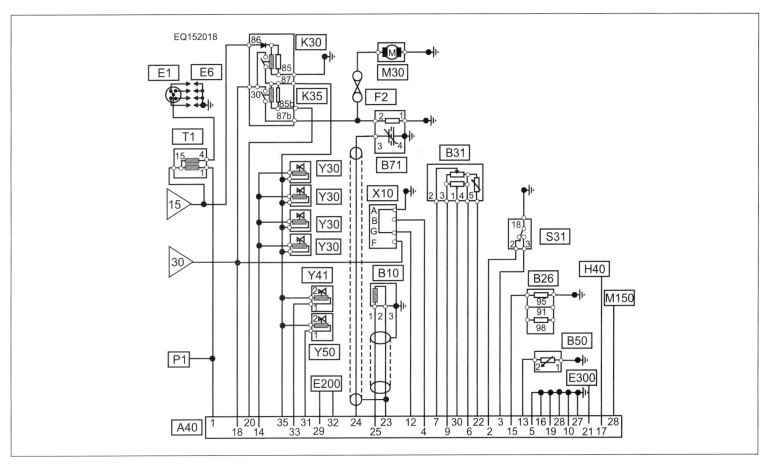

System wiring diagram, Bosch Motronic ML4.1

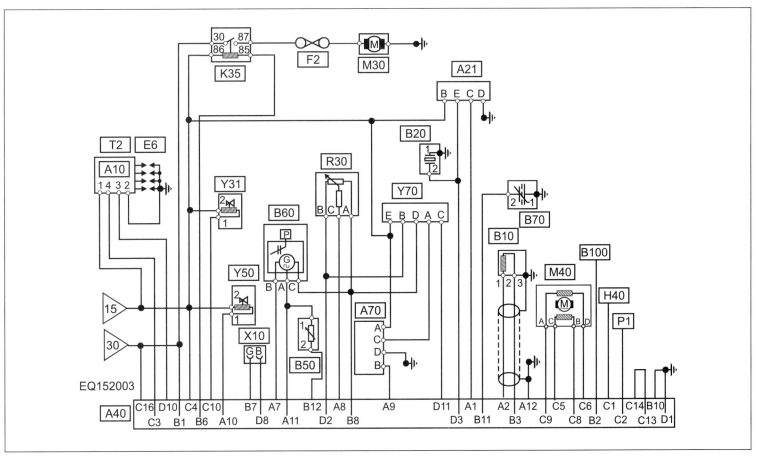

System wiring diagram, GM Multec GM-Multec CFi DIS (Corsa, X12SZ)

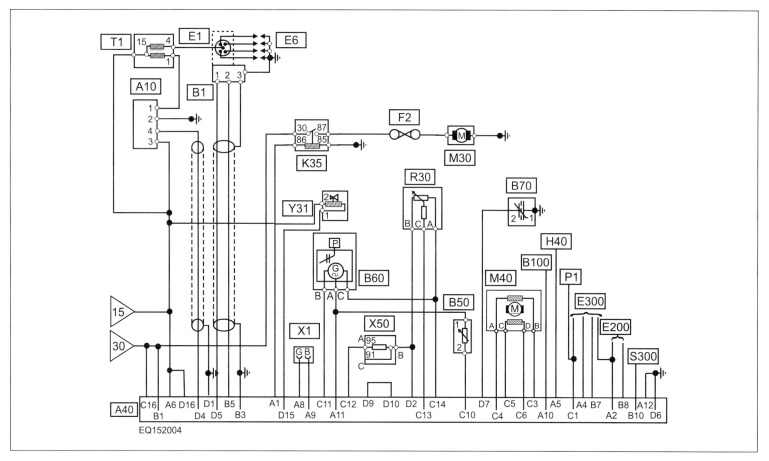

EQ152004

System wiring diagram, GM Multec CFi (Belmont, C16NZ)

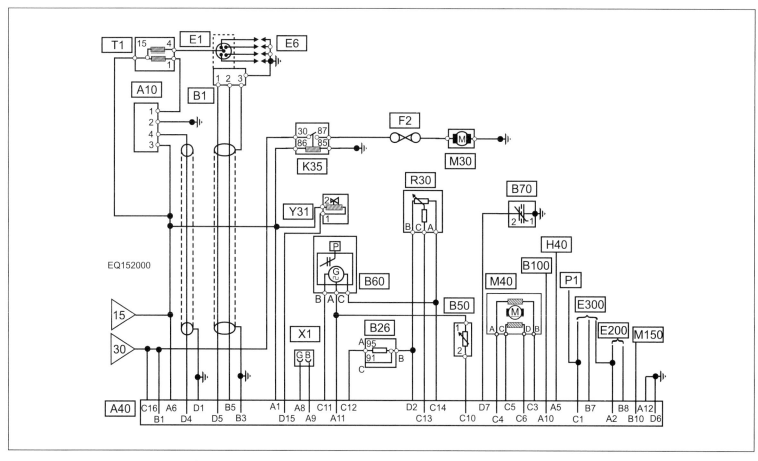

EQ152000

System wiring diagram, GM Multec CFi-HE (Nova 1.2, C12NZ)

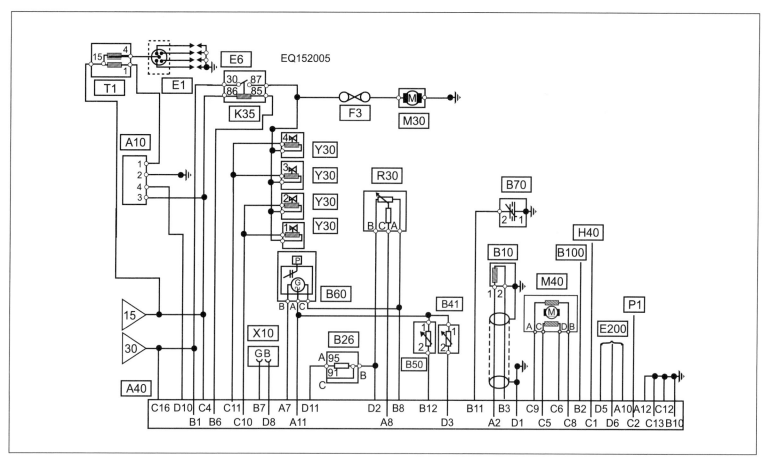

System wiring diagram, GM Multec MPi (Corsa/Nova, C14SE)

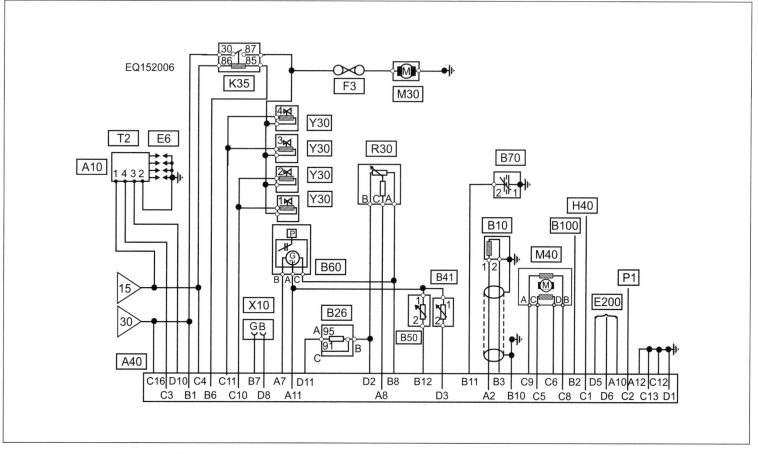

System wiring diagram, GM Multec MPi DIS (Corsa/Nova, C16SE)

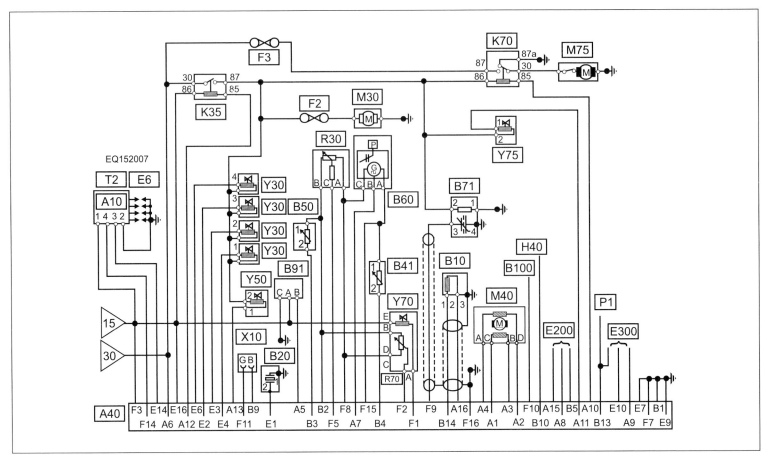

System wiring diagram, GM Multec MPi-S (Corsa 95-97, X14XE)

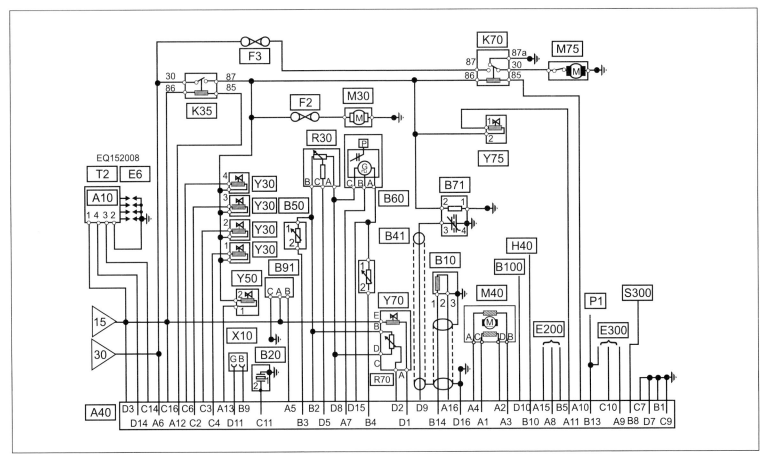

System wiring diagram, GM Multec MPi-S (Vectra X16XEL)

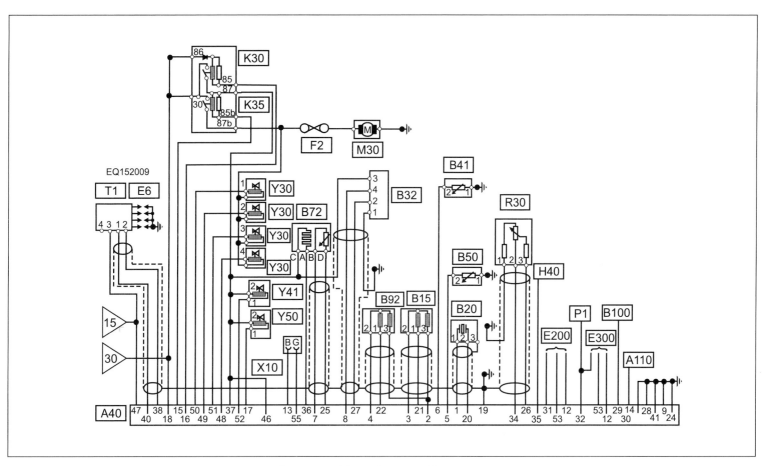

System wiring diagram, Simtec 56

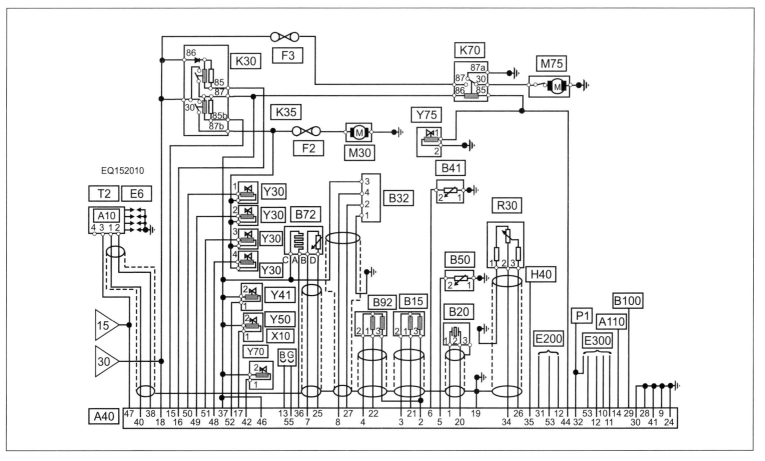

System wiring diagram, Simtec 56.1

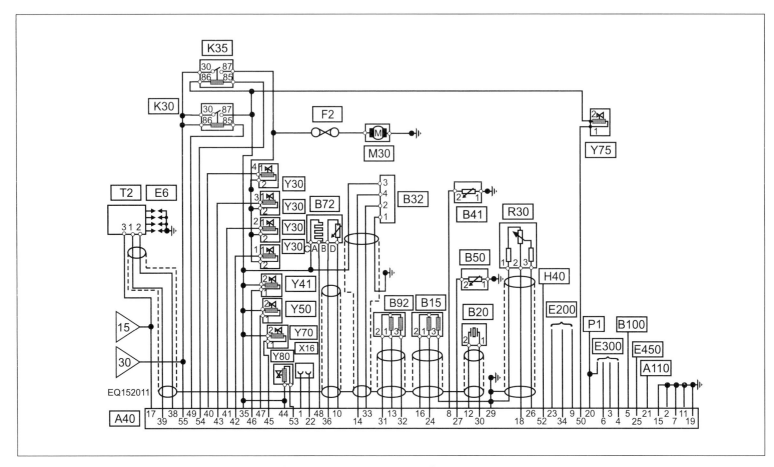

System wiring diagram, Simtec 56.5

Chapter 32
Volkswagen

Contents

Index of Volkswagen vehicles/systems

Model	Engine code	Year	System
Caddy-Pick-Up	AEE	1997 to 1998	Magneti-Marelli 1AV
Caravelle 2.0 and cat	AAC	1990 to 1992	VAG Digifant (38 pin)
Caravelle 2.5i cat	AAF	1991 to 1995	VAG Digifant (38 pin)
Caravelle 2.5i	ACU	1994 to 1997	VAG Digifant (45 pin)
Corrado (G60 supercharger) cat	PG	1992 to 1993	VAG Digifant (38 pin)
Corrado 2.0i 16v	9A	1992 to 1996	Bosch KE1.2 Motronic
Corrado	2E	1993 to 1994	VAG Digifant (45 pin)
Golf 1.3i cat	AAV	1991 to 1992	Bosch Mono-Motronic 1.2.1
Golf 1.3i cat	AAV	1991 to 1992	Bosch Mono-Motronic 1.2.3
Golf 1.3i cat	AAV	1991 to 1992	Bosch Mono-Motronic 1.3
Golf 1.4 MPi	**AEX**	**1995 to 1997**	**Bosch Motronic MP9.0**
Golf 1.4i cat	ABD	1991 to 1994	Bosch Mono-Motronic 1.2.3
Golf 1.4i cat	ABD	1991 to 1994	Bosch Mono-Motronic 1.3
Golf 1.4i cat	ABD	1991 to 1994	Bosch Mono-Motronic 1.2.1
Golf 1.6 8V	**AFT**	**1996 to 1997**	**Simos 4S2**
Golf 1.6i 8V	**AEE**	**1995 to 1997**	**Magneti-Marelli 1AV**
Golf 1.6i cat	ABU	1992 to 1994	Bosch Mono-Motronic 1.2.3
Golf 1.6i cat	ABU	1992 to 1994	Bosch Mono-Motronic 1.2.1
Golf 1.6i cat	ABU	1992 to 1994	Bosch Mono-Motronic 1.3
Golf 1.8i cat	AAM	1991 to 1994	Bosch Mono-Motronic 1.2.3
Golf 1.8i cat	AAM	1991 to 1994	Bosch Mono-Motronic 1.3
Golf 1.8i cat	ABS	1991 to 1994	Bosch Mono-Motronic 1.2.3
Golf 1.8i cat	ABS	1991 to 1994	Bosch Mono-Motronic 1.3
Golf 1.8i cat	RV	1987 to 1991	VAG Digifant (45 pin)
Golf 2.0i 16v cat	ABF	1992 to 1997	VAG Digifant (68 pin)

Index of Volkswagen vehicles/systems (continued)

Model	Engine code	Year	System
Golf 2.8i VR6	**AAA**	**1991 to 1992**	**Bosch Motronic 2.7**
Golf cabrio	2H	1989 to 1993	VAG Digifant (45 pin)
Golf Syncro 2.9	ABV	1994 to 1997	Bosch Motronic 2.9
Golf VR6 2.8i	**AAA**	**1991 to 1992**	**Bosch Motronic 2.9**
Golf VR6	AAA	1992 to 1997	Bosch Motronic 2.9
Golf	**2E**	**1991 to 1994**	**VAG Digifant (45 pin)**
Jetta 1.8i cat	RV	1987 to 1991	VAG Digifant (45 pin)
Jetta 2.0i 16v	9A	1989 to 1992	Bosch KE1.2 Motronic
Passat 1.6l	AEK	1994 to 1996	Bosch Motronic 2.9
Passat 1.8i cat	AAM	1990 to 1994	Bosch Mono-Motronic 1.2.3
Passat 1.8i cat	AAM	1990 to 1994	Bosch Mono-Motronic 1.3
Passat 1.8i cat	ABS	1991 to 1994	Bosch Mono-Motronic 1.2.3
Passat 1.8i cat	ABS	1991 to 1994	Bosch Mono-Motronic 1.3
Passat 1.8i& cat	RP	1990 to 1991	Bosch Mono-Motronic 1.2.3
Passat 1.8i& cat	RP	1990 to 1991	Bosch Mono-Motronic 1.3
Passat 2.0i & 4x4 cat	2E	1990 to 1992	VAG Digifant (38 pin)
Passat 2.0i & 4x4 cat	**2E**	**1992 to 1994**	**VAG Digifant (38 pin)**
Passat 2.0i 16v GT/GL cat	**9A**	**1988 to 1993**	**Bosch KE1.2 Motronic**
Passat 2.0i cat	**ABF**	**1994 to 1995**	**VAG Digifant (68 pin)**
Passat 2.8 VR6	AAA	1993 to 1996	Bosch Motronic 2.9
Passat 2.8i VR6	AAA	1991 to 1992	Bosch Motronic 2.7
Passat 2.9 Syncro	ABV	1994 to 1996	Bosch Motronic 2.9
Passat VR6	AAA	1991 to 1993	Bosch Motronic 2.9
Polo 1.05i cat	**AAK**	**1989 to 1990**	**Bosch Mono-Jetronic A2.2**
Polo 1.05i cat	**AAU**	**1990 to 1994**	**Bosch Mono-Motronic 1.2.1**
Polo 1.05i cat	**AAU**	**1990 to 1994**	**Bosch Mono-Motronic 1.2.3**
Polo 1.05i cat	AAU	1990 to 1994	Bosch Mono-Motronic 1.3
Polo 1.0i cat	AEV	1994 to 1995	Bosch Mono-Motronic 1.2.3
Polo 1.0i cat	AEV	1994 to 1995	Bosch Mono-Motronic 1.3
Polo 1.3i cat	AAV	1991 to 1994	Bosch Mono-Motronic 1.2.1
Polo 1.3i cat	AAV	1991 to 1994	Bosch Mono-Motronic 1.2.3
Polo 1.3i cat	AAV	1991 to 1994	Bosch Mono-Motronic 1.3
Polo 1.3i cat	ADX	1994 to 1995	Bosch Mono-Motronic 1.2.3
Polo 1.3i cat	**ADX**	**1994 to 1995**	**Bosch Mono-Motronic 1.3**
Polo 1.3i cat	ADX	1994 to 1995	Bosch Mono-Motronic 1.3
Polo 1.4 16V	AFH	1996 to 1997	Magneti-Marelli 1AV
Polo 1.4 8V 44kW	AEX	1995 to 1997	Bosch Motronic MP9.0
Polo 1.6i 8V	AEE	1995 to 1997	Magneti-Marelli 1AV
Polo 1.6i cat	AEA	1994 to 1995	Bosch Mono-Motronic 1.2.3
Polo 1.6i cat	AEA	1994 to 1995	Bosch Mono-Motronic 1.3
Polo Classic/Caddy 1.4	AEX	1996 to 1997	Bosch Motronic MP9.0
Transporter 2.0 and cat	AAC	1990 to 1992	VAG Digifant (38 pin)
Transporter 2.5i cat	AAF	1991 to 1995	VAG Digifant (38 pin)
Vento	**2E**	**1991 to 1994**	**VAG Digifant (45 pin)**
Vento 1.4 MPi	AEX	1995 to 1997	Bosch Motronic MP9.0
Vento 1.4i cat	ABD	1991 to 1994	Bosch Mono-Motronic 1.2.3
Vento 1.4i cat	ABD	1991 to 1994	Bosch Mono-Motronic 1.3
Vento 1.6i 8V	AEE	1995 to 1997	Magneti-Marelli 1AV
Vento 1.6i cat	ABU	1992 to 1994	Bosch Mono-Motronic 1.2.3
Vento 1.6i cat	ABU	1992 to 1994	Bosch Mono-Motronic 1.3
Vento 1.8i cat	AAM	1991 to 1994	Bosch Mono-Motronic 1.2.3
Vento 1.8i cat	AAM	1991 to 1994	Bosch Mono-Motronic 1.3
Vento 1.8i cat	ABS	1991 to 1994	Bosch Mono-Motronic 1.2.3
Vento 1.8i cat	ABS	1991 to 1994	Bosch Mono-Motronic 1.3
Vento 2.0i 16v cat	ABF	1992 to 1995	VAG Digifant (68 pin)
Vento 2.8i VR6	AAA	1991 to 1992	Bosch Motronic 2.7
Vento VR6	AAA	1992 to 1997	Bosch Motronic 2.9

Note: *The vehicles accentuated in bold type are the actual vehicles upon which the ECM pin tables and wiring diagrams are based. Other vehicle with the same system may be similar; but are also likely to contain some differences.*

Pin Table – Bosch KE1.2 Motronic

Pin	Item	Test Condition	Measurements
1	SD connector		data not available
2	VSS signal	drive wheels rotating	0 to 12 V (switching)
		duty cycle	50 %
3	CTS signal : t2	ignition on/engine running	20° C: 2.5 to 3.0 V
			80° C: 0.3 to 0.6 V
4-5	differential pressure regulator	idle speed, cold	55 to 75 mA (approx)
		idle speed, hot	0 to 1 mA (approx)
		deceleration from 3000 rpm	–40 mA (approx)
6	KS2 signal (rear) : t1	engine running, KS active	1.0 V AC (peak to peak)
7	oxygen sensor signal : t3	ignition on, OS multiplug disconnected	0.4 to 0.5 V
		engine running, hot	200 to 1000 mV (switching)
		throttle fully-open	0.5 to 1.0 V
		deceleration	0 to 0.5 V
8	sensor return (KS1 : t2, KS2 : t2)	ignition on/engine running	0.25 V (max)
9-10	–		
11	amplifier control signal : t2	engine cranking/running	0 to 5.0 V (switching)
12	fuel pump relay driver : t85	ignition on	nbv
		engine cranking/running	1.25 V (max)
13	–		
14	supply from ignition switch : t15	ignition on/engine running	nbv
15	CFSV driver : t1	ignition on	nbv
		engine running, above idle, operating temperature	
		CFSV inactive	nbv
		CFSV active	0 to 12 V (switching)
		duty cycle	0 to 99%
16	cold start valve (CSV) : t1	ignition on	nbv
		engine cranking:	
		CSV non-active	nbv
		CSV active	1.25 V (max)
17	ISCV driver : t1	ignition on	nbv
		engine running, idle speed:	
		hot	0 to 12.0 V (switching)
18	earth	ignition on/engine running	0.25 V (max)
19	supply from battery : t30	ignition off/on/engine running	nbv
20	earth	ignition on/engine running	0.25 V (max)
21	HES supply : t+	ignition on/engine running	5.0 V
22	SD connector		data not available
23	AFS signal : t2	ignition on:	
		voltage range	0.1 to 4.5 V
		open/close sensor plate	voltage increase/decrease
24	KS1 signal (front) : t1	engine running, KS active	1.0 V AC (peak to peak)
25	tachometer		data not available
26	AFS supply : t1	ignition on/engine running	5.0 V ± 0.1
27	TDC return : t2	ignition on/engine running	0.25 V (max)
28	idle switch : t1	ignition on/engine running:	
		throttle closed	0 V
		throttle open	12 V
29	TDC signal : t1	engine cranking	> 2.0 V AC (peak to peak)
		Idle speed	> 11.0 V AC (peak to peak)
		3000 rpm:	> 14.0 V AC (peak to peak)
30	HES signal : tO	engine running, hot	0 to 5.0 V (switching)
		duty cycle	35%
31	automatic transmission		data not available
32	full load position switch : t3	ignition on/engine running:	
		throttle closed/part open	12 V
		throttle fully open	0 V
33	air conditioning		data not available
34	earth	ignition on/engine running	0.25 V (max)
35	earth	ignition on/engine running	0.25 V (max)

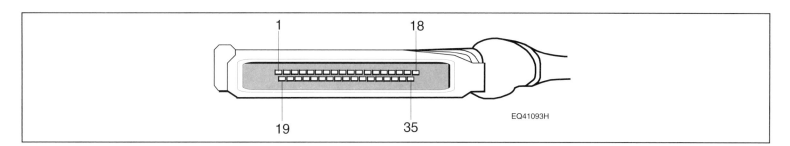

35 pin ECM multi-plug, Bosch KE1.2 Motronic

Pin Table – Bosch Mono-Jetronic A2.2

Pin	Connection	Test condition	Measurements
1	amplifier control signal : t7	engine cranking/running	0 to 12 V (switching)
2	CTS signal : t2	ignition on/engine running	20° C: 2.5 to 3.0 V
			80° C: 0.3 to 0.6 V
3	idle switch (stepper motor : t3)	ignition on/engine running:	
		idle switch closed	0.25 V (max)
		idle switch open	nbv
4	supply from battery : t30	ignition off/on/engine running	nbv
5	earth	ignition on/engine running	0.25 V (max)
6	–		
7	TPS signal : t2	ignition on/engine running:	
		throttle closed	1.0 V
		throttle fully open	4.0 V
8	TPS supply: t5	ignition on/engine running	5.0 V ± 0.1
9	supply from ignition switch : t15	ignition on/engine running	nbv
10-11	–		
12	CFSV driver : t1	engine running, above idle, operating temperature:	
		CFSV inactive	nbv
		CFSV active	0 to 12 V (switching)
		duty cycle	0 to 99%
13	Injector driver : t1	engine running, hot	1.6 ms
		deceleration	0 ms
14	ATS signal : t1	ignition on/engine running	20° C: 2.5 to 3.0 V
			80° C: 0.3 to 0.6 V
15-16	–		
17	fuel pump relay driver : t85	ignition on	nbv
		engine cranking/running	1.25 V (max)
18	TPS signal : t4	ignition on/engine running:	
		throttle closed	0 V
		throttle fully open	4.00 V (approx)
19	–		
20	OS signal : t3	ignition on, OS multiplug disconnected	0.4 to 0.5 V
		engine running, hot	200 to 1000 mV (switching)
		throttle fully open	0.5 to 1.0 V
		deceleration (fuel cut off)	0 to 0.5 V
		switching frequency	1 sec intervals (approx)
21	–		
22	SD warning lamp/SD connector	ignition on, lamp check	1.25 V (max)
		engine running:	
		no faults present	nbv
		faults present, lamp on	1.25 V (max)
23	stepper motor : t2	idle speed, active	0 to 5.0 V (switching)
24	stepper motor : t1	idle speed, active	0 to 5.0 V (switching)
25	earth	ignition on/engine running	0.25 V (max)

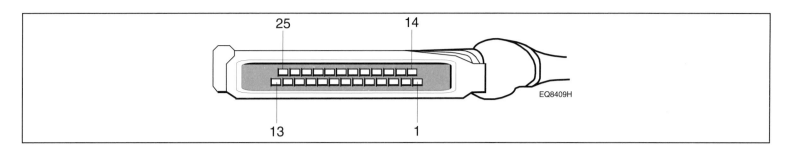

35 pin ECM multi-plug, Bosch Mono-Jetronic A2.2

Pin Table – Bosch Mono-Motronic 1.2.1

Pin	Connection	Test condition	Measurements
1	main ECM earth	ignition on/engine running	0.25 V (max)
2	supply from battery : t30	ignition off/on/engine running	nbv
3-4	–		
5	HES signal : t2	ignition on:	
		multiplug disconnected	5.0 to 10.0 V
		trigger vane cut out space in air gap	< 700 mV.
		trigger vane diverting hall voltage	5.0 to 10.0 V
		engine running	5.0 to 7.0 V
6	HES supply voltage : t3	ignition on/engine running	9.0 V (min)
7	–		
8	sensor return (CTS, ATS, TPS : t1)	ignition on/engine running	0.25 V (max)
9	–		
10	CTS signal : t2	ignition on/engine running	20° C: 2.0 to 2.5 V
			80° C: 0.2 to 0.6 V
11	earth	ignition on/engine running	0.25 V (max)
12	fuel pump relay driver : t85	ignition on	nbv
		engine cranking/running	1.25 V (max)
13	amplifier control signal : t2	engine cranking/running	0 to 12 V (switching)
14	–		
15	manifold heater relay driver : t85	engine running:	
		cold, > 55°C	1.25 V (max)
		hot, < 65°C	nbv
16	stepper motor : t2	idle speed, active	0 to 5.0 V (switching)
17	CFSV driver : t1	ignition on	nbv
		engine running, above idle, operating temperature:	
		CFSV inactive	nbv
		CFSV active	0 to 12 V (switching)
		duty cycle	0 to 99%
18	earth (final stage drivers)	ignition on/engine running	0.25 V (max)
19	supply from ignition switch : t15	ignition on/engine running	nbv
20-21	–		
22	SD connector		data not available
23	SD connector		data not available
24	TPS supply : t5	ignition on/engine running	5.0 V ± 0.1
25	TPS signal : t2	ignition on/engine running:	
		throttle closed	1.0 V
		throttle fully open	4.50 V (approx)
26	TPS signal : t4	ignition on/engine running:	
		throttle closed	0.0 V
		throttle fully open	4.00 V (approx)
27	ATS signal : t4	ignition on/engine running	20° C: 2.0 to 2.5 volts
			80° C: 0.2 to 0.6 volts
28	OS signal : t3	ignition on, OS multiplug disconnected	0.4 to 0.5 V
		engine running, hot	200 to 1000 mV (switching)
		throttle fully open	0.5 to 1.0 V
		deceleration (fuel cut-off)	0 to 0.5 V
		switching frequency	1 sec intervals (approx)

Pin Table – Bosch Mono-Motronic 1.2.1 (continued)

Pin	Connection	Test condition	Measurements
29	–		
30	idle switch (ISSM : t3)	ignition on/engine running:	
		throttle closed	0 V
		throttle open	nbv
31	instrument panel		data not available
32-33	–		
34	stepper motor : t1	idle speed, active	0 to 5.0 V (switching)
35	injector driver : t3	engine running, hot	2.0 ms
		deceleration	0 ms

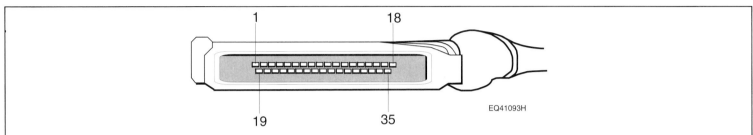

32.3 35 pin ECM multi-plug, Bosch Mono-Motronic 1.2.1

Pin Table – Bosch Mono-Motronic 1.2.3

Pin	Connection	Test condition	Measurements
1	earth	ignition on/engine running	0.25 V (max)
2	stepper motor : t2	idle speed, active	0 to 5.0 V (switching)
3	CFSV driver : t1	ignition on	nbv
		engine running, above idle, operating temperature	
		CFSV inactive	nbv
		CFSV active	0 to 12 V (switching)
		duty cycle	0 to 99%
4-6	–		
7	injector driver : t3	engine running, hot	2.0 ms
		deceleration	0 ms
8	HES supply : t3	engine cranking/running	9.0 V (min)
9	tachometer		data not available
10	idle switch : t3	ignition on/engine running:	
		idle switch closed	0.25 V (max)
		idle switch open	nbv
11	–		
12	earth	ignition on/engine running	0.25 V (max)
13	HES signal : t2	ignition on:	
		multiplug disconnected	5.0 to 10.0 V
		trigger vane cut out space in air gap	< 700 mV.
		trigger vane diverting hall voltage	5.0 to 10.0 V
		engine running	5.0 to 7.0 V
14	TPS supply : t5	ignition on/engine running	5.0 V ± 0.1
15	OS return : t4	ignition on/engine running	0.25 V (max)
16	–		
17	sensor return (CTS : t1, ATS : t4, TPS: t1)	ignition on/engine running	0.25 V (max)
18	TPS signal : t4	ignition on/engine running:	
		throttle closed	0.0 V
		throttle fully open	4.00 V (approx)
19	–		
20	earth	ignition on/engine running	0.25 V (max)
21	supply from battery : t30	ignition on/off/engine running	nbv

Pin	Connection	Test condition	Measurements
22	–		
23	supply from ignition : t15	ignition on/engine running	nbv
24	amplifier control signal : t2	engine cranking/running	0 to 12 V (switching)
25	fuel pump relay driver : t85	ignition on	nbv
		engine cranking/running	1.25 V (max)
26	stepper motor : t1	idle speed, active	0 to 5.0 V (switching)
27	–		
28	manifold heater relay driver : t85	ignition on	nbv
		engine running:	
		engine cold	1.25 V (max)
		engine hot	nbv
29	SD connector		data not available
30-32	–		
33	A/C		data not available
34	–		
35	A/C		data not available
36-37	–		
38	OS signal : t3	ignition on, OS multiplug disconnected	0.4 to 0.5 V
		engine running, hot	200 to 1000 mV (switching)
		throttle fully open	0.5 to 1.0 V
		deceleration (fuel cut-off)	0 to 0.5 V
		switching frequency	1 sec intervals (approx)
39-40	–		
41	TPS signal : t2	ignition on/engine running:	
		throttle closed	1.0 V
		throttle fully open	4.50 V (approx)
42	CTS signal : t2	ignition on/engine running	20° C: 2.0 to 2.5 volts
			80° C: 0.2 to 0.6 volts
43	ATS signal : t4	ignition on/engine running	20° C: 2.0 to 2.5 volts
			80° C: 0.2 to 0.6 volts
44-45	–		

45 pin ECM multi-plug, Bosch Mono-Motronic 1.2.3

Pin Table – Bosch Mono-Motronic 1.3

Pin	Connection	Test condition	Measurements
1	earth	ignition on/engine running	0.25 V (max)
2	stepper motor : t6	idle speed, active	0 to 5.0 V (switching)
3	CFSV driver : t1	ignition off/on	nbv
		engine running, above idle, operating temperature:	
		CFSV inactive	nbv
		CFSV active	0 to 12 V (switching)
		duty cycle	0 to 99%
4-6	–		
7	injector driver : t3	ignition on	nbv briefly, then 0 V
		engine running, hot	2.0 ms
		deceleration	0 ms
8	HES supply : t3	engine cranking/running	9.0 V (min)
9	tachometer, instrument panel		data not available

Pin Table – Bosch Mono-Motronic 1.3 (continued)

Pin	Connection	Test condition	Measurements
10	idle switch : t5	ignition on/engine running:	
		idle switch closed	0.25 V (max)
		idle switch open	nbv
11	–		
12	earth	ignition on/engine running	0.25 V (max)
13	HES signal : t2	ignition on:	
		multiplug disconnected	5.0 to 10.0 V
		trigger vane cut out space in air gap	< 700 mV.
		trigger vane diverting hall voltage	5.0 to 10.0 V
		engine running	5.0 to 7.0 V
14	TPS supply : t5	ignition on/engine running	5.0 V ± 0.1
15	OS return : t4	ignition on/engine running	0.25 V (max)
16	TVPS signal : t2	idle speed	nbv or 3 V (intermittent)
17	sensor return (ATS : t1, CTS : t1, TPS : t1)	ignition on/engine running	0.25 V (max)
18	TPS signal : t4	ignition on/engine running:	
		throttle closed	0 V
		throttle fully open	4.00 V (approx)
19	KS return : t2	engine running, KS active	0.25 V (max)
20	earth	ignition on/engine running	0.25 V (max)
21	supply from battery : t30	ignition on/off/engine running	nbv
22	–		
23	supply from ignition : t15	ignition on/engine running	nbv
24	amplifier control signal : t2	engine cranking/running	0 to 12 V (switching)
25	fuel pump relay driver : t85	ignition on	nbv
		engine cranking/running	1.25 V (max)
26	stepper motor : t1	idle speed, active	0 to 5.0 V (switching)
27	–		
28	manifold heater relay driver : t86	ignition on	nbv
		engine cold	1.25 V (max)
		engine hot	nbv
29	immobiliser control module		data not available
30-35	–		
36	instrument panel		data not available
37	–		
38	OS signal : t3	ignition on, OS multiplug disconnected	0.4 to 0.5 V
		engine running, hot	200 to 1000 mV (switching)
		throttle fully open	0.5 to 1.0 V
		deceleration (fuel cut-off)	0 to 0.5 V
		switching frequency	1 sec intervals (approx)
39	KS signal : t1	engine running, KS active	0.25 V (max)
40	–		
41	TPS signal : t2	ignition on/engine running:	
		throttle closed	1.0 V
		throttle fully open	4.50 V (approx)
42	CTS signal : t2	ignition on/engine running	20° C: 2.0 to 2.5 volts
			80° C: 0.2 to 0.6 volts
43	ATS signal : t4	ignition on/engine running	20° C: 2.0 to 2.5 volts
			80° C: 0.2 to 0.6 volts
44	–		
45	KS shield	engine running, KS active	0.25 V (max)

45 pin ECM multi-plug, Bosch Mono-Motronic 1.3

Pin Table – Bosch Motronic 2.7

Pin	Connection	Test condition	Measurements
1	amplifier control signal : t2	engine cranking/running	0 to 12.0 V (switching)
3	fuel pump relay driver : t85	ignition on	nbv
		engine cranking/running	1.25 V (max)
4	ISCV driver : t3	ignition on	nbv
		engine running, idle speed:	
		cold	6.0 to 6.5 V
		hot	7.0 to 9.0 V
		duty cycle	30 to 60%
5	CFSV driver : t1	ignition on	nbv
		engine running, above idle, operating temperature	
		CFSV inactive	nbv
		CFSV active	0 to 12 V (switching)
		duty cycle	0 to 99%
6	tachometer		data not available
7	MAF sensor signal : t3	ignition on	1.40 V
		engine running:	
		idle speed	1.90 to 2.2 V
		snap accelerate	> 3.00 V
8	HES signal (CID) : tO	engine running	0 to 5.0 V (switching)
9	instrument panel connector		data not available
10	OS return : t4	engine running	0.25 V (max)
11	KS 1 signal (front) : t1	engine running, KS active	1.0 V AC (peak to peak)
12	sensor supply (hall sensor : t+, TPS : t3)	ignition on/engine running	5.0 V ± 0.1 V
13	SD connector		data not available
14	earth	ignition on/engine running	0.25 V (max)
15	injector driver (cylinder 2) : t1	ignition on	nbv
		engine running, cold	> 4.5 ms
		engine running, hot	3.1 to 3.3 ms
16	injector driver (cylinder 5) : t1	ignition on	nbv
		engine running, cold	> 4.5 ms
		engine running, hot	3.1 to 3.3 ms
17	injector driver (cylinder 1) : t1	ignition on	nbv
		engine running, cold	> 4.5 ms
		engine running, hot	3.1 to 3.3 ms
18	supply from battery : t30	ignition off/on/engine running	nbv
19	earth	ignition on/engine running	0.25 V (max)
22	ISCV driver : t1	ignition on	nbv
		engine running, idle speed:	
		cold	6.0 to 6.5 V
		hot	7.0 to 9.0 V
		duty cycle	30 to 60%
24	earth	ignition on/engine running	0.25 V (max)
25	MAF sensor (hot wire burn-off) : t4	coolant above 31°, rpm above 1000, switch off engine	hot wire glows for 1.5 seconds
26	MAF sensor return : t2	ignition on/engine running	0.25 V (max)
27	supply from ignition switch : t15	ignition on/engine running	nbv
28	oxygen sensor : t3	ignition on, OS multiplug disconnected	0.4 to 0.5 V
		engine running, hot	200 to 1000 mV (switching)
		throttle fully-open	0.5 to 1.0 V
		deceleration	0 to 0.5 V
29	KS 2 (rear) signal : t1	engine running, KS active	1.0 V AC (peak to peak)
30	sensor return (TPS : t1, CTS : t2, KS1 : t2, KS2 : t2)	ignition on/engine running	0.25 V (max)
33	injector driver (cylinder 4) : t1	ignition on	nbv
		engine running, cold	> 4.5 ms
		engine running, hot	3.1 to 3.3 ms
34	injector driver (cylinder 6) : t1	ignition on	nbv
		engine running, cold	> 4.5 ms
		engine running, hot	3.1 to 3.3 ms

Pin Table – Bosch Motronic 2.7 (continued)

Pin	Connection	Test condition	Measurements
35	injector driver (cylinder 3) : t1	ignition on	nbv
		engine running, cold	> 4.5 ms
		engine running, hot	3.1 to 3.3 ms
36	main relay driver : t85	ignition off	
		ignition on/engine running	1.25 V (max)
37	supply from main relay : t87	ignition on/engine running	nbv
40	air conditioning		data not available
41	air conditioning		data not available
42	earth	ignition on/engine running	0.25 V (max)
45	CTS signal : t2	ignition on/engine running	20° C: 3.00 to 3.50 V
			80° C: 1.00 to 1.30 V
48	CAS return : t2	engine cranking	> 4.0 V AC (peak to peak)
		idle:	> 8.0 V AC (peak to peak)
		cruise:	> 14.0 V AC (peak to peak)
49	CAS signal : t1	engine cranking:	> 4.0 V AC (peak to peak)
		idle:	> 8.0 V AC (peak to peak)
		cruise:	> 14.0 V AC (peak to peak)
51	automatic transmission		data not available
53	TPS signal : t2	ignition on/engine running:	
		throttle closed	0.3 to 0.8 V
		throttle fully open	4.25 V
54	earth	ignition on/engine running	0.25 V (max)
55	SD connection		data not available

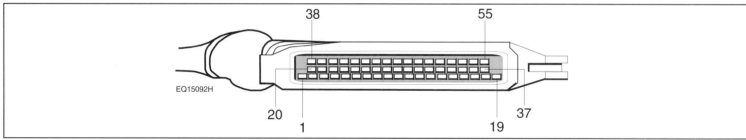

EQ15092H

55 pin ECM multi-plug, Bosch Motronic 2.7

Pin Table – Bosch Motronic 2.9

Pin	Connection	Test condition	Measurements
1	earth	ignition on/engine running	0.25 V (max)
2	injector driver (cyl 6) : t1	ignition on	nbv
		engine cranking, cold	11.0 to 12.0 ms
		engine cranking, hot	> 3.1 ms
		cold idle	> 3.5 ms
		hot idle	3.0 to 3.5 ms
		snap acceleration	> 6.0 ms
3	injector driver (cyl 2) : t1	ignition on	nbv
		engine cranking, cold	11.0 to 12.0 ms
		engine cranking, hot	> 3.1 ms
		cold idle	> 3.5 ms
		hot idle	3.0 to 3.5 ms
		snap acceleration	> 6.0 ms
4	injector driver (cyl 4) : t1	ignition on	nbv
		engine cranking, cold	11.0 to 12.0 ms
		engine cranking, hot	> 3.1 ms
		cold idle	> 3.5 ms
		hot idle	3.0 to 3.5 ms
		snap acceleration	> 6.0 ms

Pin	Connection	Test condition	Measurements
5	–		
6	fuel pump relay driver : t85	ignition on	nbv
		engine cranking/running	1.25 V (max)
7	earth	ignition on/engine running	0.25 V (max)
8	amplifier control signal	engine cranking/running	0 to 12 V (switching)
9	main relay driver : t85	ignition off	nbv
		ignition on/engine running	1.25 V (max)
10-13	–		
14	CTS signal : t2	ignition on/engine running	20° C: 1.50 V
			80° C: 0.30 V
15	–		
16	MAF return : t2	ignition on/engine running	0.25 V (max)
17	MAF sensor signal : t3	engine running:	
		idle speed	2.3 V
		3000 rpm	2.8 V
		snap accelerate	3.00 to 3.50 V (approx)
18-19	–		
20	OS return : t4	engine running	0.25 V (max)
21	SD connector		data not available
22	trip computer		data not available
23	supply from main relay : t87	ignition on/engine running	nbv
24	injector driver (cyl 1) : t1	ignition on	nbv
		engine cranking, cold	11.0 to 12.0 ms
		engine cranking, hot	> 3.1 ms
		cold idle	> 3.5 ms
		hot idle	3.0 to 3.5 ms
		snap acceleration	> 6.0 ms
25	injector driver (cyl 5) : t1	ignition on	nbv
		engine cranking, cold	11.0 to 12.0 ms
		engine cranking, hot	> 3.1 ms
		cold idle	> 3.5 ms
		hot idle	3.0 to 3.5 ms
		snap acceleration	> 6.0 ms
26	injector driver (cyl 3) : t1	ignition on	nbv
		engine cranking, cold	11.0 to 12.0 ms
		engine cranking, hot	> 3.1 ms
		cold idle	> 3.5 ms
		hot idle	3.0 to 3.5 ms
		snap acceleration	> 6.0 ms
27	ISCV supply : t2	idle speed	nbv
28	OS relay driver : t85	engine running:	
		OS heater active	1.25 V (max)
		OS heater inactive	nbv
29-30	–		
31	CFSV driver : t1	ignition on	nbv
		engine running, above idle, operating temperature:	
		CFSV inactive	nbv
		CFSV active	0 to 12 V (switching)
		duty cycle	0 to 99%
32	–		
33	sensor return (KS 1: t2, KS 2: t2, CTS: t2, ATS: t1, TPS: t1)	ignition on/engine running	0.25 V (max)
34	KS 1 signal : t1	engine running, KS active	
		idle	0.4 to 2.0 V AC
		high speed	5.1 V AC
35	–		
36	ATS signal : t2	ignition on/engine running	20° C: 3.50 to 3.75 V
			80° C: 1.25 to 1.30 V
37	A/C		data not available
38	supply from ignition switch : t15	ignition on/engine running	nbv
39	A/C diagnostic connector		data not available

Pin Table – Bosch Motronic 2.9 (continued)

Pin	Connection	Test condition	Measurements
40	TPS signal : t2	ignition on/engine running:	
		throttle closed	0.60 V
		throttle fully open	> 4.0 V
41	TPS supply : t3	ignition on/engine running	5.0 V ± 0.1
42	OS signal : t3	engine running, hot	200 to 1000 mV (switching)
		throttle fully open	0.5 to 1.0 V
		deceleration (fuel cut-off)	0 to 0.5 V
		switching frequency	1 sec intervals (approx)
43	SD connector		data not available
44	HES signal : t2	engine cranking/running	0 to nbv (switching)
45-50	–		
51	trip computer		data not available
52	–		
53	ISCV driver : t1	idle speed	0 to nbv (switching)
54	supply from battery : t30	ignition off/on/engine running	nbv
55	earth	ignition on/engine running	0.25 V (max)
56	earth	ignition on/engine running	0.25 V (max)
57	KS no2 signal : t1	engine running, KS active	
		idle:	0.4 to 2.0 V AC
		high speed:	5.1 V AC
58	–		
59	MAF Hot-wire burn-off : t4	switch off engine	hot wire glows for several seconds
60-64	–		
65	VSS signal	vehicle in motion	0 to nbv (switching)
66	–		
67	CAS signal : t1	engine cranking	> 2.0 V AC (peak to peak)
		idle:	> 11.0 V AC (peak to peak)
		cruise:	> 14.0 V AC (peak to peak)
68	CAS : t2	engine cranking	> 2.0 V AC (peak to peak)
		idle:	> 11.0 V AC (peak to peak)
		cruise:	> 14.0 V AC (peak to peak)

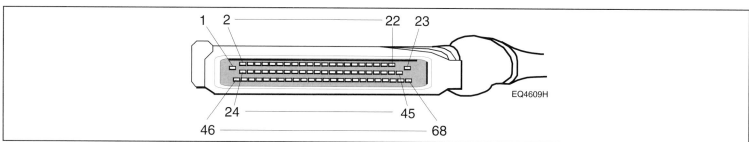

EQ4609H

65 pin ECM multi-plug, Bosch Motronic 2.9

Pin Table – Bosch Motronic MP9.0

Pin	Connection	Test condition	Measurements
1	earth	ignition on/engine running	0.25 V (max)
2	stepper motor (TCA : t1)	idle speed, active	0 to 5.0 V (switching)
		frequency	500hz
		duty cycle	30%
3	CFSV driver : t1	ignition on	nbv
		engine running, above idle, operating temperature:	
		CFSV inactive	nbv
		CFSV active	0 to 12 V (switching)
		duty cycle	0 to 99%
4	injector driver (cylinder 4) : t1	ignition on	
		engine running, hot	4.8 ms

Pin	Connection	Test condition	Measurements
5	–		
6	injector driver (cylinder 2) : t1	ignition on	
		engine running, hot	4.8 ms
7	injector driver (cylinder 1) : t1	ignition on	
		engine running, hot	4.8 ms
8	HES supply : t3	ignition on/engine running	5.0 V ± 0.1
9	tachometer		data not available
10	Idle switch (TCA : t3)	ignition on/engine running:	
		throttle closed	0.25 V (max)
		throttle open	nbv
11-12	–		
13	HES signal : t2	engine cranking/running	0 to 5.0 V (switching)
14	TPS supply (TCA : t4)	ignition on	5.0 V ± 0.1
15	OS signal : t3	engine running, hot:	
		non-active (open loop)	0.45 to 0.50 V
		active (closed loop)	0 – 0.3 to 0.7 – 1.0 V (switching)
16	TVPS signal (TCA : t8)	ignition on/engine running	2.5 V to 4.0 V
		slight variation on move throttle	
17	sensor return (CTS: t1, HES : t1,		
	TCA : t7, MAP/ATS assembly : t1)	ignition on/engine running	0.25 V (max)
18	MAP sensor signal (MAP/ATS		
	assembly: t4)	ignition on	> 4.5 V
		engine running:	
		idle speed	0.50 to 1.00 V
		wide open throttle	> 4.5 V
19	KS return: t2	engine running, KS active	0.25 V (max)
20	–		
21	supply from battery : t30	ignition off/on/engine running	nbv
22	–		
23	supply from ignition switch : t15	ignition on/engine running	nbv
24	amplifier control signal : t2	engine cranking/running	0 to 5.0 V (switching)
25	fuel pump relay driver : t85	ignition on	nbv
		engine cranking/running	1.25 V (max)
26	stepper motor (TCA : t2)	idle speed, active	0 to 5.0 V (switching)
		frequency	500Hz
		duty cycle	30%
27	–		
28	injector driver (cylinder 4) : t1	ignition on	
		engine running, hot	4.8 ms
29	immobiliser control unit		data not available
30-35	–		
36	VSS signal	vehicle in motion	0 to > 4.0 V (switching)
37	MAP supply (MAP/ATS assembly : t3)	ignition on/engine running	5.0 V ± 0.1
38	OS return : t4	engine running	0.25 V (max)
39	KS signal : t1	engine running, KS active	0.4 to 2.0 V AC (peak to peak)
40	–		
41	TPS signal (TCA : t5)	ignition on/engine running:	
		throttle closed	4.0 V
		throttle fully open	0.75 V
42	CTS signal : t3	ignition on/engine running	20° C: 2.0 to 3.0 V
			80° C: 0.5 to 1.0 V
43	ATS signal : t2 (MAP/ATS assembly : t2)	ignition on/engine running	20° C: 2.0 to 3.0 V
			80° C: 0.5 to 1.0 V
44-45	–		

EQ8509H

45 pin ECM multi-plug, Bosch Motronic MP9.0

Pin Table – Magneti-Marelli 1AV

Pin	Connection	Test condition	Measurements
1	earth	ignition on/engine running	0.25 V (max)
2	stepper motor driver : t1	idle speed, active	0 to 5.0 V (switching)
3	CFSV driver : t1	ignition off/on	nbv
		engine running, above idle, operating temperature:	
		CFSV inactive	nbv
		CFSV active	0 to 12 V (switching)
		duty cycle	0 to 99%
4	injector driver (cylinder 4) : t1	ignition on, briefly	nbv
		engine running, cold	> 3.5 ms
		engine running, hot	3.0 to 3.5 ms
		snap acceleration	> 6.0 ms (approx)
6	injector driver (cylinder 2) : t1	ignition on, briefly	nbv
		engine running, cold	> 3.5 ms
		engine running, hot	3.0 to 3.5 ms
		snap acceleration	> 6.0 ms (approx)
7	injector driver (cylinder 1) : t1	ignition on, briefly	nbv
		engine running, cold	> 3.5 ms
		engine running, hot	3.0 to 3.5 ms
		snap acceleration	> 6.0 ms (approx)
8	HES supply voltage : t+	ignition on/engine running	9.0 V (min)
9	instrument panel connection		data not available
10	idle switch	ignition on/engine running:	
		throttle closed	0.25 V (max)
		open	12.0 V
11-12	–		
13	HES signal : t0	engine running	0 to 12.0 V (switching)
		duty cycle	35% (approx)
14	TPS supply (TCA : t4)	ignition on/engine running	5.0 V ± 0.1
15	oxygen sensor signal : t3	ignition on, OS multiplug disconnected	0.4 to 0.5 V
		engine running, hot, 2000 rpm	200 to 1000 mV (switching)
		throttle fully open	0.5 to 1.0 V
16	TVPS signal (TCA : t8)	idle speed, hot:	
		range	0.5 to 4.0 V
17	sensor return (CTS : t1, HES : t-, MAP : t1, TCA : t7)	ignition on/engine running	0.25 V (max)
18	MAP sensor signal : t4	ignition on	5.0 V
		engine running:	
		idle speed	not stated, expect 1.25 V
		WOT	5.0 V
19	KS signal : t2	engine running, KS active	1.0 V AC (peak to peak)
20	–		
21	supply from ignition switch : t15	ignition on/engine running	nbv
23	supply from battery : t30	ignition off/on/engine running	nbv
24	amplifier control signal : t2	engine cranking/running	0 to 12.0 V (switching)
25	fuel pump relay driver : t3	ignition on	nbv
		engine cranking/running	1.25 V (max)
26	stepper motor driver : t2	idle speed, active	0 to 5.0 V (switching)
27	instrument panel connection		data not available
28	injector driver (cylinder 3) : t1	ignition on	nbv briefly, then 0 V
		engine running, cold	> 3.5 ms
		engine running, hot	3.0 to 3.5 ms
		snap acceleration	> 6.0 ms (approx)
29	–		
33	air conditioning		data not available
35	air conditioning		data not available
36	VSS signal : t3	vehicle in motion	0 to 12 V (switching)
37	MAP sensor supply : t3	ignition on/engine running	5.0 V ± 0.1
38	OS return : t4	ignition on/engine running	0.25 V (max)
39	KS return : t1	engine running	0.25 V (max)

Pin	Connection	Test condition	Measurements
41	TPS signal : t5	ignition on/engine running:	
		throttle closed	4.0 V
		throttle fully open	0.75 V
42	CTS signal : t2	ignition on/engine running	20° C: 2.50 to 3.00 V
			80° C: 0.30 to 0.60 V
43	ATS signal (MAP : t2)	ignition on/engine running	30° C: 2.00 to 3.00 V
45	KS : t3 shield return	engine running	0.25 V (max)

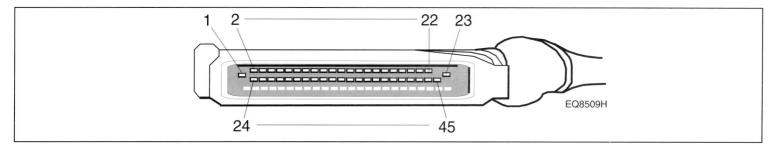

45 pin ECM multi-plug, Magneti-Marelli 1AV

Pin Table – Simos 4S2

Pin	Connection	Test condition	Measurements
1	earth	ignition on/engine running	0.25 V (max)
2	injector driver (cylinder 1) : t1	ignition on	nbv
		engine running, cold	> 3.8 ms
		engine running, hot	3.8 ms
		snap acceleration	> 6.0 ms (approx)
		deceleration (fuel cut off)	0 ms (approx)
7	amplifier control signal : t2	engine cranking/running	0 to 12.0 V (switching)
8	supply from ignition switch : t15	ignition on/engine running	nbv
9	shield return	ignition on/engine running	0.25 V (max)
11	instrument panel connector		data not available
12	CTS signal : t2	ignition on/engine running	20° C: 2.50 to 3.00 V
			80° C: 0.30 to 0.60 V
13	air conditioning		data not available
14	MAF sensor signal : t1	ignition on	1.4 V
		idle hot	1.9 to 2.2 V
16	HES return : t3	ignition on/engine running	0.25 V (max)
17	OS signal : t3	ignition on, OS multiplug disconnected	0.4 to 0.5 V
		engine running, hot	200 to 1000 mV (switching)
		throttle fully-open	0.5 to 1.0 V
		deceleration (fuel cut-off)	0 to 0.5 V
		switching frequency	1 sec intervals (approx)
18	idle switch : t3	ignition on/engine running:	
		throttle closed	0.25 V
		throttle open	12.0 V
19	instrument panel connector		data not available
20	OS heater driver : t1	ignition on	nbv
		engine running:	
		cold	0 V
		hot, non active	nbv
		hot, active	0 V
21	shield return	ignition on/engine running	0.25 V (max)
23	supply from relay : t6	ignition on/engine running	nbv
25	stepper motor : t2	idle speed, active	0 to 5.0 V (switching)
28	TVPS signal (TCA : t8)	engine running, hot	3.5 to 3.7 V
29	ATS return : t1	ignition on/engine running	0.25 V (max)

Pin Table – Simos 4S2 (continued)

Pin	Connection	Test condition	Measurements
30	stepper motor : t1	idle speed, active	0 to 5.0 V (switching)
31	fuel pump relay driver:	ignition on	nbv
		engine cranking/running	1.25 V (max)
32	starter circuit	engine cranking	nbv
33	CFSV driver : t1	ignition on	nbv
		engine running, above idle, operating temperature:	
		CFSV inactive	nbv
		CFSV active	0 to 12 V (switching)
		duty cycle	0 to 99%
34	KS signal : t2	engine running, KS active	1.0 V AC (peak to peak)
35	ground	ignition on/engine running	0.25 V (max)
36	KS signal : t1	engine running, KS active	1.0 V AC (peak to peak)
37	ATS signal : t2	ignition on/engine running	20° C: 2.50 to 3.00 V
			80° C: 0.3 to 0.6 V
38	supply from ignition switch : t15	ignition on/engine running	nbv
39	air conditioning		data not available
40	TPS signal (TCA : t5)	ignition on/engine running:	
		throttle closed	4.0 V
		throttle open	0.75 V
41	sensor supply (TCA : t4)	ignition on/engine running	5.0 V ± 0.1
42	OS return : t3	ignition on/engine running	0.25 V (max)
44	CID signal : t0	engine running:	
		hot	0 to 12.0 V (switching)
45	CID : t+	ignition on/engine running	nbv
46	injector driver (cylinder 2) : t1	ignition on	nbv
		engine running, cold	> 3.8 ms
		engine running, hot	3.8 ms
		snap acceleration	> 6.0 ms (approx)
		deceleration (fuel cut off)	0 ms (approx)
47	injector driver (cylinder 3) : t1	ignition on	nbv
		engine running, cold	> 3.8 ms
		engine running, hot	3.8 ms
		snap acceleration	> 6.0 ms (approx)
		deceleration (fuel cut off)	0 ms (approx)
48	injector driver (cylinder 4) : t1	ignition on	nbv
		engine running, cold	> 3.8 ms
		engine running, hot	3.8 ms
		snap acceleration	> 6.0 ms (approx)
		deceleration (fuel cut off)	0 ms (approx)
67	HES supply : t2	ignition on/engine running	12.0 V
68	HES signal : t1	engine running	0 to 12.0 V (switching)
		duty cycle	35%

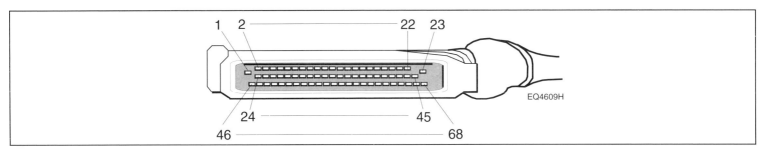

68 pin ECM multi-plug, Simos 4S2

Pin Table – VAG Digifant (38 pin)

Pin	Connection	Test condition	Measurements
1	TPS supply : t2	ignition on/engine running	5.0 V ± 0.1

Pin	Connection	Test condition	Measurements
2	injector driver : t1	engine cranking, cold	11.0 to 12.0 ms
		engine running, cold	4.0 to 4.5 ms
		engine cranking, hot	> 4.0 ms
		engine running, hot	2.0 to 2.5 ms
		2000 rpm	2.0 to 2.5 ms
		3000 rpm	2.0 to 2.5 ms
		snap acceleration	> 6.0 ms
3	cold start valve : t1	ignition on	nbv
		engine cranking	1.25 V (max)
4-6	–		
7	fuel pump relay driver : t85	ignition on	nbv
		engine cranking/running	1.25 V (max)
8	OS signal : t3	ignition on, OS multiplug disconnected	0.4 to 0.5 V
		engine running, hot	200 to 1000 mV (switching)
		throttle fully-open	0.5 to 1.0 V
		deceleration (fuel cut-off)	0 to 0.5 V
		switching frequency	1 sec intervals (approx)
9	–		
10	AT		data not available
11	HES signal : t2	engine cranking/running	5.0 to 7.0 V (mean)
12	TPS signal : t3	ignition on/engine running:	
		throttle closed	0.30 to 1.70 V
		throttle fully open	> 4.25 V
13	sensor return (HES : t1, CO pot : t1 TPS : t1, CTS : t1, AFS : t4)	ignition on/engine running	0.25 V (max)
14	CTS signal : t2	ignition on/engine running	20° C: 0.95 to 1.25 V
			80° C: 0.20 to 0.40 V
15	AFS signal (AFS : t1)	ignition on/engine running	20° C: 0.95 to 1.25 V
			80° C: 0.20 to 0.40 V
16	KS return : t1	engine running, KS active	0.25 V (max)
17	KS signal : t2	engine running, KS active	1.0 V AC (peak to peak)
18	–		
19	AFS signal : t2	ignition on	0.20 to 0.50 V
		engine cranking/idle speed	0.50 to 1.50 V
		2000 rpm	1.75 to 2.25 V
		3000 rpm	2.00 to 2.70 V
		snap accelerate	3.00 to 4.50 V
20	earth : t31	ignition on/engine running	0.25 V (max)
21-23	–		
24	AT		data not available
25	ISCV driver : t1	ignition on	nbv
		engine running:	
		cold	6.0 to 6.5 V
		hot	7.0 to 9.0 V
26	ignition switch : t50	engine cranking	nbv
27	amplifier control signal : t2	engine running	0 to nbv (switching)
28	AFS supply : t3	ignition on/engine running	5.0 V ± 0.1
29	earth	ignition on/engine running	0.25 V (max)
30	HES supply : t3	ignition on/engine running	9.0 V (min)
31	AT		data not available
32	SD connector		data not available
33	–		
34	KS shield : t3	engine running, KS active	0.25 V (max)
35	CO pot signal : t2	ignition on/engine running:	
		range	0.1 to 4.9 V
		open circuit	5.0 V
		short circuit	0 V
36	supply from ignition switch via main relay : t86a	ignition on/engine running	nbv
37	A/C compressor		data not available
38	supply from main relay : t87	ignition on/engine running	nbv

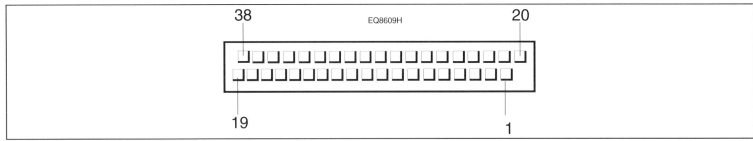

38 pin ECM multi-plug, VAG Digifant (38 pin)

Pin Table – VAG Digifant (45 pin)

Pin	Connection	Test condition	Measurements
1	earth	ignition on/engine running	0.25 V (max)
2	injectors driver : t1	ignition on	nbv briefly, then 0 V
		engine running, cold	3.0 to 3.5 ms
		engine running, hot	2.0 to 2.5 ms
		snap acceleration	> 6.0 ms
3	–		
4	supply from battery : t30	ignition off/on/engine running	nbv
5	–		
6	CSV driver : t1	ignition on	nbv
		cranking, coolant temperature > 15°C.	nbv
		cranking, coolant temperature < 15°C. (for 1 to 4 seconds depending on temperature)	1.25 V (max)
7	amplifier control signal : t2	engine cranking/running	0 to 12 V (switching)
8	supply from ignition switch : t15 (via main relay : t5/86)	ignition on/engine running	nbv
9	KS shield : t3	engine running, KS active	0.25 V (max)
10	–		
11	VSS	vehicle in motion	0 V to nbv (switching)
12	CTS signal : t2	ignition on/engine running	20° C: 0.95 to 1.25 V
			80° C: 0.20 to 0.40 V
13	–		
14	AFS signal : t2	ignition on	0.20 to 0.30 V
		idle	0.75 to 1.50 V
		2000 rpm	1.75 to 2.25 V
		snap accelerate	3.00 to 4.50 V
		wide open throttle (off-load)	> 4.50 V
15	–		
16	AFS supply : t3	ignition on/engine running:	5.0 V ± 0.1
17	OS signal : t3	ignition on, OS multiplug disconnected	0.4 to 0.5 V
		engine running, hot	200 to 1000 mV (switching)
		throttle fully-open	0.5 to 1.0 V
		deceleration (fuel cut-off)	0 to 0.5 V
		switching frequency	1 sec intervals (approx)
18	–		
19	tachometer		data not available
20	OS heater driver : t1	engine running:	
		OS heater inactive	nbv
		OS heater active	1.25 V (max)
21	earth (KS shield)	ignition on/engine running	0.25 V (max)
22	–		
23	supply from main relay : t6/87	ignition on/engine running	nbv
24-29	–		
30	ISCV driver : t1	ignition on	nbv
		engine running:	
		cold	6.0 to 6.5 V (approx)
		hot	7.0 to 9.0 V (approx)

Pin	Connection	Test condition	Measurements
31	fuel pump relay driver : t3/86	ignition on	nbv
		engine cranking/running	1.25 V (max)
32	ignition switch : t50	engine cranking	nbv
33	CFSV driver : t1	ignition on	nbv
		engine running, above idle, operating temperature:	
		CFSV inactive	nbv
		CFSV active	0 to 12 V (switching)
		duty cycle	0 to 99%
34	KS signal : t2	engine running, KS active	1.0 V AC (peak to peak)
35	sensor return (AFS : t4, CTS : t1, TPS : t3, HES : t -)	ignition on/engine running	0.25 V (max)
36	KS return : t1	engine running, KS active	0.25 V (max)
37	ATS signal (AFS : t1)	ignition on/engine running	20° C: 1.4 V
38	–		
39	A/C		data not available
40	TPS signal : t2	ignition on/engine running:	
		throttle closed	0.5 to 1.5 V
		throttle fully open	> 4.2 V
41	TPS supply : t1	ignition on/engine running:	5.0 V ± 0.1
42	OS return : t3	ignition on/engine running	0.25 V (max)
43	SD connector		data not available
44	HES signal : t0	engine cranking/running	0 to > 5 V (switching)
45	HES supply : t+	ignition on/engine running	9.0 V (min)

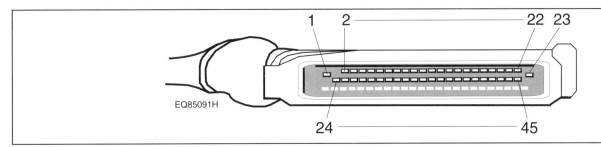

EQ85091H

45 pin ECM multi-plug, VAG Digifant (45 pin)

Pin Table – VAG Digifant (68 pin)

Pin	Connection	Test condition	Measurements
1	earth	ignition on/engine running	0.25 V (max)
2	injector driver (cylinder 4) : t1	ignition on	nbv briefly, then 0 V
		engine running, cold	> 3.5 ms
		engine running, hot	3.5 ms
		snap acceleration	20 ms (approx)
		deceleration	0 ms (approx)
3	–		
4	TPS supply : t1	ignition on/engine running	5.0 V ± 0.1
5	–		
6	fuel pump relay driver : t85	ignition on	nbv
		engine cranking/running	1.25 V (max)
7	–		
8	amplifier control signal : t2	engine cranking/running	0 to 5.0 V (switching)
9	supply from ignition switch, via main relay : t15	ignition on/engine running	nbv
10	KS shield : t3	engine running, KS active	0.25 V (max)
11	AT		data not available
12-13	–		
14	CTS signal : t2	ignition on/engine running	10° C: 1.00 V
			80° C: 0.20 V
15-17	–		

Pin Table – VAG Digifant (68 pin) (continued)

Pin	Connection	Test condition	Measurements
18	AT		data not available
19	–		
20	OS signal : t3	ignition on, OS multiplug disconnected	0.4 to 0.5 V
		engine running, hot	200 to 1000 mV (switching)
		throttle fully open	0.5 to 1.0 V
		deceleration (fuel cut-off)	0 to 0.5 V
		switching frequency	1 sec intervals (approx)
21	idle switch signal : t2	ignition on/idle speed:	
		throttle closed	0 V
		throttle open	nbv
22	–		
23	supply from main relay : t87	ignition on/engine running	nbv
24	injector driver (cylinder 1) : t1	ignition on	nbv briefly, then 0 V
		engine running, cold	> 3.5 ms
		engine running, hot	3.5 ms
		snap acceleration	20 ms (approx)
		deceleration	0 ms (approx)
25	injector driver (cylinder 2) : t1	ignition on	nbv briefly, then 0 V
		engine running, cold	> 3.5 ms
		engine running, hot	3.5 ms
		snap acceleration	20 ms (approx)
		deceleration	0 ms (approx)
26	injector driver (cylinder 3) : t1	ignition on	nbv briefly, then 0 V
		engine running, cold	> 3.5 ms
		engine running, hot	3.5 ms
		snap acceleration	20 ms (approx)
		deceleration	0 ms (approx)
27	ISCV driver : t1	ignition on	nbv
		engine running, idle speed:	
		cold	6.0 to 6.5 V
		hot	7.0 to 9.0 V
		duty cycle	30 to 60%
28	OS relay driver : t85	ignition on	nbv
		engine cranking/running	1.25 V (max)
29-30	–		
31	CFSV driver : t1	ignition on	nbv
		engine running, above idle, operating temperature:	
		CFSV inactive	nbv
		CFSV active	0 to 12 V (switching)
		duty cycle	0 to 99%
32	KS signal : t2	engine running, KS active	1.0 to 2.0 V AC (peak to peak)
33	earth	ignition on/engine running	0.25 V (max)
34	KS return : t1	engine running, KS active	0.25 V (max)
35	–		
36	ATS signal : t2	ignition on/engine running	10° C: 1.5V
37	–		
38	supply from ignition switch : t15	ignition on/engine running	nbv
39	air conditioning		data not available
40	–		
41	TPS signal : t2	ignition on/engine running:	
		throttle closed	0.5 to 1.5 V
		throttle fully open	5.0 V (max)
42	OS return : t4	ignition on/engine running	0.25 V (max)
43	SD connector		data not available
44	HES (CID) signal : t0	engine cranking/running	0 to nbv (switching)
45	HES supply : t+	ignition on/engine running	9.0 V (min)
46-50	–		
51	trip computer		data not available

Pin	Connection	Test condition	Measurements
52-54	–		
55	KS shield : t3	KS active	0.25 V (max)
56	KS signal : t2	engine running, KS active	1.0 to 2.0 V AC (peak to peak)
57	KS return : t1	engine running, KS active	0.25 V (max)
58-64	–		
65	OS shield : t3	OS active	0.25 V (max)
66	–		
67	HES (ignition) signal : t2	engine cranking/running	0 to nbv (switching)
68	HES supply : t1	ignition on/engine running	9.0 V (min)

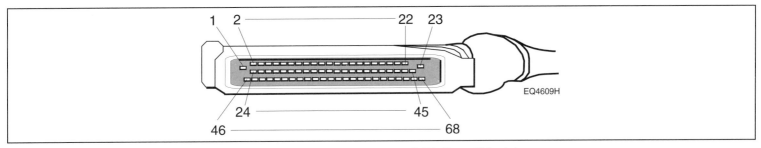

68 pin ECM multi-plug, VAG Digifant (68 pin)

Wiring Diagrams

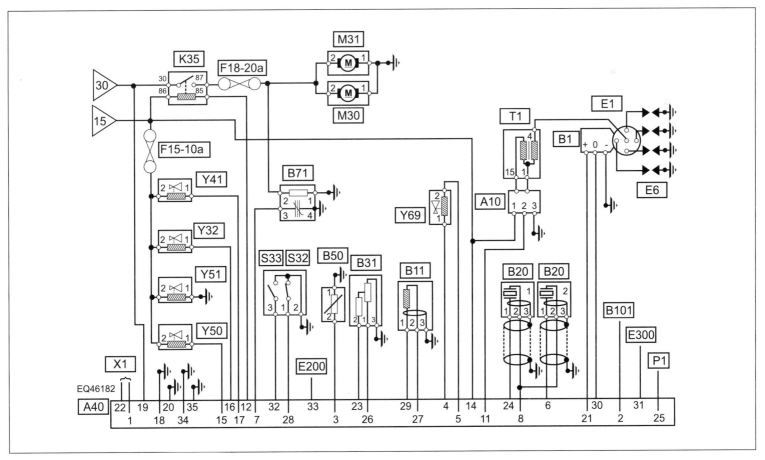

System wiring diagram, Bosch KE1.2 Motronic

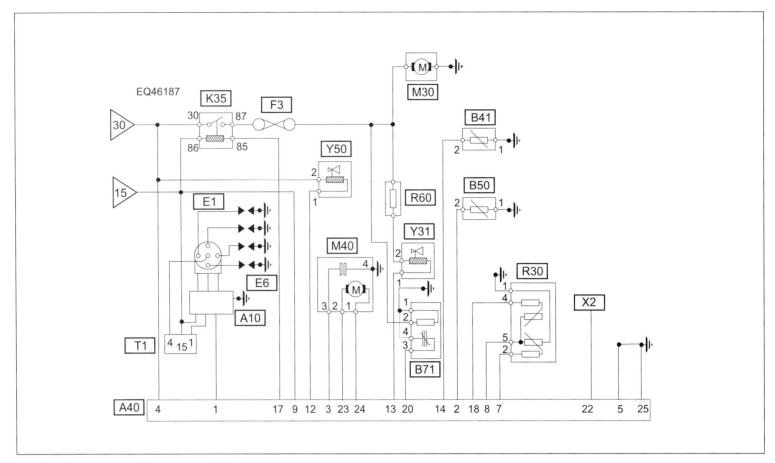

System wiring diagram, Bosch Mono-Jetronic A2.2

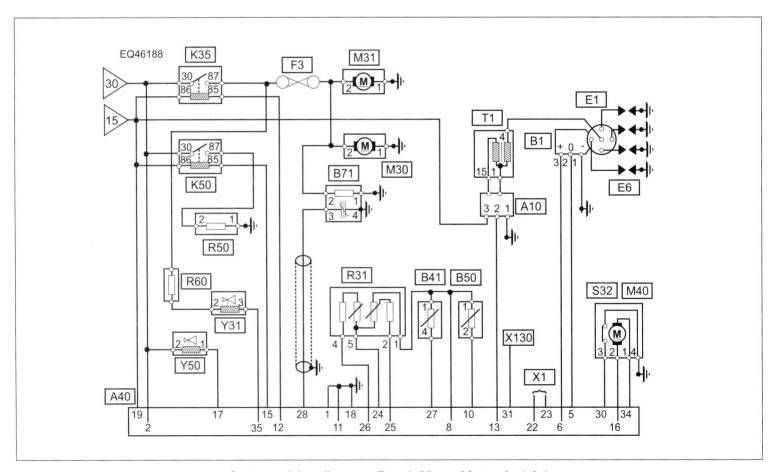

System wiring diagram, Bosch Mono-Motronic 1.2.1

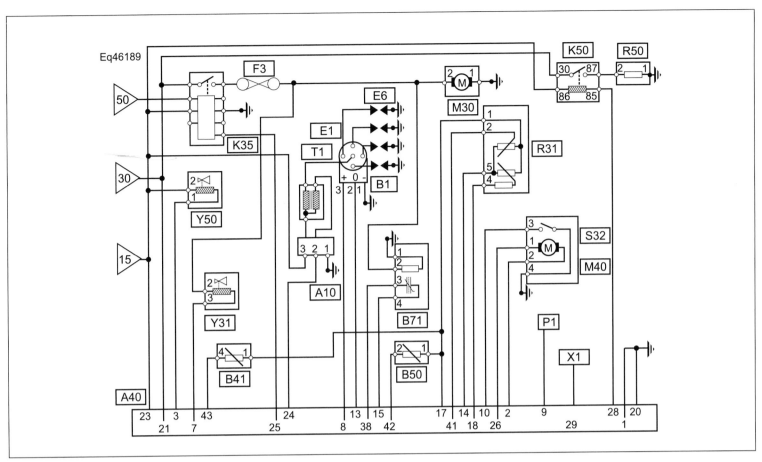

System wiring diagram, Bosch Mono-Motronic 1.2.3

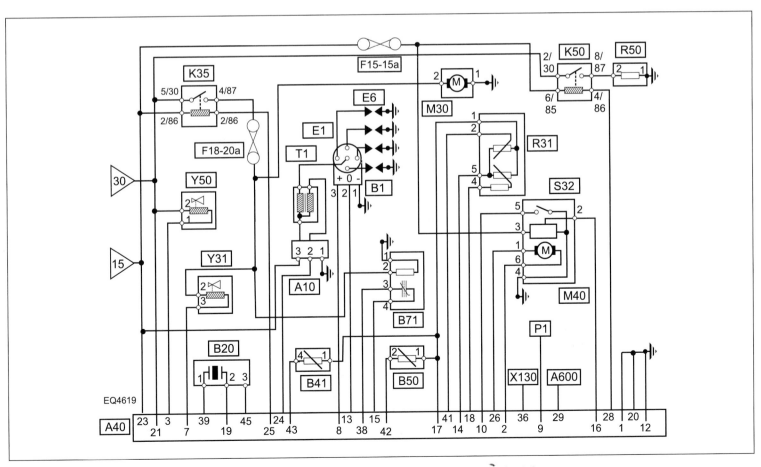

System wiring diagram, Bosch Mono-Motronic 1.3

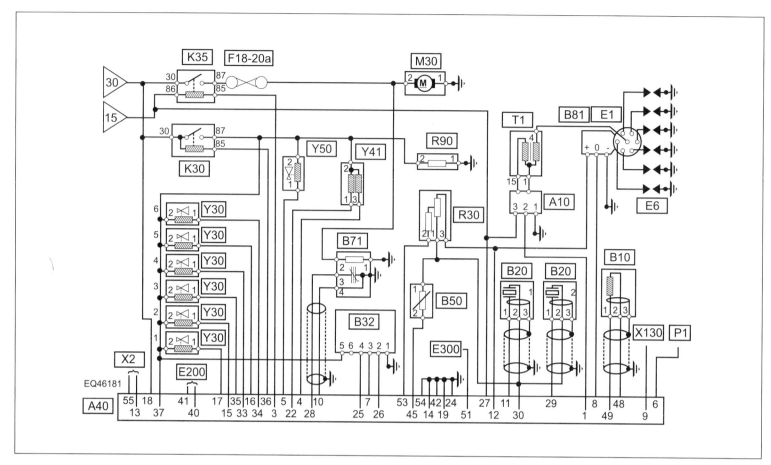

System wiring diagram, Bosch Motronic 2.7

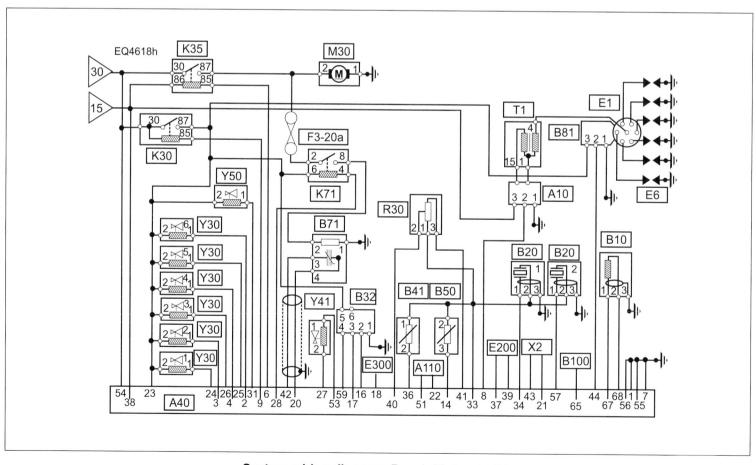

System wiring diagram, Bosch Motronic 2.9

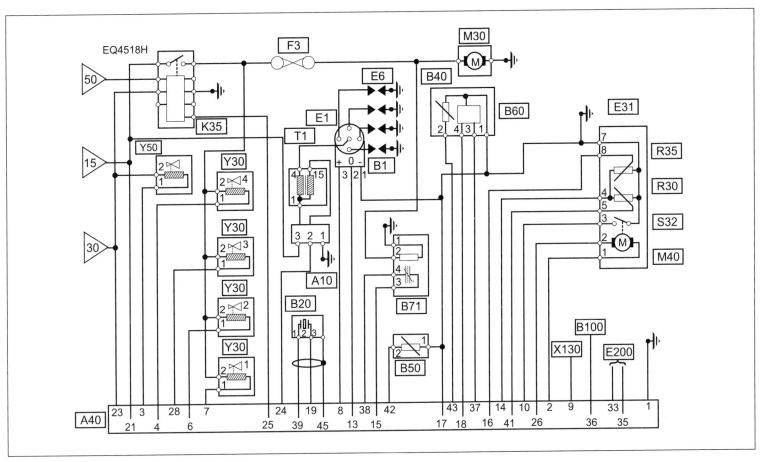

System wiring diagram, Bosch Motronic MP9.0

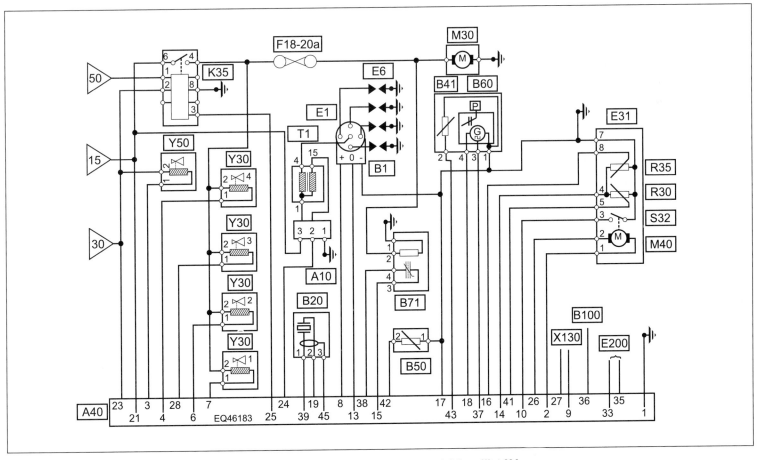

System wiring diagram, Magneti-Marelli 1AV

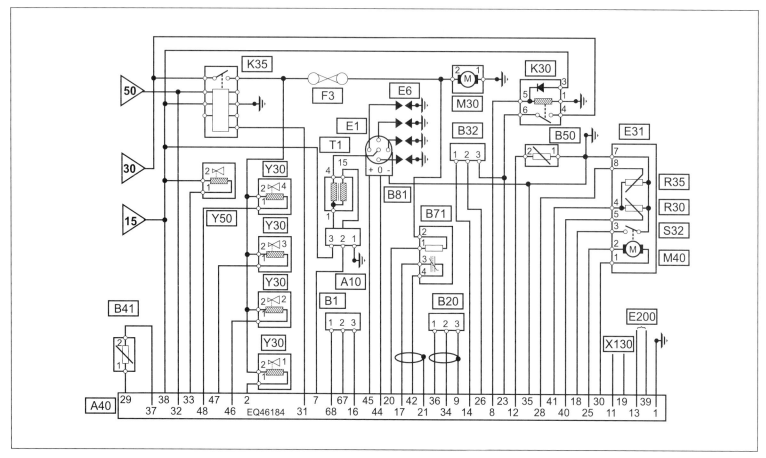

System wiring diagram, Simos 4S2

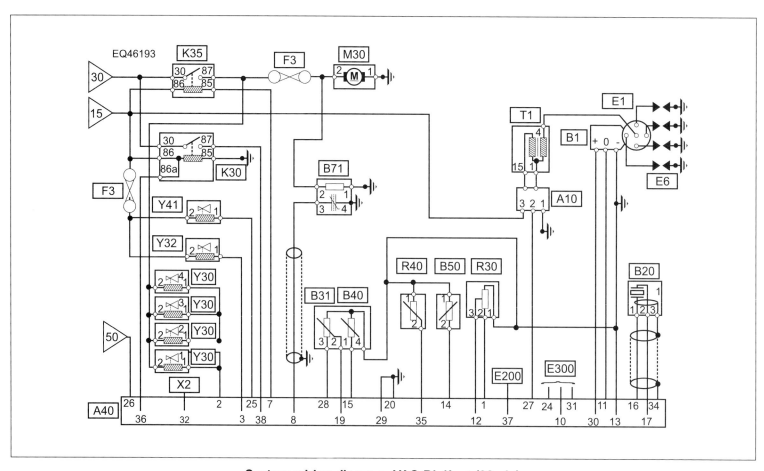

System wiring diagram, VAG Digifant (38 pin)

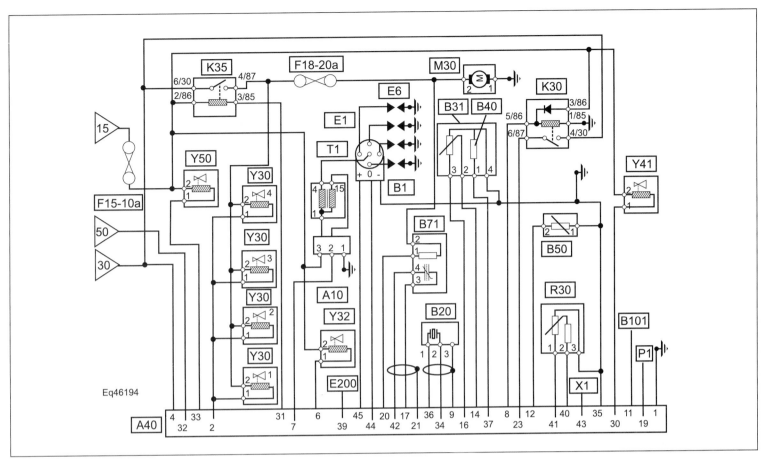

System wiring diagram, VAG Digifant (45 pin)

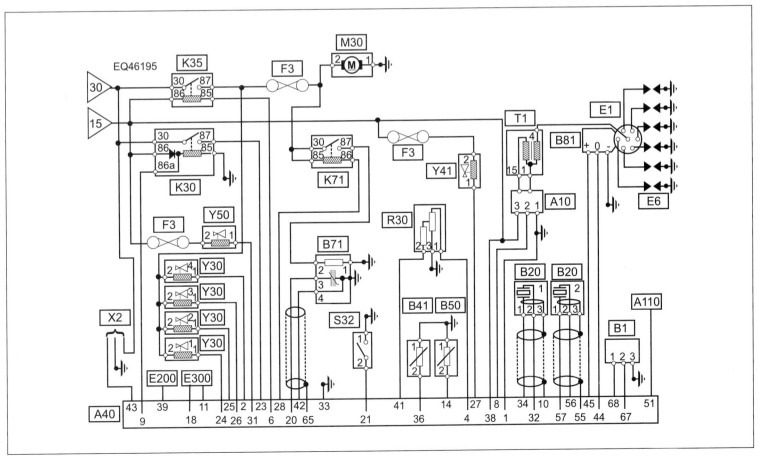

System wiring diagram, VAG Digifant (68 pin)

Notes

Chapter 33
Volvo

Contents

Index of Volvo vehicles/systems

Model	Engine code	Year	System
240 2.0i cat	B200F	1991 to 1993	Bosch LH 2.4 Jetronic
240 2.3i cat	B230F	1984 to 1991	Bosch LH 2.4 Jetronic
240 2.3i cat	B230F	1989 to 1993	Bosch LH 2.4 Jetronic
240 2.3i cat	B230FD	1993 to 1994	Bosch LH 2.4 Jetronic
400 1.8l cat SOHC 66kW	B18U-103	1992 to 1997	Fenix 3BF SPi
400 1.8l cat SOHC 66kW	B18U-103	1996 to 1997	Fenix 3BF SPi
440 1.7l cat	B18F	1988 to 1989	Bosch LH 2.2 Jetronic
440 1.7l Turbo cat	**B18FT**	**1988 to 1994**	**Bosch LH 2.2 Jetronic**
440 1.7l Turbo cat	B18FTM	1990 to 1994	Bosch LH 2.2 Jetronic
440 2.0i R Cat	B20F	1992 to 1997	Fenix 3B MPi
440/460 1.6i R Cat	B16F	1990 to 1997	Fenix 3B MPi
440/460 1.8i R Cat	B18U-103	1991 to 1997	Fenix 3B MPi
440/460 1.8i	**B18U-103**	**1991 to 1997**	**Fenix 3BF SPi**
440/460/480 1.7i	B18EP	1990 to 1992	Fenix 3B MPi
440/460/480 1.7i R Cat	**B18FP**	**1990 to 1992**	**Fenix 3B MPi**
440/460/480 1.8i Cat	B20F	1992 to 1992	Fenix 3B MPi
460 1.7l cat	B18F	1988 to 1989	Bosch LH 2.2 Jetronic
460 1.7l Turbo cat	B18FTM	1990 to 1994	Bosch LH 2.2 Jetronic
460 1.7l Turbo cat	B18FT	1988 to 1994	Bosch LH 2.2 Jetronic
480 1.7l Turbo cat	B18F	1988 to 1994	Bosch LH 2.2 Jetronic
480 1.7l Turbo cat	B18FTM	1990 to 1994	Bosch LH 2.2 Jetronic
740 2.0i cat,	B200F	1989 to 1992	Bosch LH 2.4 Jetronic
740 2.0i Turbo cat	B200FT	1991 to 1992	Bosch LH 2.4 Jetronic
740 2.3i cat	B230F	1989 to 1992	Bosch LH 2.4 Jetronic
740 2.3i cat	B230FB	1991 to 1992	Bosch LH 2.4 Jetronic
740 2.3i DOHC 16v cat	B234F	1989 to 1990	Bosch LH 2.4 Jetronic
740 turbo	**B230ET**	**1985 to 1989**	**Bosch Motronic 1.0**
740, 760 2.3i Turbo non-cat	B230GT	1989 to 1990	Bosch LH 2.4 Jetronic
760 2.3i Turbo cat	**B230FT**	**1989 to 1992**	**Bosch LH 2.4 Jetronic**
760 2.8l cat	B280F	1986 to 1991	Bosch LH 2.2 Jetronic
760 2.8l	B280E	1986 to 1991	Bosch LH 2.2 Jetronic
760 turbo	**B230ET**	**1985 to 1989**	**Bosch Motronic 1.0**

Index of Volvo vehicles/systems (continued)

Model	Engine code	Year	System
850 2.0i 20v	**B5204FS**	**1991 to 1997**	**Bosch LH 3.2 Jetronic**
850 2.0 20V Turbo	**B5204T**	**1994 to 1997**	**Bosch Motronic M4.3**
850 2.0 20V Turbo	B5204T	1994 to 1997	Bosch Motronic M4.3
850 2.0I 10v SOHC	**B5202S**	**1995 to 1997**	**Fenix 5.2**
850 2.5i 20v	B5254FS	1991 to 1997	Bosch LH 3.2 Jetronic
850 2.5I 10v SOHC	B5252S	1993 to 1997	Fenix 5.2
850 T5 DOHC 20V	B5234T	1994 to 1997	Bosch Motronic M4.3
850 T-5R	B5234T-5	1994 to 1997	Bosch Motronic M4.3
850 R	B5234T-5	1994 to 1997	Bosch Motronic M4.3
940 2.0i cat	B200F	1990 to 1997	Bosch LH 2.4 Jetronic
940 2.0i Turbo cat	B200FT	1991 to 1997	Bosch LH 2.4 Jetronic
940 2.3i cat	B230F	1992 to 1994	Bosch LH 2.4 Jetronic
940 2.3i cat	B230FB	1990 to 1997	Bosch LH 2.4 Jetronic
940 2.3i cat	B230FD	1992 to 1997	Bosch LH 2.4 Jetronic
940 2.3i DOHC 16v cat	B234F	1990 to 1992	Bosch LH 2.4 Jetronic
940 2.3i LPT Turbo cat	B230FK	1995 to 1997	Bosch LH 2.4 Jetronic
940 2.3i Turbo cat	B230FT	1990 to 1997	Bosch LH 2.4 Jetronic
960 2.0i 16v Turbo	B204FT	1991 to 1994	Bosch LH 2.4 Jetronic
960 2.3i Turbo cat	B230FT	1990 to 1994	Bosch LH 2.4 Jetronic
960 2.4I 24v	B6244F	1995 to 1997	Bosch Motronic M1.8
960 2.5I 24v	B6254F	1995 to 1997	Bosch Motronic M1.8
960 3.0I 24v	**B6304F**	**1990 to 1997**	**Bosch Motronic M1.8**
S40/V40 1.6i	**B4164S**	**1997 to 1999**	**Fenix 5.1 MPi**
S40/V40 1.8 16v	B4184S	1996 to 1999	Fenix 5.1 MPi
S40/V40 2.0 16v	B4204S	1996 to 1999	Fenix 5.1 MPi
S70/V70 2.0 turbo	B5204T	1997 to 1998	Bosch Motronic M4.3
S70/V70 2.0	B5202S	1997 to 1999	Fenix 5.2
S70/V70 2.5 20v	B5254S	1997 to 1999	Bosch LH 3.2 Jetronic

Note: *The vehicles accentuated in bold type are the actual vehicles upon which the ECM pin tables and wiring diagrams are based. Other vehicles with the same system may be similar; but are also likely to contain some differences.*

Pin Table – Bosch LH2.2 Jetronic

Pin	Connection	Test Condition	Measurements
1	rpm signal from ignition ECM : t17	engine cranking/running	0 to nbv (switching)
2	CTS signal : t2	ignition on/engine running	20° C: 2.2 V 80° C: 0.4 V
3	TPS, idle contact : t4	ignition on/engine running:	
		throttle closed	0 V
		throttle part/fully open	5.0 V ± 0.1
4	ignition switch : t50	engine cranking	nbv
5	earth	ignition on/engine running	0.25 V (max)
6	MAF sensor return : t2	ignition on/engine running	0.25 V (max)
7	MAF sensor signal : t3	ignition on	0.20 to 0.70 V
		idle	1.5 V
		3000 rpm	2.4 V
		snap open throttle	> 4.0 V
8	MAF sensor hot wire burn-off : t4	coolant above 65° C, rpm above 2500, switch off engine	hot wire glows for 1.0 second
9	supply from main relay : t87	ignition on/engine running	nbv
10	ISCV signal : t1	ignition on	nbv
		idle speed, duty cycle	30 to 40%
11	earth	ignition on/engine running	
12	idle speed test connector OR signal from ignition ECM : t4	engine cranking/running	0 to nbv (switching)

Pin	Connection	Test Condition	Measurements
13	injectors driver : t1	ignition on	nbv briefly, then 0 V
		engine running, cold	3.8 ms
		engine running, hot	2.4 ms
		2000 rpm	2.2 ms
		3000 rpm	2.1 ms
		snap acceleration	> 6.0 ms
		deceleration	0 ms
14	CO pot (MAF: t6), non cat only	ignition on/engine running:	
		voltage range	0.1 to 4.0 V
15	–		
16	A/C		data not available
17	fuel pump relay driver : t85	ignition on	nbv
		engine cranking/running	1.25 V (max)
18	supply from ignition switch : t15	ignition on/engine running	nbv
19	auxiliary water pump relay driver : t85	engine running:	
		water pump active	1.25 V (max)
		water pump inactive	nbv
20	OS signal (some models)	ignition on, OS multiplug disconnected	0.4 to 0.5 V
		engine running, hot	200 to 1000 mV (switching)
		throttle fully-open	0.5 to 1.0 V
		deceleration (fuel cut-off)	0 to 0.5 V
		switching frequency	1 sec intervals (approx)
21	main relay driver : t85	ignition off	nbv
		ignition on/engine running	1.25 V (max)
22	SD connector (some models)		data not available
23	ISCV signal : t3	ignition on	nbv
		idle speed:	
		duty cycle	30 to 40%
24	ignition ECM : t8 (some models)	engine cranking/running	0 to nbv (switching)
25	earth	ignition on/engine running	0.25 V (max)

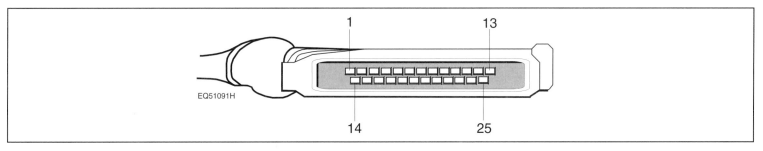

35 pin ECM multi-plug, Bosch LH 2.2 Jetronic + EZ210/EZ210Ka

Pin Table – Bosch LH2.4 Jetronic

Pin	Connection	Test condition	Measurements
1	injection system control unit (engine speed signal) : t17	ignition on	500 mV (min)
		engine running:	
		voltage & frequency	7-8 V, 27Hz (approx), increases with engine speed
2	TS, idle contact : t2	ignition on/engine running:	
		throttle closed	0 V
		throttle part/fully open	nbv
3	TS, full-load contact : t3	ignition on/engine running:	
		throttle closed/part open	nbv
		throttle fully open	0 V
4	supply from battery : t30	ignition off/on/engine running	nbv
5	earth	ignition on/engine running	0.25 V (max)
6	MAF sensor return : t2	ignition on/engine running	0.25 V (max)

Pin Table – Bosch LH2.4 Jetronic (continued)

Pin	Connection	Test condition	Measurements
7	MAF sensor signal : t3	ignition on	1.4 V (approx)
		idle	2.3 V increases with engine speed
8	MAF sensor hot wire burn-off : t4	coolant above 65° C, rpm above 2500, switch off engine	hot wire glows for 1.0 second
9	supply from main relay : t87/1	ignition on/engine running	nbv
10	half speed electronic fan control		data not available
11	full speed electronic fan control		data not available
12	SD connector : t2	ignition on	11 V (approx)
13	CTS signal : t1	ignition on/engine running	20° C: 1.6 to 2.5 V
			80° C: 0.4 to 0.6 V
14	A/C compressor		data not available
15	A/C control		data not available
16	–		
17	earth	ignition on/engine running	0.25 V (max)
18	injectors driver : t1	ignition on	nbv
		engine running, cold	3.8 ms
		engine running:	
		hot idle	2.4 ms
		2000 rpm	2.2 ms
		3000 rpm	2.1 ms
		snap acceleration	> 6.0 ms
		deceleration (fuel cut off)	0 ms
19	earth	ignition on/engine running	0.25 V (max)
20	fuel pump relay driver : t86/2	ignition on	nbv
		engine cranking/running	1.25 V (max)
21	main relay driver : t86/1	ignition off	nbv
		ignition on/engine running	1.25 V (max)
22	SD warning lamp	ignition on, lamp on	1.25 V (max)
		engine running:	
		no faults present	nbv
		faults present, lamp on	1.25 V (max)
23	–		
24	OS signal (some models)	ignition on, OS multiplug	
		disconnected	0.4 to 0.5 V
		engine running, hot	200 to 1000 mV (switching)
		throttle fully-open	0.5 to 1.0 V
		deceleration (fuel cut-off)	0 to 0.5 V
		switching frequency	1 sec intervals (approx)
25	ignition system control unit : t8 (load signal)	ignition on	250-300 mV
		idle speed	370 mV
26	gear shift indicator (some models)		data not available
27	CFSV driver (some models) : t1	ignition on	nbv
		engine running, above idle, operating temperature:	
		CFSV inactive	nbv
		CFSV active	0 to 12 V (switching)
		duty cycle	0 to 99%
28	ignition system control unit : t4 (knock signal)	ignition on	900-950 mV
		engine running	7 V (approx)
29	earth	ignition on/engine running	0.25 V (max)
30	AT		data not available
31	–		
32	cold start valve driver : t1 (some models)	engine cranking:	
		above 16°C	nbv
		below 16°C	1.25 V (max)

Pin	Connection	Test condition	Measurements
33	ISCV signal : t1	ignition on	nbv
		engine running:	
		cold	6.0 to 6.5 V
		hot	7.0 to 9.0 V (approx)
34	VSS signal	vehicle in motion	0 to nbv (switching)
35	supply from ignition switch : t15	ignition on/engine running	nbv

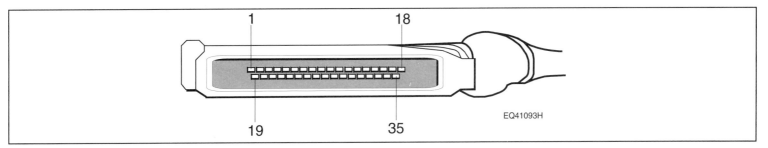

35 pin ECM multi-plug, Bosch LH2.4 Jetronic + EZ116K

Pin Table – Bosch LH3.2 Jetronic

Connector A

Pin	Connection	Test condition	Measurements
A1	TPS signal : t3	ignition on/engine running:	
		throttle closed	0.6 V
		throttle fully open	4.2 V
A2	TPS supply : t2	ignition on/engine running	5.0 V ± 0.1
A3-A7	–		
A8	MAF sensor return : t2	ignition on/engine running	0.25 V (max)
A9	injector driver : t1	ignition on	nbv
		idle speed	2.0 to 2.5 ms (2.1 ms typical)
A10	supply from battery : t30	ignition off/on/engine running	nbv
A11	–		
A12	MAF sensor signal : t1	ignition on	1.4 V (approx)
		idle	2.3 V increases with engine speed
A13	MAF sensor hot wire burn-off : t4	coolant above 65° C, rpm above 2500, switch off engine	hot wire glows for 1.0 second
A14	sensor return (TPS : t1, CTS : t1)	ignition on/engine running	0.25 V (max)
A15	CTS signal : t2	ignition on/engine running	20° C: 1.8 V
			80° C: 0.25 V
A16	ISCV driver : t3	ignition on	11.0 V
		engine running, idle speed:	
		cold	6.0 to 6.5 V
		hot	7.0 to 9.0 V
		duty cycle	33%
A17	ISCV driver : t1	ignition on	5.0 V
		engine running, idle speed:	
		cold	6.0 to 6.5 V
		hot	7.0 to 9.0 V
		duty cycle	66.5
A18	–		
A19	supply from relay : t87	ignition on/engine running	nbv
A20	earth	ignition on/engine running	0.25 V (max)
A21	–		
A22	OS signal : t3	ignition on, OS multiplug disconnected	0.4 to 0.5 V
		engine running, hot	200 to 1000 mV (switching)
		throttle fully-open	0.5 to 1.0 V
		deceleration (fuel cut-off)	0 to 0.5 V
		switching frequency	1 sec intervals (approx)

Pin Table – Bosch LH3.2 Jetronic (continued)

Connector A (continued)

Pin	Connection	Test condition	Measurements
A23	OS return : t4	ignition on/engine running	0.25 V (max)
A24	main relay driver : t86	ignition off	nbv
		ignition on/engine running	1.25 V (max)
A25	A/C clutch : t2	ignition on/engine running:	
		A/C compressor off	0 V
		A/C compressor on	nbv
A26-A27	–		
A28	OS heater driver : t1	ignition on	nbv
		engine running:	
		cold	1.25 V (max)
		hot	nbv
A29	earth	ignition on/engine running	0.25 V (max)
A30	supply from ignition switch : t15	ignition on/engine running	nbv

Connector B

Pin	Connection	Test condition	Measurements
B1-B4	–		
B5	SD connector		data not available
B6	–		
B7	SD warning lamp : t1	ignition on, lamp on	1.25 V (max)
		engine running:	
		no faults present, lamp off	nbv
		faults present, lamp on	1.25 V (max)
B8-B11	–		
B12	load signal to ignition ECM : tB12	engine running, idle:	
		frequency	34 Hz
		duty cycle	99.8 %
B13	–		
B14	knock signal from ignition ECM : tB14	engine running, KS active	0 to 5 V (switching)
B15-B17	–		
B18	cruise control		data not available
B19	–		
B20	TPS signal to ignition ECM : tB20	engine running:	
		idle speed	0.6 V
		full load	4.2 V
B21	RPM signal from ignition ECM : tB21	engine running, idle:	
		frequency (increase with speed)	32 to 36 Hz
		mean voltage	4 to 7 V
B22	–		
B23	temperature signal to ignition ECM : tB23	ignition on/engine running:	
		voltage/frequency	20° C: 6 V (mean), 46 Hz
		voltage/frequency	80° C: 6 V (mean), 22 Hz
B24	AT-ECM (if fitted): t14	ignition on/engine running:	
		AT in P or N	5 V
		AT not in P or N	0 V
B25	–		
B26	idle signal from ignition ECM : tB26	ignition on	11 V
		engine running, idle:	
		cooling fan on	0.7 V
		cooling fan off	nbv
B27-B28	–		
B29	trip computer		data not available
B30	–		

60 pin ECM Multi-plug, Bosch LH3.2 Jetronic

Pin Table – Bosch Motronic M1.0

Pin	Item	Test Condition	Measurements
1	ignition coil driver : t1	ignition on	nbv
		engine running:	
		dynamic volt drop	2.0 V (max)
		primary switching	200 V (min)
2	TS idle contact : t2	ignition on/engine running:	
		throttle closed	0 V
		throttle part open	5.0 V ± 0.1
4	ignition switch : t50	engine cranking	nbv
5	earth (inlet manifold)	ignition on/engine running	0.25 V (max)
6	AFS return : t6	ignition on/engine running	0.25 V (max)
7	AFS signal : t7	ignition on	0.20 to 0.60 V
		idle	0.50 to 0.60 V
		2000 rpm	0.75 to 1.0 V
		3000 rpm	1.20 to 2.50 V
		snap accelerate	3.00 to 4.50 V
		fully open	> 4.50 V
8	RPM sensor signal : t2	engine cranking	> 2.5 V AC (peak to peak)
		idle:	> 11.0 V AC (peak to peak)
		cruise:	> 14.0 V AC (peak to peak)
9	AFS supply : t9	ignition on/engine running	5.0 V ± 0.1
10-12	–		
13	CTS signal : t2 (dual resistor)	ignition on/engine running	80° C: 0.5 to 0.9 V
			20° C: 2.0 to 3.0 V
14	injectors, power amplifier : t16	engine cranking cold	11.0 to 12.0 ms
		engine running cold	3.0 to 3.5 ms
		engine cranking hot	4.0 to 4.5 ms
		engine running hot	2.0 to 2.5 ms
		2000 rpm	2.0 to 2.5 ms
		3000 rpm	2.0 to 2.5 ms
		snap acceleration	6.0 ms
		deceleration (fuel cut off)	0 ms
15	–		
16	earth (1985 only)	ignition on/engine running	0.25 V (max)
17-18	–		
19	earth	ignition on/engine running	0.25 V (max)
20	fuel pump relay driver : t86/1	ignition on	nbv
		engine cranking/running	1.25 V (max)
21	idle speed control ECM : t12	engine running	0 to nbv (switching)
22	ATS : (AFS : t22)	ignition on/engine running	20° C: 2.0 to 3.0 V
23	earth return (RPM sensor shield, TCATS) : t1	ignition on/engine running	0.25 V (max)
24	–		
25	TDC sensor return : t1	ignition on/engine running	0.25 V
26	TDC sensor signal : t2	engine cranking:	> 4.0 V AC (peak to peak)
		idle:	> 11.0 V AC (peak to peak)
		cruise:	> 14.0 V AC (peak to peak)
27	RPM sensor return : t1	ignition on/engine running	0.25 V
28-29	–		

Pin Table – Bosch Motronic M1.0 (continued)

Pin	Item	Test Condition	Measurements
30	TCATS signal (PTC) : t2	ignition on/engine running	0.1 to 4.9 V
		open circuit:	5.0 V ± 0.1
31-34	–		
35	supply from relay : t30	ignition on/engine running	nbv

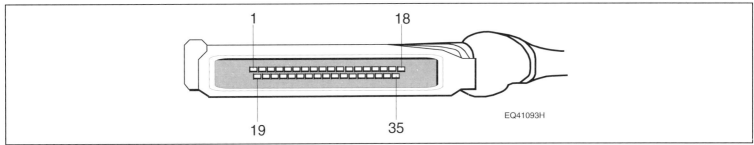

35 pin ECM multi-plug, Bosch Motronic 1.0

Pin Table – Bosch Motronic M1.8

Pin	Connection	Test condition	Measurements
1	amplifier control signal : t2	engine cranking/running	0.1 to 0.3 V (switching)
		frequency	6 Hz
2	amplifier control signal : t7	engine cranking/running	0.1 to 0.3 V (switching)
		frequency	6 Hz
3	fuel pump relay driver: t4	ignition on	nbv
		engine cranking/running	1.25 V (max)
4	ISCV driver : t3	ignition on	nbv
		engine running, idle speed:	
		cold	6.0 to 6.5 V
		hot	7.0 to 9.5 V
		duty cycle	40 to 60%
5	secondary air injection relay (if fitted)	engine running, cold:	
		inactive	nbv
		active	1.25 V (max)
6	tachometer	ignition on	11 V
		engine, idle	7 V
7	MAF sensor signal : t3	ignition on	1.5 V
		idle	2.5 V
8	camshaft sensor supply : t2	ignition on/engine running	5 V
9	VSS signal : t49	vehicle in motion	0 to 12 V (switching)
10	camshaft sensor signal : t3	engine running	0 to 5 V (switching)
11	KS1 (front) signal : t2	engine running, KS active	1.0 to 2.0 V AC (peak to peak)
12	TPS supply : t2	ignition on/engine running	5.0 V ± 0.1
13	amplifier control signal : t5	engine cranking/running	0.1 to 0.3 V (switching)
		frequency	6 Hz
14	engine cooling fan	ignition on/engine running:	
		engine coolant fan on	0 V
		engine coolant fan off	nbv
15	SD warning lamp : t1	ignition on, lamp on	1.25 V (max)
		engine running:	
		no faults present	nbv
		faults present, lamp on	1.25 V (max)
16	injector driver (cyls 3,5,6) : t1	ignition on	nbv
		engine running, cold	> 4.0 ms
		engine running, hot	4.0 ms
		snap acceleration	20 ms (approx)
		deceleration	0 ms (approx)

Pin	Connection	Test condition	Measurements
17	injector driver (cyls 1,2,4) : t1	ignition on	nbv
		engine running, cold	> 4.0 ms
		engine running, hot	4.0 ms
		snap acceleration	20 ms (approx)
		deceleration	0 ms (approx)
18	supply from battery : t30	ignition off/on/engine running	nbv
19	earth	ignition on/engine running	0.25 V (max)
20	amplifier control signal : t5	engine cranking/running	0.1 to 0.3 V (switching)
		frequency	6 Hz
21	amplifier control signal : t2	engine cranking/running	0.1 to 0.3 V (switching)
		frequency	6 Hz
22	ISCV driver : t1	ignition on	nbv
		engine running, idle speed:	
		cold	6.0 to 6.5 V
		hot	7.0 to 8.5 V
		duty cycle	50 to 70%
23	A/C control signal	ignition on:	
		A/C on	0 V
		A/C off	11 to 14 V
24	earth	ignition on/engine running	0.25 V (max)
25	MAF hot wire burn off : t4	coolant above 65° C, rpm above 2500, switch off engine	hot wire glows for 1.0 second
26	earth	ignition on/engine running	0.25 V (max)
27	supply from ignition switch : t15	ignition on/engine running	nbv
28	OS signal : t3	ignition on, OS multiplug disconnected	0.4 to 0.5 V
		engine running, hot	200 to 1000 mV (switching)
		throttle fully-open	0.5 to 1.0 V
		deceleration (fuel cut-off)	0 to 0.5 V
		switching frequency	1 sec intervals (approx)
29	KS2 (rear) signal : t2	engine running, KS active	1.0 to 2.0 V AC (peak to peak)
30	sensor return (KS1 : t1, KS2 : t1,CTS : t1)	ignition on/engine running	0.25 V (max)
31	amplifier control signal : t7	engine cranking/running	0.1 to 0.3 V (switching)
32	–		
33	EGR solenoid valve driver : t1 (if fitted)	ignition on	nbv
		engine running:	
		EGR inactive	nbv
		EGR active	1.25 V (max)
34	engine cooling fan	ignition on/engine running	
		engine coolant fan on	0 V
		engine coolant fan off	nbv
35	–		
36	main relay driver : t2	ignition off	nbv
		ignition on/engine running	1.25 V (max)
37	supply from ignition switch : t15	ignition on/engine running	nbv
38	connector (2 pin)		data not available
39	AT-ECM signal : tB16	ignition on	nbv
		engine running, idle	0.4 V
40	A/C compressor	ignition on/engine running, idle:	
		A/C compressor on	nbv
		A/C compressor off	0 V
41	A/C-ECM : t	ignition on/engine running, idle:	
		A/C off	nbv
		A/C on	0 V
42	AT-ECM P/N : tB15	ignition on/engine running, idle:	
		AT in P or N	6 V
		AT not in P or N	0.6 V
43	AT-ECM : tB5	ignition on	5 V
44	–		
45	CTS signal : t2	ignition on/engine running	20° C: 1.7 V
			50° C: 0.8/3.9 V (dual scales)
			90° C: 2.2 V

Pin Table – Bosch Motronic M1.8 (continued)

Pin	Connection	Test condition	Measurements
46	–		
47	camshaft sensor (inductive) return : t1	ignition on/engine running	0.25 V (max)
48	earth	ignition on/engine running	0.25 V (max)
49	AT-ECM : tB1	engine running:	
		idle	0.5 V
		full load	4.5 V
50	AT-ECM : tB7	ignition on	5.0 V
51	AT-ECM : tB6	ignition on	< 5.0 V
52	–		
53	TPS signal : t3	ignition on/engine running:	
		throttle closed	0.5 V
		throttle fully open	4.5 V
54	connector (2 pin)		data not available
55	SD connector		data not available

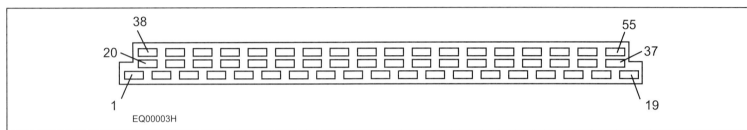

55 pin ECM multi-plug, Bosch Motronic 1.8

Pin Table – Bosch Motronic M4.3

Connector A

Pin	Connection	Test condition	Measurements
A1	–		
A2	KS2 (rear) signal : t2	engine running, KS active	1.0 to 2.0 V AC (peak to peak)
A3	MAF sensor return : t1	ignition on/engine running	0.25 V (max)
A4	MAF sensor signal : t4	engine running:	
		idle speed	0.7 to 1.0 V
		3000 rpm	1.25 V
		snap accelerate	3.00 to 3.50 V (approx)
A5	MAF sensor return : t2	ignition on/engine running	0.25 V (max)
A6	CAS signal : t2	engine cranking:	0.3 V AC
		idle:	1.5 V AC
A7	cooling fan relay : t1B	ignition on/engine running:	
		radiator fan on, low speed	1.25 V (max)
		radiator fan off, low speed	nbv
A8	–		
A9	injector driver (cyl 5) : t1	ignition on	nbv
		engine running, idle	2.2 to 3.6 ms
		snap acceleration	6.0 ms
		deceleration (fuel cut off)	0 ms (approx)
A10	injector driver (cyl 1) : t1	ignition on	nbv
		engine running, idle	2.2 to 3.6 ms
		snap acceleration	6.0 ms
		deceleration (fuel cut off)	0 ms (approx)
A11	ISCV driver : t3	ignition on	nbv
		engine running, idle speed:	
		cold	6.0 to 6.5 V
		hot	7.0 to 9.0 V
		duty cycle	30 to 60%

Pin	Connection	Test condition	Measurements
A12	supply from ignition switch : t15	ignition on/engine running	nbv
A13	earth	ignition on/engine running	0.25 V (max)
A14	OS heater driver : t1	ignition on	nbv
		engine running, idle:	
		heater on	1.25 V (max)
		heater off	nbv
A15	TPS sensor supply : t2	ignition on/engine running	5.0 V ± 0.1
A16	TPS signal : t1	ignition on/engine running:	
		throttle closed	1.0 V
		open	5.0 V (approx).
A17	sensor return (KS1 : t1, KS2 : t1)	ignition on/engine running	0.25 V (max)
A18	sensor return (CTS : t1, TPS : t3 camshaft sensor : t1)	ignition on/engine running	0.25 V (max)
A19	–		
A20	CAS signal : t1	engine cranking:	0.3 V AC
		idle:	1.5 V AC
A21	camshaft sensor signal : t2	ignition on	0 V or 5.0 V
		engine running:	
		idle	0 to 5.0 V (switching)
		idle frequency	7 Hz
A22	cooling fan relay : t2B	ignition on/engine running:	
		radiator fan on, high speed	1.25 V (max)
		radiator fan off, high speed	nbv
A23	injector driver (cyl 4) : t1	ignition on	nbv
		engine running, idle	2.2 to 3.6 ms
		snap acceleration	6.0 ms
		deceleration (fuel cut off)	0 ms (approx)
A24	injector driver (cyl 3) : t1	ignition on	nbv
		engine running, idle	2.2 to 3.6 ms
		snap acceleration	6.0 ms
		deceleration (fuel cut off)	0 ms (approx)
A25	ISCV driver : t1	ignition on	nbv
		engine running, idle speed:	
		cold	6.0 to 6.5 V
		hot	7.0 to 9.0 V
		duty cycle	30 to 60%
A26	supply from battery : t30	ignition off/on/engine running	nbv
A27	supply from main relay : t3	ignition on/engine running	nbv
A28	earth	ignition on/engine running	0.25 V (max)
A29	–		
A30	KS1 signal (front): t2	engine running, KS active	1.0 to 2.0 V AC (peak to peak)
A31	CTS sensor : t2	ignition on/engine running	20° C: 1.8 V
			100° C: 0.5 V
A32	OS signal : t3	ignition on, OS multiplug disconnected	0.4 to 0.5 V
		engine running, hot	200 to 1000 mV (switching)
		throttle fully-open	0.5 to 1.0 V
		deceleration (fuel cut-off)	0 to 0.5 V
A33	OS return : t4	ignition on/engine running	0.25 V (max)
A34-A35	–		
A36	camshaft sensor supply : t3	ignition on/engine running	nbv
A37	–		
A38	injector driver (cyl 2) : t1	ignition on	nbv
		engine running, idle	2.2 to 3.6 ms
		snap acceleration	6.0 ms
		deceleration (fuel cut off)	0 ms (approx)
A39	CFSV driver : t1	ignition on	nbv
		engine running, above idle, operating temperature:	
		CFSV inactive	nbv
		CFSV active	0 to 12 V (switching)
		duty cycle	0 to 99%

Pin Table – Bosch Motronic M4.3 (continued)

Connector A (continued)

Pin	Connection	Test condition	Measurements
A40	EGR solenoid : t2 (if fitted)	ignition on/engine running	nbv
A41	main relay driver : t1	ignition off	nbv
		ignition on/engine running	1.25 V (max)
A42	earth	ignition on/engine running	0.25 V (max)
A43	–		

Connector B

Pin	Connection	Test condition	Measurements
B1	suspension G-force sensor signal : t1	ignition on/engine running	5 V
B2	AT-ECM signal : t2	ignition on/engine running	9 to 12 V
B3	AT-ECM signal : t3	ignition on/engine running	9 to 12 V
B4	AT-ECM signal : t4	ignition on/engine running	9 to 12 V
B5	SD connector : t2	ignition on/engine running	nbv
B6	A/C pressure switch : t9	ignition on/engine running:	
		engine running, idle:	
		A/C compressor on	nbv
		A/C compressor off	0V
B7	SD warning lamp : t26	ignition on, lamp on	1.25 V (max)
		engine running:	
		no faults present	nbv
		faults present, lamp on	1.25 V (max)
B8	–		
B9	A/C pressure sensor : t2	ignition on/engine running, idle:	
		A/C off	nbv
		A/C on	0V
B10	–		
B11	amplifier control signal : t4	engine cranking/running	0 to 5.0 V (switching)
B12	AT-ECM signal : t12	ignition on	0.8 V
		engine running, idle	35 Hz
B13-B17	–		
B18	VSS signal : t3	vehicle in motion	0 to 12 V (switching)
B19	–		
B20	AT-ECM signal : t20	ignition on/engine running:	
		idle	0.5 V
		throttle fully open	4.2 V
B21	tachometer		data not available
B22	–		
B23	engine coolant temperature gauge : t32	ignition on/engine running:	20° C: 40 Hz
			100° C: 21 Hz
B24	AT-ECM signal : t14	ignition on/engine running:	
		AT in P or N	nbv
		AT not in P or N	0 V
B25	AT- ECM supply from relay : t87	ignition on/engine running:	
		relay on	0 V
		relay off	nbv
B26	AT-ECM signal : t15	ignition on/engine running	< 1 V
		idle	nbv
B27	fuel pump relay driver : t31B	ignition on	nbv
		engine cranking/running	1.25 V (max)
B28	A/C pressure sensor earth : t2	ignition on	0 V
B29	A/C pressure sensor : t3	ignition on	5 V
B30-B31	–		
B32	suspension G-force sensor return : t3	ignition on/engine running	2.5 V
B33-B35	–		
B36	AT-ECM signal : t22		data not available
B37-B38	–		
B39	trip computer		data not available
B40	A/C supply from relay : t85	ignition on/engine running	nbv

Pin	Connection	Test condition	Measurements
B41	TBCV driver : t1	ignition on	nbv
		engine running:	
		TBCV inactive	nbv
		TBCV active	0 to 12 V (switching)
		duty cycle	0 to 99%
B42	AT-ECM signal : t1	ignition on/engine running	nbv
		engine running, idle	0 to 3 V
B43	–		

86 pin ECM multi-plug, Bosch Motronic 4.3

Pin Table – Fenix 3B MPi

Pin	Connection	Test condition	Measurements
1	earth	ignition on/engine running	0.25 V (max)
2	earth shield	ignition on/engine running	0.25 V (max)
3	supply from ignition switch : t15	ignition on/engine running	nbv
4	supply from battery : t30	ignition off/on/engine running	nbv
5	CFSV driver : t1	fuel pump relay t87 and t30	
		bridge with jumper wire	nbv
		engine running:	
		inactive	nbv
		active	0 to 12 V (switching)
6	fuel pump relay driver : t85	ignition on	nbv
		engine cranking/running	1.25 V (max)
7	A/C		data not available
8	–		
9	TPS signal : t3	ignition on/engine running:	
		throttle closed	0.8 V (approx)
		throttle open	4.5 V (approx)
10	coolant pump relay driver : t86	ignition off/on	nbv
		engine running, inactive	nbv
		engine running, active	1.25 V (max)
11	CAS sensor : tA	engine cranking	> 2.5 V AC (peak to peak)
		idle:	> 11.0 V AC (peak to peak)
		cruise:	> 14.0 V AC (peak to peak
12	SD connector : t2		data not available
13	–		
14	ATS signal : tB	ignition on/engine running	20° C: 2.0 V (approx)
15	CTS signal : tA	ignition on/engine running	20° C: 2.0 V (approx)
			50° C: 0.5 V (approx)
			80° C: 0.35 V (approx)
16	sensor supply (MAP sensor : tC, TPS : t2)	ignition on/engine running	5.0 V ± 0.1
17	sensor return (OS : t4, ATS : t1, CTS : t1, TPS : t1, MAP : tA)	ignition on/engine running	0.25 V (max)
18	–		
19	supply from main relay : t87	ignition on	11.0 V
		engine running	nbv
20	main relay driver : t85	ignition on	11.0 V
		engine running	1.25 V (max)

Pin Table – Fenix 3B MPi (continued)

Pin	Connection	Test condition	Measurements
21	injectors driver : t1	fuel pump relay t87 and t30	
		bridge with jumper wire	nbv
		engine cranking/running	nbv
		engine running hot	2.0 to 3.0 ms
		snap acceleration	> 6.0 ms
		deceleration (fuel cut off)	0 ms
22	–		
23	SD connector		data not available
24	ISCV signal : t2	fuel pump relay t87 and t30	
		bridge with jumper wire	nbv
		idle speed	2.0 to 12 V (switching)
25	SD connector		data not available
26	–		
27	amplifier control signal : tB	engine cranking/running	0 to 5.0 V (switching)
28	CAS return : tB	engine cranking/running	0.25 V (max)
29	–		
30	signal from AT		data not available
31	KS signal : tA	engine running, KS active	1.0 V AC peak to peak (approx)
32	KS return : tB	ignition on/engine running	0.25 V
33	MAP sensor signal : t2	ignition on	> 4.0 V
		engine running, WOT	> 4.0 V
		50 kPa	2.2 V
34	–		
35	OS signal	ignition on, OS multiplug disconnected	0.4 to 0.5 V
		engine running, hot	200 to 1000 mV (switching)
		throttle fully-open	0.5 to 1.0 V
		deceleration (fuel cut-off)	0 to 0.5 V
		switching frequency	1 sec intervals (approx)

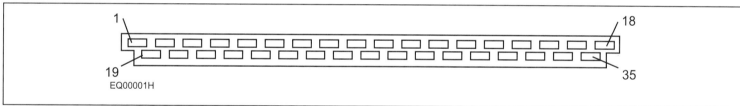

1 18
19 35
EQ00001H

35 pin ECM multi-plug, Fenix 3B MPi

Pin Table – Fenix 3BF SPi

Pin	Connection	Test condition	Measurements
1	earth	ignition on/engine running	0.25 V (max)
2	earth	ignition on/engine running	0.25 V (max)
3	VSS signal	drive wheels rotating or vehicle in motion	0 to 12 V (switching)
4	supply from battery : t30	ignition off/on/engine running	nbv
5	CFSV driver	ignition on	nbv briefly then 0 V
		engine running, above idle,	operating temperature:
		CFSV inactive	nbv
		CFSV active	0 to 12 V (switching)
		duty cycle	0 to 99%
6	fuel pump relay driver: t85	ignition on	nbv
		engine cranking/running	1.25 V (max)
7	air conditioning		data not available
8	idle switch : t3	ignition on/engine running:	
		throttle closed	0 V
		throttle fully open	5.0 V

Pin	Connection	Test condition	Measurements
9	TPS signal : t4	ignition on/engine running:	
		throttle closed	0.7 V
		throttle open	4.5 V
10	–		
11	CAS signal : tB	engine cranking	> 4.0 V AC (peak to peak)
		idle	> 8.0 V AC (peak to peak)
		cruise	>14.0 V AC (peak to peak)
12	SD connector		data not available
13	–		
14	ATS signal : t4	ignition on/engine running	20° C: 2.00 to 2.50 V
15	CTS signal : t2	ignition on/engine running	20° C: 2.00 to 2.50 V
			80° C: 0.30 to 0.50 V
16	sensor supply (MAP sensor : tC, TPS : t2)	ignition on/engine running	5.0 V ± 0.1
17	sensor return (MAP sensor : tA, CTS : t1, TPS : t1, ATS : t1, idle switch : t4)	ignition on/engine running	0.25 V (max)
18	tachometer		data not available
19	supply from main relay : t87	ignition on/engine running	nbv
20	main relay driver : t85	ignition off	
		ignition on/engine running	1.25 V (max)
21	injector driver : t3	ignition on	nbv briefly then 0 V
		engine running, hot:	
		idle	0.7 ms
		deceleration (fuel cut off)	0 ms
22	supply from ignition switch : t15	ignition on/engine running	nbv
23	stepper motor : t1	idle speed, active	0 to 5.0 V (switching)
24	stepper motor : t2	idle speed, active	0 to 5.0 V (switching)
25	cranking signal : t50	engine cranking	nbv
26	–		
27	amplifier control signal : tB	engine cranking/running	0 to 5.0 V (switching)
28	CAS return : tA	engine running	0.25 V (max)
29	supply from ignition switch : t15	ignition on/engine running	nbv
30	air conditioning		data not available
31	KS signal : tB	engine running, KS active	1.0 to 2.0 V AC (peak to peak)
32	KS return : tA	ignition on/engine running	0.25 V
33	MAP sensor signal : tB	ignition on	5.0 V
		engine running:	
		WOT	> 4.0 V
		250 mbar	3.4 V
		500 mbar	2.0 V
34	–		
35	OS signal : t3	ignition on, OS multiplug disconnected	0.4 to 0.5 V
		engine running, hot	200 to 1000 mV (switching)
		throttle fully-open	0.5 to 1.0 V
		deceleration (fuel cut-off)	0 to 0.5 V
		switching frequency	1 sec intervals (approx)

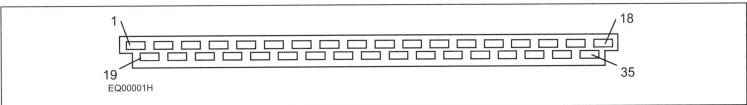

1

18

19

35

EQ00001H

35 pin ECM multi-plug, Fenix 3BF SPi

Pin Table – Fenix 5.1

Pin	Connection	Test condition	Measurements
1	–		
2	earth	ignition on/engine running	0.25 V (max)
3	earth	ignition on/engine running	0.25 V (max)
4	injector driver (cylinder 3) : t1	ignition on	nbv
		engine running, cold	> 3.5 ms
		engine running, hot	3.5 ms
		snap acceleration	20 ms (approx)
		deceleration (fuel cut off)	0 ms (approx)
5	–		
6	camshaft sensor signal : t2	ignition on	5.0 V or 0 V
		engine running	0 to 5 V (switching)
7	AT-ECM : t11	ignition on:	
		AT in P or N	5 V
		AT not in P or N	0.5 V (max)
8	KS signal : t1	idle speed	5.0 V
		> 4000 rpm	variable
9	–		
10	A/C pressure switch	ignition on	0 V
		engine running, idle speed:	
		A/C on	10 V
		A/C off	0 V
11	SD connector : t11		data not available
12	–		
13	trip computer		data not available
14	–		
15	CTS signal : t2	ignition on/engine running	20° C: 2 V
			80° C: 0.5 V
			100° C: 0.22 V
16	MAP sensor signal : tB	ignition on	5.0 V
		engine running, WOT	> 4.0 V
		250 mbar	3.4 V
		500 mbar	2.0 V
17	OS signal : t3	ignition on, OS multiplug disconnected	0.4 to 0.5 V
		engine running, hot	200 to 1000 mV (switching)
		throttle fully-open	0.5 to 1.0 V
		deceleration (fuel cut-off)	0 to 0.5 V
		switching frequency	1 sec intervals (approx)
18	OS return : t4	ignition on/engine running	0.25 V (max)
19	TPS signal : tC	ignition on/engine running:	
		throttle closed	0.7 V
		throttle open	4.7 V
20	ATS signal : t2	ignition on/engine running	20° C: 2 V
21-22	–		
23	engine radiator fan motor relay	ignition on/engine running:	
		radiator fan off	nbv
		radiator fan on	1.0 V (max)
24	supply from ignition switch : t15	ignition on/engine running	nbv
25	injector driver (cylinder 2) : t1	ignition on	nbv
		engine running, cold	> 3.5 ms
		engine running, hot	3.5 ms
		snap acceleration	20 ms (approx)
		deceleration (fuel cut off)	0 ms (approx)
26	SD warning lamp : t1	ignition on, lamp on	1.25 V (max)
		engine running:	
		no faults present	nbv
		faults present, lamp on	1.25 V (max)
27	secondary air pump relay driver : t4	ignition off	nbv
		engine running:	
		air pump on	< 1.0 V
		air pump off	nbv

Pin	Connection	Test condition	Measurements
28	ignition coil driver (cyls 1& 4) : t1	ignition on	nbv
		engine running:	
		dynamic volt drop	2.0 V (max)
		primary switching	200 V (min)
29	ignition coil driver (cyls 2 & 3) : t1	ignition on	nbv
		engine running:	
		dynamic volt drop	2.0 V (max)
		primary switching	200 V (min)
30	injector driver (cylinder 4) : t1	ignition on	nbv
		engine running, cold	> 3.5 ms
		engine running, hot	3.5 to 5.0 ms
		snap acceleration	20 ms (approx)
		deceleration (fuel cut off)	0 ms (approx)
31	–		
32	supply from battery : t30	ignition off/on/engine running	nbv
33	CAS signal : t2	engine running, idle	1.8 V AC
34	CAS signal : t1	engine running, idle	1.8 V AC
35	immobiliser control module : t6	ignition on/engine running	2 to 4 V (switching)
36-37	–		
38	SD connector : 15		data not available
39-40	–		
41	traction control – ECM/AT-ECM	ignition on	50 Hz
		throttle closed	3 ms
		throttle fully open	15 ms
42	traction control – ECM signal	ignition on/engine running	5 V after 3 seconds
		engine running, idle	2 V with traction control
43	tachometer	ignition on	0 V
		engine running, idle	25 Hz
44	sensor return (MAP : tA, KS : t2, CTS : t1)	ignition on/engine running	0.25 V (max)
45	sensor supply (MAP sensor : tC, TPS : tB, camshaft sensor : t3)	ignition on/engine running	5.0 V ± 0.1
46	sensor return (TPS : tA, ATS : t1, camshaft sensor : t1)	ignition on/engine running	0.25 V (max)
47	–		
48	main relay driver : t4	ignition on	nbv
		engine cranking/running	1.25 V (max)
49	–		
50	CFSV driver : t1	ignition on	nbv
		engine running, above idle, operating temperature:	
		CFSV inactive	nbv
		CFSV active	0 to 12 V (switching)
		duty cycle	0 to 99%
51	A/C clutch relay	ignition on	10 V
		engine running, idle:	
		A/C off	10 V
		A/C on	< 1.0 V
52	supply from main relay : t2	ignition on/engine running	nbv
53	injector driver (cylinder 1) : t1	ignition on	nbv
		engine running, cold	> 3.5 ms
		engine running, hot	3.5 to 5.0 ms
		snap acceleration	20 ms (approx)
		deceleration (fuel cut off)	0 ms (approx)
54	ISCV driver : t1	ignition on	nbv
		engine running, idle speed:	
		cold	6.0 to 6.5 V
		hot	7.0 to 10.0 V
		duty cycle	15 to 25%
55	–		

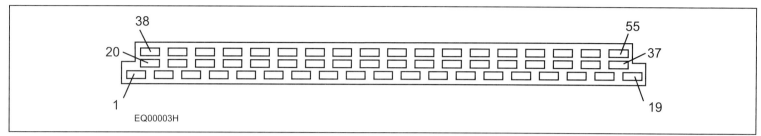

55 pin ECM multi-plug, Fenix 5.1

Pin Table – Fenix 5.2

Connector A

Pin	Connection	Test condition	Measurements
A1	ISCV driver : t1	ignition on	nbv
		engine running, idle speed:	
		cold	6.0 to 6.5 V
		hot	7.0 to 9.0 V
		duty cycle	30 to 60%
A2	KS1 signal (front) : t1	engine running, KS active	> 0.1 V AC
A3	ATS signal : t1	ignition on/engine running:	20° C: 2.5 V
A4	MAP sensor signal : tB	ignition on	5.0 V
		engine running:	
		wide open throttle (WOT)	5.0 V
		idle speed	0.9 to 1.4 V
A5	–		
A6	CAS signal : t2	engine running, idle	1.2 V AC
A7	engine coolant blower motor relay : tB	ignition on/engine running:	
		coolant blower motor off	nbv
		coolant blower motor on	1.25 V (max)
A8	module cooling fan (if fitted)	ignition on/engine running:	
		cooling fan on	1.25 V (max)
		cooling fan off	nbv
A9	injector driver (cylinder 5) : t1	ignition on/engine running	nbv
		engine running, idle speed	3.0 ms
A10	injector driver (cylinder 1) : t1	ignition on/engine running	nbv
		engine running, idle speed	3.0 ms
A11	–		
A12	supply from ignition switch : t15	ignition on/engine running	nbv
A13	earth	ignition on/engine running	0.25 V (max)
A14	OS signal : t3	ignition on, OS multiplug disconnected	0.4 to 0.5 V
		engine running, hot	200 to 1000 mV (switching)
		throttle fully-open	0.5 to 1.0 V
		deceleration (fuel cut-off)	0 to 0.5 V
		switching frequency	1 sec intervals (approx)
A15	sensor return (MAP sensor : tC, TPS : t2)	ignition on/engine running	0.25 V (max)
A16	TPS signal : t3	ignition on/engine running:	
		throttle closed	0.5 V
		throttle fully open	4.2 V
A17	KS return : t2	ignition on/engine running	0 V
A18	sensor return (MAP sensor : tA, ATS : t1, camshaft sensor : t1, TPS : t1, CTS : t1)	ignition on/engine running	0.25 V (max)
A19	–		
A20	CAS return : t1	engine running	0.25 V (max)
A21	camshaft sensor signal : t2	engine running	0 to 5 V (switching)
A22	engine coolant blower motor relay : t2B	engine running, idle:	
		coolant blower on	1.25 V (max)
		coolant blower off	nbv

Pin	Connection	Test condition	Measurements
A23	injector driver (cylinder 4) : t1	ignition on/engine running	nbv
		engine running, idle speed	3.0 ms
A24	injector driver (cylinder 3) : t1	ignition on/engine running	nbv
		engine running, idle speed	3.0 ms
A25	–		
A26	supply from battery : t30	ignition off/on/engine running	nbv
A27	supply from main relay : t3	ignition on/engine running	nbv
A28	earth	ignition on/engine running	0.25 V (max)
A29	–		
A30	KS2 signal (rear) : t2	engine running, KS active	> 0.1 V AC
A31	CTS sensor	ignition on/engine running	20° C: 1.8 V
			80° C: 0.25 V
A32	OS signal : t3	ignition on, OS multiplug disconnected	0.4 to 0.5 V
		engine running, hot	200 to 1000 mV (switching)
		throttle fully-open	0.5 to 1.0 V
		deceleration (fuel cut-off)	0 to 0.5 V
		switching frequency	1 sec intervals (approx)
A33	OS return : t4	ignition on/engine running	0.25 V (max)
A34-A35	–		
A36	camshaft sensor supply : t3	ignition on/engine running	9.0 V (min)
A37	–		
A38	injector driver (cylinder 2) : t1	ignition on/engine running	nbv
		engine running, idle speed	3.0 ms
A39-A40	–		
A41	main relay driver : t1	ignition off	
		ignition on/engine running	1.25 V (max)
A42	earth	ignition on/engine running	0.25 V (max)
A43	–		

Connector B

Pin	Connection	Test condition	Measurements
B1	–		
B2	AT-ECM signal : t2	ignition on/engine running	nbv
B3	AT-ECM signal : t3	ignition on/engine running	nbv
B4	AT-ECM : t4	ignition on/engine running	nbv
B5	SD connector		data not available
B6	A/C pressure switch	ignition on/engine running	0 V
		engine running, idle	
		A/C off	1.25 V (max)
		A/C on	nbv
B7	SD warning lamp : t1	ignition on, lamp on	1.25 V (max)
		engine running:	
		no faults present	nbv
		faults present, lamp on	1.25 V (max)
B8	–		
B9	A/C pressure switch : t3	ignition on/engine running	0 to 5 V increasing with pressure
B10	–		
B11	amplifier control signal : t5	engine cranking/running	0 to 5.0 V (switching)
B12	AT-ECM : t12	ignition on/engine running	
		idle speed:	nbv
		frequency	34 Hz
		duty cycle	99.8%
B13-B17	–		
B18	VSS signal	vehicle in motion	0 to 12 V (switching)
B19	–		
B20	AT-ECM : t20	ignition on/engine running:	
		throttle closed	0.5 V
		throttle fully open	4.2 V
B21	tachometer	ignition on	nbv
		engine running, idle	7 V
		frequency	27 Hz
B22	–		

Pin Table – Fenix 5.2 (continued)

Connector B (continued)

Pin	Connection	Test condition	Measurements
B23	engine coolant temperature gauge	ignition on/engine running:	7 V
B24	AT-ECM signal : t24	ignition on/engine running:	
		AT in P or N	nbv
		AT not in P or N	0.6 V
B25	A/C pressure switch	engine running, idle:	
		A/C on	nbv
		A/C off	1.25 V (max)
B26	–		
B27	fuel pump relay driver: t31B	ignition on	nbv
		engine cranking/running	1.25 V (max)
B28	AT-ECM : t1	ignition on/engine running	0 V
B29	A/C pressure switch : t3	ignition on/engine running	5 V
B30-B37	–		
B38	secondary air pump relay : t1B	engine running, cold:	
	(if secondary air fitted)	secondary air pump on	< 1.0 V
		secondary air pump off	nbv
B39	trip computer		data not available
B40	A/C relay	ignition on	0 V
		engine running:	
		A/C off	nbv
		A/C on	1.25 V (max)
B41-B43	–		

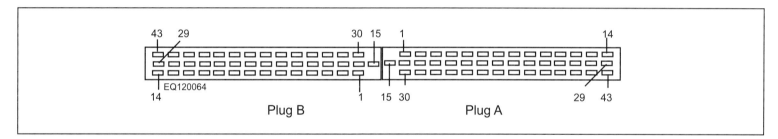

33.10 86 pin ECM multi-plug, Fenix 5.2

Wiring Diagrams

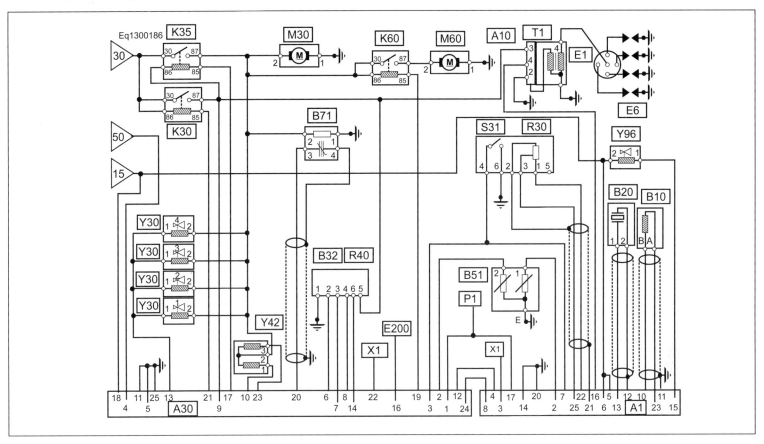

System wiring diagram, Bosch LH2.2 Jetronic + EZ210/EZ210Ka

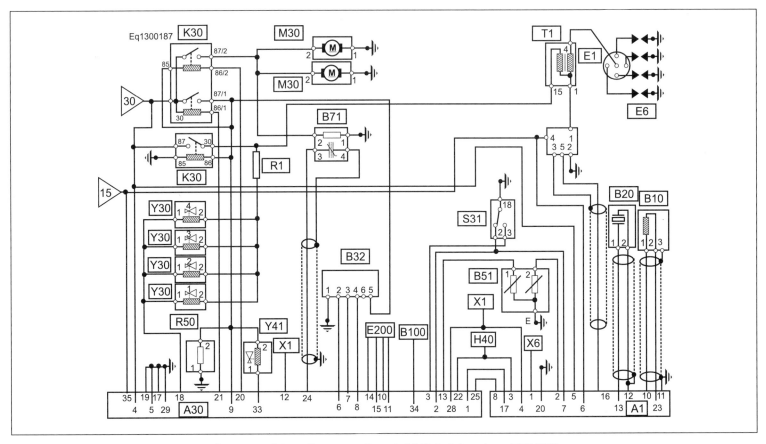

System wiring diagram, Bosch LH2.4 Jetronic + EZ116K

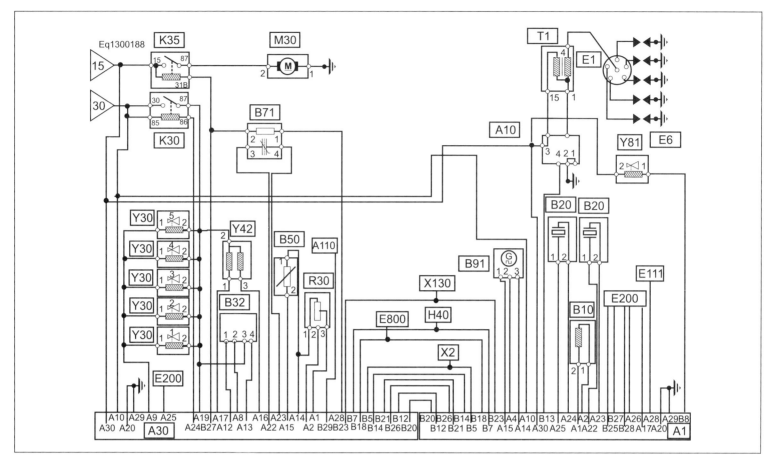

System wiring diagram, Bosch LH3.2 Jetronic

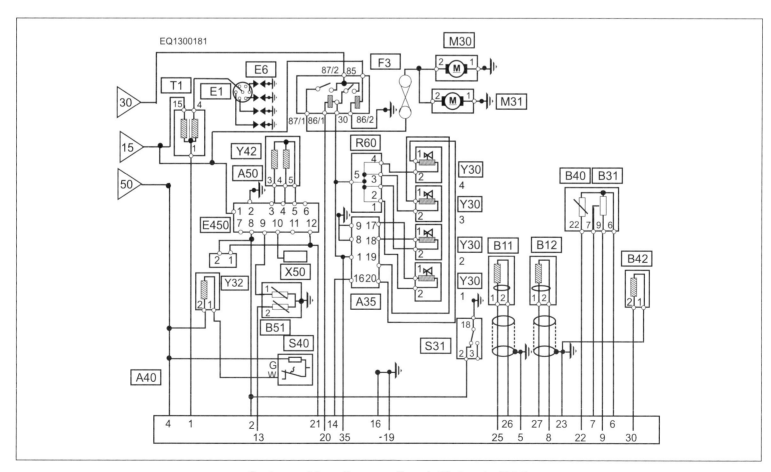

System wiring diagram, Bosch Motronic M1.0

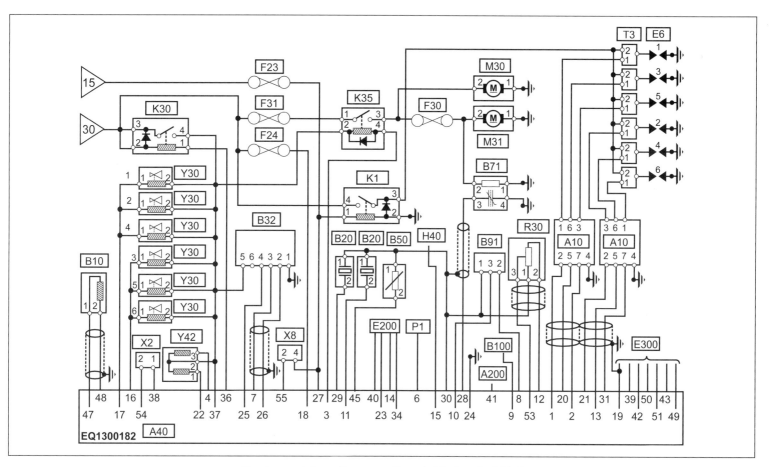

System wiring diagram, Bosch Motronic M1.8

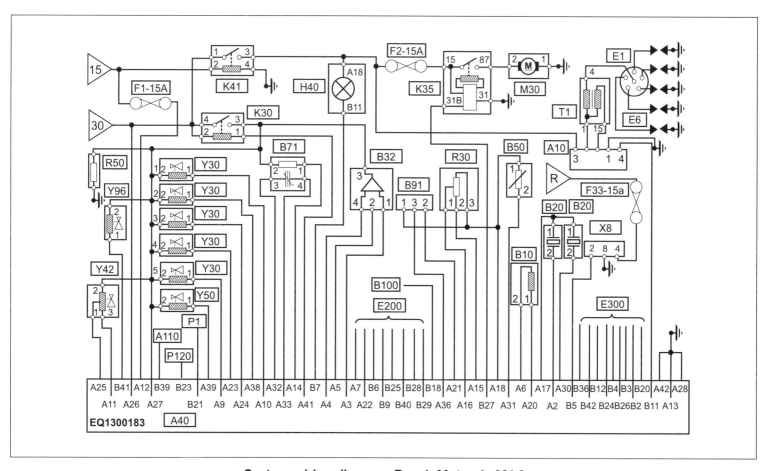

System wiring diagram, Bosch Motronic M4.3

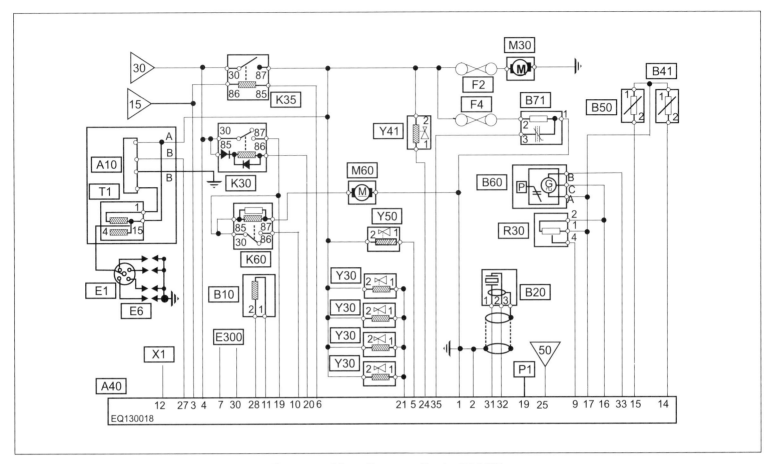

System wiring diagram, Fenix 3B MPi

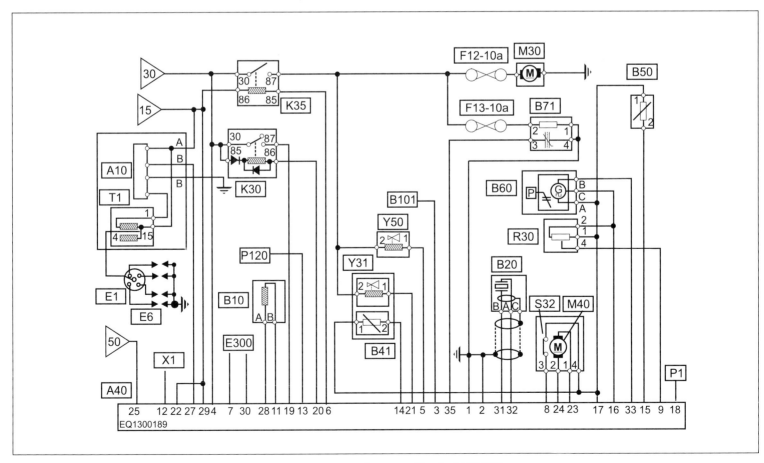

System wiring diagram, Fenix 3BF SPi

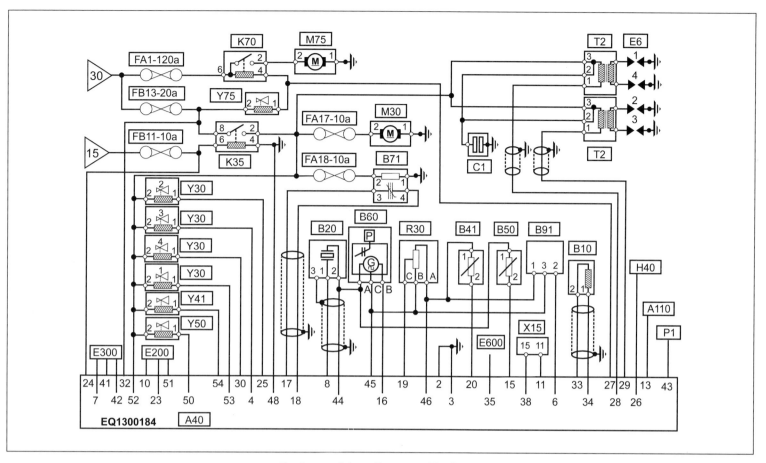

System wiring diagram, Fenix 5.1

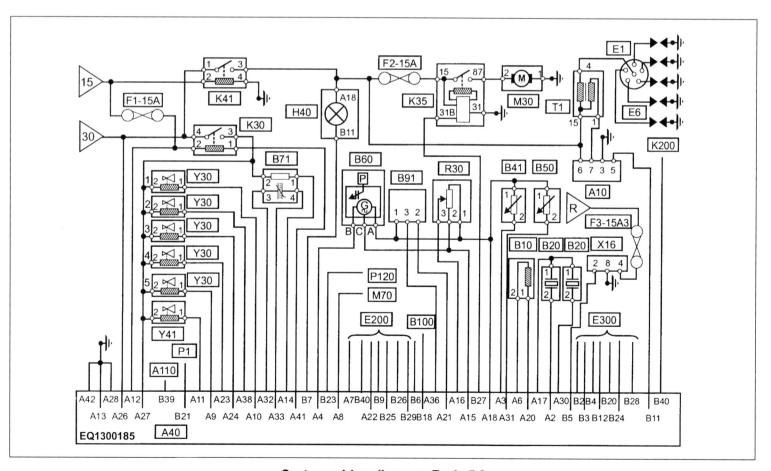

System wiring diagram, Fenix 5.2

Notes

Abbreviations and Glossary of technical terms

A

A/C (Air Conditioning)

AATS (Ambient Air Temperature Sensor)

AAV (Auxiliary Air valve)

ABS (Anti-lock Braking System)

AC (Alternating Current) An electric current that first flows in one direction and then the opposite.

ACAV (Variable Acoustic Characteristic Induction - PSA term) See Induction ChangeOver Valve (ICOV) and Variable Induction System (VIS)

ACC (Air Conditioning compressor Clutch - Ford term)

ACS (Air Conditioning Switch - Ford term)

ACT (Air Charge Temperature - Ford term - see ATS) Usually refers to a sensor that is located within the inlet manifold or throttle body, as distinct to one that is integrated into the AFS.

Actuator A device controlled by the ECM. Examples are injectors, ISCV etc.

Actuator driver Refer to driver (actuator), relay driver, control signal and final stage

ACW (anti clockwise) Direction of rotation

Adaptive system An EMS that is able to learn the best setting during changing operating or engine conditions is said to be adaptive.

ADC (Analogue to Digital Converter)

AFM (Air Flow Meter - see AFS)

AFR (Air Fuel Ratio.) Ratio of air to fuel by weight in a vaporised charge: i.e. 14.7 kilos of air to 1.0 kilo of fuel. See AFR/Lambda chart.

AFR/Lambda Chart

AFR: = 14.7: 1 by weight

AFR	Lambda
0.7	10.29
0.8	11.76
0.9	13.23
0.97	14.26) Lambda
1.0	14.70) window
1.04	15.29)
1.1	16.17
1.2	17.64
1.3	19.11

AFS (Air Flow Sensor) A sensor that measures the volume of air being drawn into the engine and passes this to the ECM as an electrical signal so that the ECM can calculate the load factor and compute an appropriate injection duration. Common types of AFS would include hot-wire & hot film (Mass Air Flow), Karmen Vortex and vane (mechanical).

ALDL (Assembly Line Diagnostic Link) The name given to the self diagnostic connector used on GM vehicles.

Air Air is a mixture of nitrogen (79%), oxygen (20%), carbon dioxide (0.04%) and inert gases (0.06%).

Alternator A current generating device used in a vehicle charging system.

Ammeter An instrument for measuring current in amperes.

Amp (abbreviation for ampere) A unit measurement of current flow.

Amplifier In a conventional ignition, the CB switches the negative side of the coil on and off to produce a spark. The electronic system is very similar in operation but uses (typically) a pulse generator and amplifier to achieve the same result.

A pulse generator provides the amplifier with correctly timed electrical pulses to trigger the ignition. The generated pulse is too weak to operate the switching transistor and must be amplified. The amplifier senses the trigger pulse and amplifies the voltage to the correct level to operate the switching transistor. The coil negative (-) terminal is thus switched on by the amplifier circuitry to build the magnetic field, and switched off by the switching transistor to collapse the magnetic field and induce the secondary spark. In an EMS, the amplifier may be an integral part of the ECM, or may be a separate amplifier that is switched by the ECM. When located within the ECM, no separate wiring is required. However, if the amplifier fails, the only course of action is to renew the ECM.

Amplitude

Square waveform: Difference between the maximum and minimum voltage.

AC waveform: Difference between zero and either the maximum or minimum peak. The positive amplitude is likely to be slightly greater than the negative amplitude in CAS waveforms.

Analogue signal An analogue signal is defined as a continuous signal that can change by an infinitely small amount. Any sensor that meets these conditions can also be called an analogue sensor. Typically, an instrument that uses a needle to progressively sweep across a fixed scale may be used to measure an analogue signal. Any change in the signal will cause the needle to move by a similar amount. One example would be the throttle pot. As the throttle is opened and closed, the voltage output signal from the throttle pot increases and decreases and an analogue signal is passed to the ECM.

Annular coil A type of signal generator that utilises a coiled wire magnet attached to a stator plate. The plate contains a number of magnetised upright arms equal to the number of cylinders and also equal to the number of arms on the reluctor.

APS (Absolute Pressure Sensor - see MAP sensor)

APS (Atmospheric Pressure Sensor – see BPS)

ASV (Air Switching Valve) A vacuum switching valve - often found on Asian vehicles.

Asynchronous Refers to an injection system that is not synchronised to the ignition. Asynchronous pulses may occur at a set time interval or be intermittent in operation.

AT (Automatic Transmission)

ATDC (After Top Dead Centre.) A point in the four stroke cycle where the piston has passed TDC and is descending.

ATF (Automatic Transmission Fluid.)

Atmospheric pressure The weight of atmosphere per unit area. At sea level the atmospheric pressure is 14.7 psi absolute or 102 KPa. See pressure conversion table under 'Pressure'.

ATR (Automatic Transmission Relay - Ford term)

ATS (Air Temperature Sensor) A thermistor that changes in resistance according to temperature. Most ATS usually work on the NTC principle. However, the ATS fitted to a number of Renix equipped EMS may be NTC or PTC. As the temperature changes, the thermistor resistance changes, and thus the ECM is able to calculate the air temperature from the level of voltage (or current) that is registered on the sensor signal wire.

B

Backprobe A method of obtaining voltage from the multi-plug pin of an electronic component or sensor. The multi-plug must remain connected to the component. The multi-plug insulating boot should be peeled back and the voltmeter positive probe attached to the relevant pin - ignition key on. **Note:** *In this book the multi-plug diagram shows the terminals of the harness connector. When back-probing the multi-plug (or viewing the sensor connector terminals), the terminal positions will be reversed.*

Ballast resistor A current compensating device that alters current flow in direct proportion to the temperature of the resistor. When used in the primary ignition circuit it serves two purposes.
1) *By providing the proper current level to a low primary resistance coil, it promotes cool coil running under all operating conditions.*
2) *When a full 12 volt by-pass supply is introduced to the coil under cranking, the coil output will be greater and starting will therefore be aided.*

The ballast resistor was mainly use in conventional CB ignition systems to compensate in part for some of the deficiencies of that system. A number of the early electronic ignition systems, that were not of the constant energy type, also utilised a ballast resistor for current control purposes. The ballast resistor can also be found in other circuits where current compensation is necessary. An example would be the fuel pump circuit on the Lucas LH system fitted to some Rover fuel injected systems.

Banked or simultaneous injection Injectors connected in parallel circuits. In some four cylinder engines the four injectors may be connected together so that they all open at the same moment. In other four cylinder systems, the four injectors are connected in two banks of two cylinders. However, all injectors may still be actuated simultaneously. In a six-cylinder engine the six injectors may be connected in two banks of three cylinders. In an eight-cylinder engine the eight injectors may be connected in two banks of four cylinders. In a twelve-cylinder engine the twelve injectors may be connected in four banks of three cylinders.

Bar A unit of pressure. One bar is almost equal to atmospheric pressure. See pressure conversion table under 'pressure'.

Barometric pressure Equal to atmospheric pressure. At sea-level, this is 100 KPa. See pressure conversion table under 'pressure'.

Battery A storage device for electrical energy in chemical form. The primary function of the battery is to provide ignition current during the starting period and power to operate the starter motor. This must be accomplished irrespective of adverse temperature conditions. The battery also serves, for a limited time, as a current source to satisfy the electrical demands of the vehicle, which are in excess of the generator output.

BBDC (Before Bottom Dead Centre)

BOB (Break Out Box) A box that connects between the ECM and its multiplug. Each terminal in the box is thus connected in series to the equivalent ECM pin. Easy access to the ECM input and output signals is thus possible without directly probing the ECM pins.

BOO (Brake On/Off switch - Ford term)

BPC (Boost Pressure Control solenoid (turbo) - Ford term)

BPS (Barometric Pressure Sensor) A sensor to measure atmospheric pressure.

BTDC (Before Top Dead Centre) A point in the four stroke cycle where the piston is approaching TDC and is ascending.

Burn time See Spark duration.

C

C (Celsius or Centigrade) Measurement of temperature. Centigrade is also used as a measurement of angle.

Cable Heavy electrical wire used to conduct high voltage or high current. i.e. spark plug cables or battery cables.

Calibrate The setting of an instrument to base zero for greatest accuracy.

CANP (CANister Purge solenoid valve) See CFSV

Capacitor A device that absorbs electricity by offering an alternative path.

CAS (Crank Angle Sensor) The CAS works on the same principle as the inductive permanent magnet pick-up. A number of steel pegs or pins are set at regular intervals around the circumference of the flywheel or crankshaft. Typically, a peg may be set at every 10° - 36 in all. One or more of the pegs may be removed at TDC, BDC or a known distance from these points. The flywheel thus becomes a reluctor.

A permanent magnet inductive signal generator is mounted in close proximity to the flywheel. As the flywheel spins, an alternating (AC) waveform is produced which signals RPM and flywheel position to the ECM. Although most modern systems utilise a single CAS, some of the older systems use two CAS - one for RPM and one for position.

Cat (catalytic converter) A catalyst is something which promotes a reaction, but itself remains unaffected by the reaction. The catalytic converter consists of a stainless steel housing containing a ceramic monolith with a honeycomb of passages called cells.

CCO (Clutch Converter lock-up solenoid - Ford term)

Cell A single battery unit consisting of positive and negative plates covered by Electrolyte. A twelve volt battery consists of six cells connected in series and measuring approximately 2.1 volts each.

CEL (Check Engine Light - self diagnostic warning lamp)

Celsius See C

CFI (Central Fuel Injection - Ford/ Vauxhall term - see SPi)

CFCV (Carbon Filter Control Valve) Mechanically operated valve used in the evaporation control system to control recycling of vapours from the carbon canister.

CFSV (Carbon Filter Solenoid Valve) Electrically operated solenoid valve used in the evaporation control system to control recycling of vapours from the carbon canister. Sometimes termed a purge valve.

CFCOSV (Carbon Filter Cut-off Solenoid Valve) This valve is often fitted to Peugeot and Citroen vehicles. The CFCOSV is actuated by the ignition key and is used in conjunction with the CFSV. When the ignition is switched off, the valve closes and fumes are retained in the system.

CID (Cylinder Identification) sensor A sensor used to determine which cylinder is at TDC on the firing stroke and thereby establish the engine firing order. Typical mounting positions are on the camshaft or in the distributor.

Circuit An electrical path through which current can flow and that begins and ends at the current source.

CIS (Continuous Injection System.) A fuel injection system in which the fuel injectors spray fuel continuously during engine operation. Most common type is the Bosch 'K' or 'KE' Jetronic.

Clear flood If a fuel injected vehicle fails to start, continued cranking could result in excessive fuel being injected into the cylinders. Where the fuel injection system has a 'clear flood' facility, full depression of the throttle during engine cranking will result in a reduced volume of fuel being injected.

Closed loop control An engine operates under closed loop control when the ECM responds to the signal from the oxygen sensor to prevent emissions from deviating from the stoichiometric point.

CO (Carbon Monoxide) Carbon Monoxide is formed by the partial burning of the fuel due to a lack of oxygen.

CO_2 (Carbon Dioxide) CO_2 is the product of an efficient engine. With low CO and HC levels, the percentage of CO_2 in the exhaust is likely to be 13 to 15%. CO_2 is directly proportional to the AFR, but inversely proportional to CO. The less fuel, the higher the CO_2. One molecule of CO_2 contains one atom of carbon and two of oxygen.

Coil (ignition) A device that transforms low (battery) voltage into the high voltage required to bridge the rotor and spark plug gaps.

Cold start device A choke or a starting device to enrich the air/fuel ratio during cold starting and during the warm-up period.

Combustion During the combustion process, oxygen combines with carbon to form carbon dioxide (CO_2), and with hydrogen to form water (H_2O).

Compression The charging of a maximum volume of air and fuel into a minimum volume.

Conductor A material that will pass electrical current efficiently. A good conductor depends on material used, length, cross sectional area and temperature.

Constant energy The use of high primary current limited, to a pre-set figure, for efficient electronic ignition operation.

Control signal see also relay driver, driver, final stage

Conversion tables See Pressure conversion table, Vacuum conversion table, temperature conversion table

Corrosion Deterioration and crumbling of a component by chemical action. Sensor terminals and multi-plugs are particularly susceptible to this complaint.

Corrosion inhibitor A preparation to prevent corrosion. Often used to prevent corrosion of the radiator internal channels by water action.

CPS (Crankshaft Position Sensor See CAS) Ford term corresponding to CAS.

CPU (Central processing unit) See ECM

Cranking Rotating the engine with the aid of the starter motor.

CSI (cold start injector see Cold Start Valve)

CSV (Cold Start Valve) An injector mounted in the inlet manifold that is only actuated during cold starts when the engine temperature is below a certain threshold. Usually operated through a TTS that completes the CSV earth path. The CSV is not fitted to the modern EMS.

CTS (Coolant Temperature Sensor) A thermistor that changes in resistance according to temperature. Most CTS usually work on the NTC principle. However, CTS fitted to Renix equipped EMS may be NTC or PTC. As the temperature changes, the thermistor resistance changes, and thus the ECM is able to calculate the engine coolant temperature from the level of voltage (or current) that is registered on the sensor signal wire.

Current The flow of electrons through a conductor and measured in amps.

Current controlled or pulse modulation injection See EFi systems

CVH (Compound Valve angle Head - Ford term) Cylinder head with valves arranged in two planes in a V configuration

Cw (clockwise) Direction of rotation

D

Dashpot A device that enables the throttle to close slowly rather than suddenly, thus preventing the removal of droplets of fuel from the inlet manifold walls due to the high vacuum present during deceleration. These droplets are emitted as excess HC during this operation.

Datastream This data is essentially electrical data on voltage, frequency, dwell or pulse duration, temperature etc, provided by the various sensors and actuators and obtained through the ECM self-diagnosis system. Such data is not available from all vehicle systems. Since the data is in real time, various tests can be made and the response of the sensor or actuator evaluated.

DC (Direct Current) An electrical current source which flows in only one direction.

DC - ISC (Throttle plate control motor - Ford term)

Deceleration Closing the throttle and allowing the engine speed to reduce to idle.

Degree (°) 1/360 part of a circle. Also used to indicate temperature (°C).

Detonation refer to knock

Diaphragm A thin sheet of rubber that is moved by vacuum to actuate a mechanical device.

Digital signal A digital signal is represented by a code that has two states, on and off. In simple terms, the signal consists of a series of digital pulses when the frequency, pulse width or number of pulses is used to indicate a specific value.

DIN International standard used in the automotive industry

Diesel A fuel injected engine that uses the high temperature generated in compression to ignite the charge.

Dieseling A fault condition where a petrol engine continues running after the ignition has been switched off. Often caused by cylinder hot spots or carbon deposits that continue to glow and which are hot enough to explode the air/fuel charge.

Differential pressure The method by which air is drawn through a carburettor and into an engine. By the rules of physics, air will flow from high (atmospheric) pressure to low pressure (depression caused by fall of piston).

Diode A transistor that allows current flow in one direction alone.

DIS (Distributorless Ignition System)

Distributor A component that distributes the secondary voltage to the correct spark plug in firing order. It is also used to house the reluctor and stator in some electronic ignition systems. The distributor turns at the same speed as the camshaft and at half the speed of the flywheel.

Distributor cap An insulated cap with a centre tower and a circular series of terminals, one for each cylinder. The secondary HT pulses travel from the coil to the centre tower and are delivered, in firing order, to each terminal by the rotor.

DME Digital Motor Electronics Generic term often used to describe the Bosch Motronic EMS.

DMM (Digital Multi-Meter)

DOHC (Double Over Head Camshaft) A set of two camshafts mounted in the cylinder head. Operation is similar to the SOHC type except that one of the camshafts opens the inlet valves, and the other one opens the exhaust valves. This leads to more efficient valve operation and improved engine efficiency.

DPFE (Delta Pressure Feedback Electronic system - Ford term) An ECM controlled valve that regulates the flow of exhaust gas to the EGR valve.

Driver (actuator) The system actuators are supplied with a voltage feed from either the ignition switch or from one of the system relays. The earth point is then connected to an ECM driver pin. When the ECM actuates the component, it drives the appropriate ECM driver pin to earth by connecting the driver pin to one of the ECM pins that are directly connected to earth. The circuit connection to earth is thus completed internally for as long as actuation is required. In general, the earth connection will only be completed after the ECM has received one or more signals from relevant sensors and either looked up pulse duration in an associated map or calculated the correct actuator 'on' time.

Examples of an actuator driver are: injector, relay, ISCV, CFSV, EGR solenoid etc. Refer also to relay driver, control signal and final stage.

Duty cycle The period of time in % or ms, during which a component is switched on or energised. Also see Dwell.

DVM (Digital Volt Meter)

Dwell angle A definition of a dwell angle is the time or rotational period through which a device passes when it is energised. Dwell could thus be measured in terms of degrees of rotation, time 'on' - (or off) in percentage (%) compared with the total time for one occurrence, or time on or off in milliseconds (ms). Usually, dwell is measured in degrees, but if either (%) or (ms) is measured, it is more common to refer to the value as 'duty cycle'. See also Duty Cycle.

To convert dwell degrees to dwell percent and vice versa, use the following formulae:

$$\text{Dwell}° \times \frac{\text{cylinders} \times 100}{360 \quad 1} = \text{Dwell \%}$$

$$\text{i.e. } 45° \times \frac{4}{360} \times \frac{100}{1} = 50\%$$

$$\frac{\text{Dwell \%}}{100} \times \frac{360}{\text{cylinders}} = \text{Dwell}°$$

$$\text{i.e. } \frac{50\%}{100} \times \frac{360}{6} = 30°$$

Dwell meter An instrument used to measure dwell angle.

Dynamic volt drop In vehicles with electronic ignition, the dynamic volt drop refers to the volt drop over the primary circuit from the coil negative terminal to earth through the amplifier final driver stage. This measurement is only available with the engine cranking or running, because current must be flowing in the circuit before a measurement can be taken. Not all DMMs are capable of measuring this circuit.

E

Earth A path for current to return to the power source.

EACV (Electronic Air Control Valve - Honda, Rover Term)

EAI (Electronic Advance Ignition GM term)

EBCV (Electronic Air Bleed Control Valve)

EC (European Community.)

ECM (Electronic control module) A computer control unit that assimilates information from various sensors and computes an output. Can be used to control the engine ignition timing, injection duration, opening of the ISCV, ABS brakes, air bag etc etc.

ECT (Engine Coolant Temperature) Refer to CTS.

ECOTEC (Emission Consumption Optimised TECnology) GM term to describe a range of vehicles.

ECU (Electronic Control Unit) Term has now been largely replaced by ECM. Refer to ECM.

EDIS (Electronic Distributorless Ignition System - Ford term)

EDIS-4 Applied to EDIS - 4 cylinder engines

EDF (Electro Drive Fan - Ford term)

EDM (EDIS Diagnostics Monitor Signal - Ford term)

EEC (Electronic Engine Control - Ford term)

EEC IV (Electronic Engine Control 4th generation (module) - Ford term)

EEC V (Electronic Engine Control 5th generation (module) - Ford term)

EFi (Electronic Fuel injection) A fuel injection system where the injectors are opened (pulsed) by an ECM. There are two kinds of injection system in current use and a description of each type now follows.

Standard injection In the standard EFi system, the injector is simply pulsed by the ECM for a calculated period of time. During this time, known as the pulse duration or the injector `on' time, the injector solenoid operates and fuel is injected.

Current controlled or pulse modulation injection

Some systems rely on the principle that more current is required to open the injector than to actually keep it open. The injector solenoid circuit is pulsed - but for only about one millisecond, which is just long enough to open the injector. The opening circuit is then switched off, and another circuit rapidly closed and opened, to apply a small holding current to the injector so that it remains open for the correct time duration. The pulsing is so fast that the injector does not have time to close, and current flow is therefore much reduced.

EFi pulse duration The period of time that the injector is held open. Can be measured in ms or as a duty cycle.

EGOS (Exhaust Gas Oxygen Sensor) See Oxygen Sensor – Ford term

EGR (Exhaust Gas Recirculation.) A method of recycling a small amount of exhaust gas into the intake system. This leads to lower peak combustion temperature with a reduction in NOx emissions.

EHPR (Electro-Hydraulic Pressure Regulator - Ford term)

Electrode An electrical conductor.

Electrolyte A sulphuric acid and water solution used in a lead / acid batteries. Chemical reaction between the acid and battery plates produce voltage and current.

Electro-magnet A magnet that requires electrical energy to create an electrical field.

Electronic 'MAP' See mapped timing/injection advance.

EI (Electronic Ignition) An ignition system that uses a magnetic sensor and transistors to switch the coil negative terminal on and off.

Emissions Pollution of the atmosphere by fumes from the exhaust, breather vent or fuel tank.

Emission control Devices used to control and minimise poisonous fume emissions from the automotive engine.

Emission standards

US 79: This standard was set in the USA in 1979 and has been superseded by the US83 standard. The vehicle must be equipped with a regulated three way catalyst with OS.

US 83: This is the most stringent of the current European emission levels and the standard was set in the USA in 1983. The vehicle must be equipped with a regulated three way catalyst with OS and evaporative emission control.

US 88 LDT (Light Duty Truck): This standard sets the same requirements as the US83 standard. However, commercial vehicles over a certain weight will fall into this category.

NEEC 5th amendment: This is an European standard for emission control and vehicles equipped with at least one of the following systems will meet the standard. Unregulated Catalytic converter; Pulse air system; EGR; EMS calibrated for engines less than a certain size

15.04: This is not a standard and is a category applied to vehicles that do not meet a particular emission standard. Vehicles without a catalytic converter, EGR, pulse air system or evaporative emission control will fall into this category.

Energised The period during which an electrical device is switched on.

EMR (Engine Management Relay - Ford term)

EMS (Engine Management System) An EMS is essentially an electronic system whereby the engine ignition and fuelling functions are controlled by one or more Electronic Control Modules (ECM). When separate ECM's are provided for ignition and fuelling, the two units do not operate independently and connections are made so that they can communicate with each other.

ENR (ENgine run Relay - Ford term)

EPT (Electronic Pressure Transducer - Ford term)

ERIC (Electronically Regulated Ignition & Carburettor - Rover term)

ESA (Electronic Spark Advance - Toyota term)

ESC (Electronic Spark Control - Ford term)

ESC II (Electronic Spark Control 2nd generation (module) - Ford term)

Exhaust gas Burned and unburned gases that are exhausted after combustion.

External influences An influence that is not directly attributable to a particular component but could affect the operation of that component .

EVAP (EVAPorative emission control systems) - see CFSV

EVR Electronic Vacuum Regulator - Ford term)

F

Fahrenheit Temperature scale

Fast codes Digital fault codes emitted by an EMS that are too fast to be displayed on an LED lamp or on a dash mounted warning lamp. A digital FCR instrument is required for capturing fast codes.

Fault codes Electronics are now extensively used throughout the modern vehicle and may control functions such as the transmission, suspension, automatic gearbox, air conditioning and myriad others.

Most modern vehicle EMS or ECM have the facility of making self-diagnostic checks upon the sensors and actuators that interface with the vehicle computer or computers. A fault in one of the component circuits causes a flag or code to be set in the ECM memory. If a suitable code reading device is attached to the serial port on the vehicle harness, these faults can then be read out from the vehicle computer and displayed in the form of a two or three digit output code.

FCR (Fault Code Reader) A device that can be connected to the vehicle serial (diagnostic port) to interrogate the vehicle ECM. Fault codes and Datastream information can then be read from the ECM. In some instances, vehicle actuators can be actuated from the controls on the FCR. Where adjustments to the ignition timing or fuel system are possible, for example on some Ford or Rover systems, then these adjustments must be made through an FCR. Fault Codes may be described as being slow or fast and some ECM's are capable of emitting both types. Slow codes can be captured by an LED tool, whereas fast codes must be captured by a digital FCR.

FI (Fuel Injection)

Final stage See driver, relay driver and control signal

FIR (Fuel Injection Relay - Ford term)

Firing line The actual firing voltage as represented on an oscilloscope.

Firing order The order in which the cylinders are fired.

Firing voltage The secondary voltage required to overcome the rotor and spark plug gaps.

Flash codes Fault codes of the slow variety that are output on a dash mounted warning lamp or via an LED lamp.

Flashshield A cover used in the distributor to prevent secondary arcing interfering with primary operation.

Flat spots Hesitation of the engine under acceleration.

Flow rate Describes the volume of fuel pumped during a pre-determined period of time in order to test fuel system output.

FLW (Fuse Link Wire - Ford term)

Flywheel sensor see CAS

FO (Fuel Octane - Ford term)

FP (Fuel Pump)

FPR (fuel pressure regulator)

FPR (Fuel Pump Relay - Ford term)

Frequency Pulse Frequency measured in Hz.

FRS (Fuel Restrictor Solenoid - Rover term)

FRTS (Fuel Rail Temperature Sensor)

FTVV (Fuel Tank Vent Valve) A solenoid valve used to control evaporation emissions in GM vehicles. See CFSV.

FTS (Fuel Temperature Sensor)

FTS (Fuel Temperature Switch)

Fuel atomisation Proper mixing of air and fuel to ensure good combustion.

Fuel injector (EFI systems) The injector is a solenoid operated valve that delivers an exact amount of fuel according to an opening duration signal from the ECM.

Fuse A small component containing a sliver of metal that is inserted into a circuit. The fuse will blow at a specified current rating, in order to protect the circuit from voltage overload.

Fuselink (also known as fusible link). A heavy duty circuit protection component that can burnout if the circuit becomes overloaded

G

Gas analyser A device used to sample gases at the exhaust pipe, so that an analysis may be made of the exhaust constituents.

Generator An alternator or dynamo that produces voltage and current. See also alternator.

GM (General Motors) Manufacturer of Opel and Vauxhall vehicles in Europe. The parent company is based in the USA.

GND (ground)

Ground USA term for earth. See also earth.

H

Hall-Effect generator A type of pulse generator which returns a small digital voltage to signal the exact position of a particular component. Often used to signal flywheel, distributor or camshaft position.

HES (Hall Effect Switch) - see above

Hard faults Generally refers to faults logged by an ECM self-diagnosis routine. The faults are usually present at the moment of testing,

HC (Hydrocarbons) 15% Hydrogen and 85% carbon. Petrol is almost pure hydrocarbons. HC is a generic term and refers to unburnt fuel and partially burnt fuel. It is measured in ppm - parts per million).

HCS (High compression swirl - Ford term)

Heat range With reference to a spark plug, the operating range in which the plug will safely and effectively operate.

Heat sink A component to dissipate high operating temperatures.

HEDF (High speed Electro Drive Fan - Ford term)

HEGOG (see HEGOS) Heated Exhaust Gas Oxygen sensor Ground - Ford term

HEGOS (HEGO, Heated Exhaust Gas Oxygen Sensor – Ford term) See also Oxygen Sensor.

HG Chemical symbol for measurement of mercury.

HLG (Hall effect generator)

Hot-film AFS - very similar in operation to the hot-wire sensor

Hot-wire sensor A type of AFS in which the resistance of an electrically heated wire is measured and converted into a measurement of engine load. The volume, temperature and density of air, at all altitudes can be more accurately measured by hot-wire or hot-film than by the Vane type of AFS systems.

HT (High tension) High voltage induced in the secondary windings of the ignition coil.

HT lead (High Tension lead.) Cable used to distribute secondary ignition to the distributor cap and to the spark plugs.

Hybrid All the semi-conductor modules are densely packed and encased in resin.

Hydrogen An odourless gas. Highly explosive. Forms 67% of the chemical make-up of water.

Hz (Hertz) Frequency measurement in cycles per second.

I

IA (Idle Adjust - Ford term)

IBR (Injector Ballast Resistor - Ford term)

ICOV (Induction ChangeOver Valve) An ECM controlled solenoid valve used to vary the airflow through the inlet manifold, in order to improve torque and power at different engine speeds and loads.

ID (Identification)

Idle speed control On most modern engines, speed at idle is maintained at a constant speed irrespective of engine load or temperature. As idle conditions alter, or a temperature or an electrical load condition occurs, the ECM actuates either a solenoid controlled ISCV or a stepper motor to maintain the correct idle position - no matter the speed or load. This prevents poor idle and stalling with heavy electrical loads and a lean mixture.

Idle switch Fulfils the same function as the Throttle Switch, idle contact.

idle up - Asian term. Any mechanical or electronic system that is used to increase the idle speed according to temperature or engine load could be termed an idle-up system.

IDM (Ignition Diagnostics Monitor signal - Ford term)

IGC (Ignition coil Ford term)

IGf (Ignition confirmation signal – Asian vehicle manufacturer term)

IGt (Ignition trigger signal from the ECM – Asian vehicle manufacturer term)

IGN (Ignition switch - Ford term)

Igniter (Ignition module or amplifier) Term commonly used by Asian vehicle manufacturers to describe the ignition amplifier

Ignition module term used to describe the ignition amplifier

Ignition switch An on-off switch that provides current to the primary ignition and other important circuits.

Ignition timing The correct moment at which the compressed air/fuel charge is ignited to allow maximum force to be exerted upon the piston.

IIA (Integrated Ignition Assembly - Toyota term) Ignition module integral with the distributor

IMA (Idle Mixture adjuster Honda, Rover Term)

Impedance Resistance to the flow of current and often used to describe the resistance of a voltmeter. A minimum 10 megohm impedance is recommended for instruments used to measure values in automotive electronic circuits.

IMPH (Inlet Manifold Pre-Heater) see manifold heater

Intake system The components responsible for the intake of the air/fuel mixture. i.e. air filter, throttle body, inlet manifold and inlet valve.

Inductive (permanent magnet) pick-up The pick-up is a permanent magnet and inductive coil wound around a pole piece. It is usually fixed securely in the distributor and radiates a magnetic field. The two most common types in current service are the pick-up limb or the annular coil.

Insulator A material that will not pass current readily, and therefore used to prevent electrical leakage.

Inst panel Abbreviation for Instrument panel on the vehicle dashboard

Intercooler A device for cooling the air charge supplied to the engine from the TurboCharger. Cooler air is denser than hot air and so a greater volume of air is inducted into the engine. The greater the volume of air inducted, the greater will be the horsepower produced by the engine.

IS (Inertia switch)

ISC (Idle speed control) See ISCV

ISCV (Idle Speed Control Valve) A gate or rotary valve that is actuated by the ECM to maintain the correct idle speed, no matter the load or temperature.

ISO (International Standards Organisation)

ISSM (Idle Speed Stepper Motor) See stepper motor

ITS (Idle Tracking Switch - Ford term)

IV PWR (Ignition voltage power - Ford term)

J

Jumper lead A small electrical cable that is used to temporarily bridge an electrical circuit

J1930 SAE standard for acronyms describing electrical and electronic components.

K

KA PWR (Keep Alive PoWeR - Ford term)

KAM (Keep Alive Memory) Ford term for a dynamic memory in the EEC IV/V ECM. This memory retains soft faults and also the engine adaptive settings.

Karmen Vortex A type of AFS fitted to some Asian vehicles. The Vortex AFS relies on the inlet manifold design to create a turbulent air flow. A radio signal is passed through the air flow as it flows through the sensor. Variations in the turbulence cause a change in frequency that the sensor returns to the ECM as a measure of air flow into the engine.

KCM (Knock Control Module - Ford term)

KDS (Kick-Down Switch - Ford term)

KEM (KE Module - Ford term)

KEMKE (fuelling module - Ford term)

King HT lead The cable that carries secondary voltage from the coil to the distributor cap. King lead is a slang term in common use

KNK (Knock signal, from knock sensor - Ford term)

Knock The spontaneous explosion of the remaining air/fuel charge in the combustion chamber when only a portion of it has burnt progressively. A direct result of excessive combustion chamber temperature. Known also as detonation..

KS (Knock Sensor) A sensor that outputs a small electrical signal on detecting `engine knock' . On receiving a knock signal, the ECM will temporarily adjust (retard) the ignition timing to prevent the condition. Some engine systems with KS can detect engine knock in an individual cylinder. In this case, the ECM will retard ignition timing on an individual cylinder basis until knock ceases on one or all cylinders.

Knock threshold During engine operation, the actual moment when knocking commences.

kohms (Kilohms) A resistance measurement equal to 1000 ohms.

kPa (KiloPascals) International standard for the measurement of pressure and vacuum. See pressure conversion table and vacuum conversion table

kV KiloVolt A unit of secondary voltage measurement equal to 1000 volts.

L

Lambda Greek word for the 'stoichiometric symbol'. As the engine operates, fuel and air are mixed together and drawn into each cylinder. The AFR at which fuel burns most efficiently is called the Stoichiometric point and this is where HC and CO are lowest and CO<288> is highest. This ratio is 14.7:1 by weight, and it is also called Lambda = 1 which is the Greek word for correct.
A catalyst equipped engine will attempt to maintain the AFR between a Lambda factor of 0.97 and 1.04.

Lambda /AFR Chart
Although Lambda = 1 is not the best point for best fuel consumption, we have already established that it is the best compromise for using a Catalytic Converter to oxidise CO, HC and NOx. Therefore, if the engine's AFR can be contained within the 'window' of 0.98 to 1.02, the resultant engine emissions will raise the efficiency of the Catalytic Converter to about 95 %. The reason is that the lower the emissions from the engine, the less work the cat has to do and the more efficient it will become. Moreover, by reducing the engine emissions - the cat will also last much longer.

Lambda sensor see Oxygen Sensor. A sensor that monitors the amount of oxygen in the exhaust stream and passes a voltage signal back to the ECM. The ECM then alters the amount of fuel passed to the engine. In an effort to maintain the AFR at the most suitable ratio for perfect combustion.

LDT (Light Duty Truck) see emission standards. Refers to the US88 LDT emission standards for commercial vehicles.

Lead A substance (tetra-ethyl or TEL) that is added to petrol to assist the fuel's ability to resist knocking and pre-ignition. Lead also lubricates the valves and seats in the engine. Lead levels in petrol have gradually been reduced in recent years and even leaded petrol contains a far smaller concentration than at one time.
Lead is a poisonous substance and progressively and irreversibly reduces the efficiency of the blood to transport oxygen. It functions as cellular poison for blood, bone marrow and nerve cells. Lead also poisons the catalytic converter and clogs the cells thus quickly reducing efficiency.

LED (Light Emitting Diode

lb/in² (Pounds per Square Inch) an Imperial measurement of pressure. See pressure conversion table

LHS (Left Hand Side) Viewed from the drivers seat.

Limp home See LOS

LAF (Linear Air Flow sensor (Honda)) Digital type of oxygen sensor

LOS (Limited Operating Strategy) Often called Limp Home, this is a safety system that allows the vehicle to be driven to a service area if a fault occurs. When the system perceives that a sensor is operating outside of its design parameters, a substitute value is used which allows the engine to function satisfactorily. However, this value is often that for a hot or semi-hot engine and this means that the engine may be difficult to start and run badly when it is cold. Some LOS systems are so smart that the driver may be unaware, from the way that the vehicle functions that a fault has indeed occurred. In some systems certain engine functions may also be restricted to allow safe engine operation. The self-diagnostic warning light (where fitted) may be switched on to indicate that a fault has occurred.

LT (low tension) Primary ignition circuit.

LUS (Lock-up Solenoid - automatic transmission - Ford term)

M

ma (milliamperes)

MAF (Mass Air Flow sensor - term used to describe hot-wire or hot-film types of AFS)

Magnet A substance that has the ability to attract iron.

Magnetic field The space around a magnet that is filled by invisible lines of magnetic force.

Manifold heater A heater inserted into the inlet manifold so that the cold charge may be heated more quickly after a cold engine start. Sometimes termed a 'hedgehog' because of its distinctive shape, the manifold heater usually functions on the PTC principle and is often used in single point injection engines.

MAP (Manifold Absolute Pressure sensor) This is an inexpensive and less accurate alternative to the AFS for measuring engine load. The MAP sensor measures the manifold vacuum or pressure and uses a transducer to pass an electrical signal back to the ECM. The unit may be located in the engine compartment or in the ECM. Used in both simultaneous MPi and SPi systems, the MAP sensor is particularly popular in SPi systems. MAP is calculated from the formula: Atmospheric pressure - vacuum = MAP.
MAP sensors may take one of two forms. Older generation vehicles use an analogue sensor where the voltage signal output is proportional to the load. A newer system used in Ford vehicles is the digital type which sends a square waveform in the form of a frequency. As the load increases, the frequency also increases and the time in ms between pulses becomes shorter.

Mapped ignition timing or injection Electronic timing advance or injection pulse that is controlled by the ECM from a 'map' placed within the ECM. A three dimensional map contains settings for a number of engine load, speed and temperature variations. Timing and injection settings are usually contained in separate maps within the ECM.

MAS (mixture adjustment screw)

Max abbreviation for maximum

Mean average measurement value

MEMS (Modular Engine Management System) A type of EMS manufactured by Rover.

MFU (Multi Function Unit) A relay box containing 3 to 4 control relays. Found in Rover vehicles amongst others.

Mixture adjustment Device provided to allow a small measure of CO adjustment.

Molecule The smallest particle into which a chemical compound may be divided.

Motronic a type of EMS manufactured by Bosch.

MPi (Multi-Point injection) One injector per cylinder. May be triggered in banks (simultaneous) or sequentially.

Multi-Point injection - simultaneous This is the most common type of EFi system in current use. A number of injectors are looped together in a parallel 'bank' with a single connection to the ECM. Where an engine has more than one bank, each bank has its own ECM connection.

Multi-Point injection - sequential A system where each injector opens in cylinder sequence. The sequential MPi system uses the same sensors as other injection systems. However, an additional sensor pinpoints the correct cylinder for the sequential system. This may be a Hall-effect switch located in the distributor or on the camshaft or an inductive pulse generator located close to the camshaft.

ms (millisecond) 1/1000 second (0.001).

MSTS-h) (Microprocessor Spark Timing System - HES ignition - GM term)

MSTS-i) (Microprocessor Spark Timing System - inductive ignition - GM term)

MT (Manual Transmission)

Multimeter An instrument designed for automotive use that can measure voltage, current, resistance and sometimes covers other functions such as dwell, duty cycle, frequency, rpm and amps etc .

Multiplug A connecting plug in the wiring harness. Often used to connect the harness to a sensor or actuator. In this book the multi-plug diagram shows the terminals of the harness connector. When back-probing the multi-plug (or viewing the sensor connector terminals), the terminal positions will be reversed.

mV (milliVolt) one milliVolt = 1/1000 of a volt

MY (Model Year) Most vehicle manufacturers start manufacturing their latest models in the months leading up to the end of a particular year. The actual date when manufacturing commences is usually termed the model year date and the year used is usually that of the following year. For example a model year date of September 1995 could mark the commencement of manufacture of the 1996 models.

N

nbv (nominal battery voltage) Nominally 12 volt, the voltage will vary under engine operating conditions:
Engine stopped: 12 - 13 volts.
Engine cranking: 9.0 to 12.0 volts.
Engine running: 13.8 to 14.8 volts.

NDS (Neutral Drive Switch - Ford term

Nearside Side nearest to the kerb on any vehicle - irrespective of whether LH or RH drive.

NE (RPM signal from the pick-up coil - Toyota term)

NEEC (New European Economic Community)

Newton (N) An international unit of force that is independent of gravity. This unit was introduced because gravity varies in different parts of the world. The Newton is defined as: The force required to accelerate a mass of 1kg at 1 metre per second per second. Newton units of force are measured as N/m^2 and called Pascal units. This unit is very small and measured in MPa (1,000,000) or kPa (1,000). See also Pascal.

Nitrogen An atmospheric gas.

Non-cat (non catalyst) Vehicles without a catalytic converter.

Non-sinusoidal Irregular waveforms such as sawtooth (i.e. Ford ISCV), square, ripple etc.

Non volatile memory ECM memory that is able to retain information - even when the vehicle battery is disconnected.

NOx (Oxides of Nitrogen) NOx is a poisonous gas formed due to high temperatures (exceeding 1300° C - 2500° F). and high compression. (and power) by recycling the inert exhaust gas.

NTC (Negative Temperature Co-efficient) A thermistor in which the resistance falls as the temperature rises. An NTC resistor decreases (negatively) in resistance as the temperature (i.e. coolant temperature) rises.

O

OA (Octane Adjuster) A device to finely tune the engine timing for fuels of differing octane levels.

OAI (Octane Adjust Input - Ford term)

OBD1 (On Board Diagnostics 1) Original US standard for OBD

OBD2 (On Board Diagnostics 2) US standard for OBD

OBDE (On Board Diagnostics Europe) Proposed OBD standard for Europe and based upon OBD2 with local (European) changes.

OCAS (Optical Crank Angle Sensor) See Optical distributor

OCID (Optical Cylinder Identification)

Octane level The level of fuel resistance to knock. The higher the octane level, the more resistance to knock.

OHC (Overhead camshaft)

Ohm A unit of resistance that opposes current flow in a circuit.

Ohmmeter An instrument used to measure resistance in ohms.

Ohms law
Volts = Amps x Ohms (V = I x R)
Amps = Volts / Ohms (I = V / R)
Ohms = Volts / Amps (R = V / I)
Also:
Power (Watts) = Volts x Amps

Optical distributor Mainly used in some Asian vehicles. The optical distributor consists of two LEDs (Light Emitting Diodes), a thin disk or rotor with two rows of slits and two optical diodes or pick-ups.

OTS (Oil Temperature Sensor)

Open circuit A break in an electrical circuit which prevents the flow of current.

Open loop control When an engine with Lambda control is operating outside of closed loop control, it is in 'open loop'. This may occur during acceleration, WOT, or during the warm-up period, and when in LOS. Some system may go into open loop at idle speed. When the system is under 'open loop' control, a richer mixture is allowed to prevent hesitation or poor driveability.

OS (Oxygen Sensor) An Oxygen Sensor is a ceramic device placed in the engine exhaust system. Essentially, the OS contains two porous platinum electrodes. The outer surface electrode is exposed to exhaust air and coated in porous ceramic. The inner surface electrode is exposed to ambient atmospheric air. The difference in oxygen at the two electrodes generates a voltage signal which is transmitted to the ECM. This voltage is inversely proportional to the amount of oxygen in the exhaust. Various names have been given to this sensor and it could equally be called a Lambda Sensor or even an EGOS.

OS heater Because the sensor does not operate efficiently below about 300°C, many Oxygen sensors incorporate a heater element for rapid warm-up. Such sensors may be termed HEGOS.

Oscilloscope A high speed voltmeter that visually displays a change in voltage against time. Used to display ignition, alternator and engine sensor or actuator waveforms.

Overrun See deceleration.

OVP (Over Voltage Protection - Ford term)

Oxidation A chemical change in a lubricating oil caused by combustion, heat and oxygen.

Oxides of nitrogen refer to NOx

O_2 (Oxygen) A harmless gas that is present in about 21% of air and is necessary for proper combustion.

O_2 consists of two oxygen atoms and is measured in % volume. A small proportion of Oxygen (1 - 2%) will be left after proper combustion.

P

Pascal International standard for the measurement of pressure and vacuum. See pressure conversion table and vacuum conversion table refer also to Newton

PA (Pressure atmospheric - Honda, Rover term)

PAS (Power Assisted Steering)

PASV (Pulse Air Solenoid Valve)

PCS (Pressure Control Switch - Ford term)

PCV (Positive Crankcase Ventilation) A control system used to recycle crankcase fumes into the intake system where they are reburnt during the combustion process..

Percent Part of a hundred

Permanent magnet A magnet that has a magnetic field at all times.

Petrol A hydrocarbon fuel composed of a mixture of hydrogen and carbons.

Pick-up see also inductive. Used as a trigger in an electronic system. The pick-up generates a small voltage which signals the amplifier or ECM to switch and thus instigate ignition. The pick-up is usually some form of permanent magnet fixed in the distributor or on the flywheel. When a reluctor is rotated in the magnetic field, the signal to switch occurs when the signal is at its strongest.

Pick-up air gap A specified and often adjustable gap between reluctor and pick-up.

PIM (MAP sensor signal - Toyota term)

Pinging The audible sound produced by detonation.

Pinking A commonly used aberration of pinging.

P / N (Park Neutral switch) A switch to cut the electrical supply to the starter motor and so prevent the engine from being started in gear. Usually found in vehicles with Automatic Transmission.

PIP (Profile Ignition Pick-up - Ford term) Term used to describe the basic timing signal.

Plugged exhaust An exhaust blockage causing back pressure and lack of performance.

Polarity A positive or negative state with reference to two electrical poles.

Pollutants see emissions.

Ported vacuum A vacuum source located in front of the throttle valve. The valve must be opened before a vacuum signal is produced.

Pot (potentiometer) A variable resistance.

PPM : (Parts Per Million) A measurement of unburned HC.

PRC (Pressure Regulator Control – Asian term)

Pre-emission Engines that do not have emission control devices.

Pre-ignition The premature explosion of the compressed air/fuel charge before proper ignition by the spark plug. Usually caused by excessive combustion temperature.

Pressure conversion table

Bar	lb/in²	kPa
0.1	1.45	10
0.2	2.90	20
0.3	4.35	30
0.4	5.80	40
0.5	7.25	50
1.0	14.50	100
1.02	14.75	102 **
1.1	15.95	110
1.2	17.40	120
1.3	18.85	130
1.4	20.30	140
1.5	21.75	150
1.6	23.20	160
1.7	24.65	170
1.8	26.10	180
1.9	27.55	190
2.0	29.00	200
3.0	43.50	300
4.0	58.00	400
5.0	72.50	500

** approximate atmospheric pressure at sea level

Pressure regulator The fuel pump supplies fuel at a pressure that exceeds the required system pressure. A spring loaded diaphragm relieves this pressure by allowing excess fuel to flow back to the tank via the fuel return line.

Primary switching The switching of the primary coil windings in order to initiate the high tension current required for ignition.

Primary windings. The outer windings of relatively heavy wire in an ignition coil in which the primary current flows.

Prom (programmable read only memory)

Pulse air system The Pulse air system bleeds fresh air into the exhaust system which allows the rich cold start mixture to continue burning. The exhaust temperature rises and very quickly achieves the objective.

PSA (Citroen and Peugeot group)

PSI (Pounds per Square Inch) An Imperial measurement of pressure. See pressure conversion table

PSPS (Power Steering Pressure Switch)

PU (inductive pick-up coil)

PUA (Pulse Air solenoid - Ford term)

PTC (Positive Temperature Co-efficient) A thermistor in which the resistance rises as the temperature rises. A PTC resistor increases (positively) in resistance as the temperature (i.e. coolant temperature) rises.

Pulse A digital signal sent by the ECM.

Pulse generator The pulse generator is a trigger used to initiate ignition. It sends a correctly timed signal to the amplifier, which then amplifies the signal to switch the coil negative terminal. Examples of pulse generators are:

1 *An inductive permanent magnet pick-up located inside the distributor.*

2   An inductive permanent magnet located adjacent to the flywheel (CAS).

3   Hall Effect trigger located inside the distributor.

Pulse width The time period during which an electronic component is energised. It is usually measure in milliseconds or as an duty cycle.

Purge valve refer to CFSV

PVS (Ported Vacuum Switch)

R

RAM (Random Access Memory - computer term)

Reference voltage During normal engine operation, battery voltage could vary between 9.5 (cranking) and 14.5 (running). To minimise the effect on engine sensors (for which the ECM would need to compensate), many ECM voltage supplies to the sensors are made at a constant value (known as a reference voltage) of 5.0 volts.

REG (Regulator)

Relay An electro-magnetic switching solenoid controlled by a fine shunt coil. A small current activates the shunt winding, which then exerts magnetic force to close the relay switching contacts. The relay is often used when a low current circuit is required to connect one or more circuits that operate at high current levels. In European vehicles the relay terminal numbers are often annotated to the DIN standard.

Typical relay annotation to DIN standard

30   Supply voltage direct from the battery positive terminal.

31   Earth return direct to battery.

85   Relay earth for energising system. May be connected direct to earth, or 'driven' to earth through the ECM.

85b Relay earth for output. May be connected direct to earth, or 'driven' to earth through the ECM.

86   Energising system supply. May arrive from battery positive, ignition switch or another relay.

87   Output from first relay or first relay winding. This terminal will often provide power to the second relay terminal 86 and provide voltage to the ECM, injectors, ISCV etc.

87b Output from second relay or second relay winding. Often provides power to the fuel pump and OS.

Note: *in some relays the function of terminals 30 & 87 and 85 & 86 may be reversed.*

Relay control see relay driver

Relay driver The system relays are supplied with a voltage feed from either the battery, ignition switch or from another system relay. The earth terminal is then connected to an ECM earth pin. When the ECM actuates the relay, it drives the appropriate ECM pin to earth by completing the circuit internally for as long as the actuation is required. In general, the relay earth connection will only be completed once the ECM receives a pre-determined sensor input signal.

Depending upon the relay, the input signal may be instigated by switching on the ignition or cranking the engine (i.e. CAS signal). Once the ECM has received the signal, the ECM will 'drive' the relay to earth by completing the circuit internally. The signal could be termed a 'driver' or a 'final stage' or a 'control' signal. Examples of other actuator drivers are: injector, ISCV, CFSV etc.

Reluctor A metal rotor with a series of arms equal to the number of cylinders.

REMCO (Remote adjustment for CO pot - Ford term)

Renix A type of EMS used mainly on Renault and Volvo vehicles.

Required voltage The minimum amount of secondary voltage that must be produced to bridge the rotor and spark plug gaps.

Res. Abbreviation for resistance

Resistance Opposition to the flow of current.

Retarded timing Opposite to advance timing. When the ignition timing fires AFTER the correct moment. Can also be used to describe ignition timing that occurs ATDC.

Return Term used to describe the earth return path to an ECM or module of a sensor when the return is not directly connected to earth. The ECM or module will internally connect the return to one of its own earth connections. By this method the number of earth connections is much reduced.

RFI (Radio Frequency Interference) The EMS is susceptible to outside interference. Radiated RFI can be a problem if the levels are high enough and this can emanate from items such as a faulty secondary HT circuit or a faulty alternator. Excess RFI can disrupt and affect ECM and EMS operation - particularly where both ignition and fuelling are located in the same ECM.

RHS (Right Hand Side) Viewed from the drivers seat.

RMS (Root mean square) AC equivalent to DC voltage. Can be calculated from AC amplitude by the formula:

AC amplitude x 0.707.

ROM (Read Only Memory - computer term)

Rotor Rotating part of a component such as a rotor arm or an electro-magnet used in an alternator.

Rotor air gap The space between the rotor tip and the distributor cap terminal.

Rotor arm The rotor is keyed to the distributor shaft so that it points directly at the correct distributor cap terminal in order to relay HT voltage to the correct sparkplug.

Rotor register

The alignment of the rotor tip to the distributor cap terminal. Where the register is mis-aligned then the resulting large air gap will cause high firing voltages.

Rpm (revolutions per minute) A measure of engine speed.

S

SAE (Society of Automotive Engineers) The Society sets standards for automotive engineering. See also BCI and J1930

SAW (Spark Advance Word) A Ford term for the modified timing signal passed from the EEC IV/V ECM to the EDIS module.

Scanner US term for a FCR. See FCR

Scope Abbreviation for an oscilloscope.

Screen Term usually applied to the insulation applied to a particular electrical cable. Used to reduce the effects of RFI.

SD (Self Diagnosis)

Secondary air system It is important that the catalytic converter and OS reach their respective operating temperatures as soon after the engine is started as possible. The secondary air system pumps fresh air into the exhaust system, which allows the rich cold start mixture to continue burning. The exhaust temperature rises and very quickly achieves the objective.

Secondary ignition circuit The high voltage circuit used to distribute secondary voltage to the spark plug.

Secondary voltage Output from ignition coil.

Secondary windings

SEFI (Sequential Electronic Fuel Injection - Ford term)

Self-diagnosis of serial data see fault codes

Sensor Electronic systems. A component that can measure one or more of the following engine parameters:

temperature, position, airflow, pressure etc. The sensor returns this information to the ECM, in the form of a voltage or current signal, for processing by the ECM.

Serial data port The serial port is an output terminal from the ECM for relaying digital information. See Fault Codes.

Sequential injection See MPi systems

SG (Signal Generator) Pickup coil in distributor.

Short Short circuit to earth. When electricity flows directly to earth and takes a shorter path back to the power source. Because extremely high current values are present, the condition is dangerous and can cause an electrical fire.

Signal generator Pickup coil in distributor. See pulse generator.

Signal voltage A voltage returned to the ECM by a sensor for the ECM to detect load or temperature.

Simultaneous injection An injection system in which all the injectors are pulsed simultaneously (all fire at the same time). Refer to MPi systems.

Sinusoidal A sine wave. i.e. a CAS or inductive pick-up waveform where the amplitude of the positive part of the waveform is roughly equal to the amplitude of the negative part of the waveform.

Slow codes Fault codes emitted by an EMS that are slow enough to be displayed on an LED lamp or on a dash mounted warning lamp.

Smog So-called 'photo-chemical smog'. Formed by combining HC and NOx in the presence of strong sunshine. A particular problem in car-dense, sunny climates such as California in the USA.

Soft faults Generally refers to intermittent faults logged by an ECM self-diagnosis routine. The faults are often not present at the moment of testing, but have been logged at some period in the past.

SOHC (Single Over Head Camshaft) A single rotating camshaft that controls the opening and closing of both inlet and exhaust valves. The camshaft is mounted above the valves in the cylinder head and acts directly upon them.

Solenoid An electrical device that produces a mechanical effort when energised.

Spark advance See timing advance.

Spark control Spark advance control by electronic or thermostatic means.

Spark duration The time taken for a spark to bridge the spark plug electrodes. Shown as a spark line on the oscilloscope.

Spark line see spark duration. Also known as burn time.

Sparkplug A device screwed into the cylinder head for igniting the compressed air/fuel charge.

Sparkplug electrodes
1   *The centre rod passing through the spark plug insulator.*
2   *The rod welded to the outer shell.*

Sparkplug gap The clearance between the sparkplug electrodes.

SPi (Single Point injection)
   Sometimes known as throttle body injection (TBI), the SPi system utilises a single injector (normally of the current controlled type) that injects fuel into a distributing manifold in much the same fashion as a carburettor.

SPOUT (Spark Out) A Ford term used to describe the modified timing signal passed from the EEC IV/V ECM to the TFI or EDIS module.

Square waveform A waveform that illustrates the switching on and off of a particular circuit. The higher voltage line defines supply voltage & the lower voltage defines earth potential. The transitions should be straight and the distance between the transitions defines the time or duration of `switch on'.

STA (starter motor signal - Toyota term)

STAR (Self Test Automatic Readout, electronic FCR test - Ford term)

starter motor An electrical motor that rotates the engine to starting speed.

Static ignition This term is often used by some European vehicle manufacturer's to describe the Distributorless ignition system.

Stator Used in electronic ignition or an alternator. As the rotating reluctor and stationery stator become opposite then AC voltage is induced.

STC (Self-Test Connector Ford term) Refer to Self Diagnosis

Stepper motor
   A description of the two most common types of stepper motor follows:
1   *A motor is used to drive a valve which opens or closes an air by-pass passage in the inlet manifold.*
2   *A motor is used to increment the throttle plate by so many steps, thereby allowing more or less air through the opening.*

STI (Self-test Input - Ford term)

STO (Self-test Output - Ford term)

Stoichiometric ratio The point at which fuel burns most efficiently is called the Stoichiometric ratio and this is where HC and CO are lowest and CO_2 is highest. The air / fuel ratio by weight at this point is approximately 14.7:1. i.e. 14.7 kilograms of air to 1 kilogram of fuel.

Strobe abbreviation for stroboscope

Stroboscopic Used to measure ignition timing. A strobe light flashes in unison with the number one spark plug, giving the impression of a 'frozen' timing point when the strobe is pointed at the engine timing marks..

Superimposed An oscilloscope display pattern where all cylinder traces are placed on top of each other. Differences between the various cylinders will tend to 'stick out'.

Suppression Reduction of radio or television interference generated by the high voltage ignition system. Typical means used are radio capacitors or resistive components in the secondary ignition circuit.

Suppresser Used to prevent radio interference. See capacitor.

SVC (Service Connector, octane/idle adjustment - Ford term)

Synchronised Usually refers to an injection pulse that is synchronised with the ignition system. The injector will be pulsed at a pre-determined time interval before ignition occurs.

SYOV (System Overview) A term used to describe the technical description of how the system operates.

T

Tacho (tachometer) A device used to indicate engine speed in RPM.

Tachometric relay A relay that requires a speed signal from the ignition to function.

TAD (Thermactor Air Diverter vacuum solenoid valve - Ford term)

TBH (Throttle Body Heater) An PTC device that quickly warms-up the throttle area; thereby preventing ice from forming during engine operation at low and moist temperatures.

TBI (Throttle Body Injection) see SPi

TBCV (Turbo Boost Control Valve) Solenoid valve used to control Turbo boost.

TCA (Throttle Control Assembly) An assembly than incorporates several throttle sensors and actuators into one unit. Typically, this may include the TS, TPS, TVPS and idle speed stepper motor.

TCATS (Turbo Charge Air Temperature Sensor)

TDC (Top Dead Centre.) Position of the piston at the top of its stroke

Temp Abbreviation for temperature

Temperature conversion table

° C	° F
-17.8	0
-17.2	1
-15	5
-12.2	10
-9.4	15
-6.7	20
-3.9	25
-1.1	30
0	32
4.4	40
7.2	45
10.0	50
12.8	55
15.6	60
18.3	65
21.1	70
23.8	75
26.7	80
29.4	85
32.2	90
35.0	95
37.8	100
40	105
43	110

Temperature conversion table (continued)

°C	°F
46	115
49	120
52	125
54	130
57	135
60	140
63	145
66	150
68	155
71	160
74	165
77	170
79	175
82	180
85	185
88	190
91	195
93	200
96	205
99	210
100	212
102	215
149	300
204	400
260	500
316	600
371	700
427	800
482	900
538	1000
743	1370
1206	2202

Conversion Formula

$(°C \times 1.8) + 32 = °F$

$(°F - 32) \times 0.56 = °C$

Terminal An electrical connecting point.

TFI (Thick Film Ignition - Ford term) ignition module used in some Ford ignition systems

THA (Air Temperature Sensor - Toyota term) see ATS

Thermistor A potentiometer controlled by temperature.

Three wire sensor The three wire sensor has a voltage supply of 5 volts, an earth connection (often made through the ECM) and an output (signal) wire. The signal wire returns a variable voltage signal to the ECM. The two most common forms of output are by resistance track and wiper arm, or via a transducer. Examples include the AFS and TPS (wiper arm) and MAP (transducer).

Throttle valve A valve that controls the volume of airflow into the engine. Sometimes known as throttle plate or disc.

Throttle valve positioner VAG term - see stepper motor

THS 3/4 (Transmission Hydraulic Switch (3rd/4th gear solenoid) - Ford term)

THW (Coolant Temperature Sensor - Toyota term) See CTS

Timing advance As engine speed increase, combustion must occur earlier so that a correctly timed maximum force is exerted upon the piston.

Timing light A stroboscopic light used to check and set ignition timing.

Timing marks Two marks, or a scale and a mark, to indicate TDC or the timing point when aligned. These marks may be located on the timing case and front pulley, or on the flywheel where they may be viewed through an inspection hatch.

Titania Oxygen Sensor A digital type of OS.

TP (Throttle plate)

TPS (Throttle Position Sensor) The throttle pot is a potentiometer that sends a variable voltage signal to the ECM to indicate (depending on system), throttle position, idle mode, WOT and rate of throttle opening.

Transducer A device that converts pressure or vacuum etc into an electrical signal. I.e. Manifold vacuum may be piped to a transducer (MAP sensor) which turns it into an electrical load signal.

Transistor An electronic switching component.

Trigger See pulse generator

Trigger wheel See reluctor.

Trouble codes US term for fault codes.

TS (Throttle Switch) The throttle switch informs the ECM when the engine is in idle mode. An additional contact may indicate WOT.

Tss (throttle stop screw)

TSS (Turbo Speed Sensor)

TTS (Thermo Time Switch) A switch that responds to both time and temperature.

Turbocharger An exhaust gas driven compressor that compresses the air inducted by the engine to increase the horsepower for any given engine capacity.

TVPS (Throttle Valve Position Sensor) A sensor that continually monitors the exact position of the throttle valve as it is moved by the ISSM and returns the signal to the ECM.

TVS (Thermal Vacuum Switch) Used to control vacuum according to engine temperature. Mainly used in carburettor systems.

TVSV (Thermostatic Vacuum Switching Valve - see VSV)

Two wire sensor The two wire sensor utilise an earth wire and a 5 volt supply wire in a circuit that begins and ends at the ECM. The supply wire also doubles as the signal wire in the following manner. Once the supply and earth wires are connected to the sensor, the resistance value of the sensor causes the voltage value of the supply to vary. Thus, if we take an example of a two wire CTS, the supply value of 5 volts will reduce (typically) to between two and three volts if the engine is cold (20° C), and to between 0.6 and 0.8 volts once the engine has become warm (80° C). Examples of two wire sensors would include the ATS and CTS.

U

UESC (Universal Electronic Spark Control (module) - Ford term)

Unleaded petrol A type of petrol blended without addition of lead. Even unleaded petrol contains a very small amount of natural lead that is not usually removed during refining. This amount is insignificant from an emissions viewpoint, and has no adverse effect upon the catalytic converter.

Unported vacuum A vacuum source located on the manifold side of the throttle plate. A vacuum signal is produced irrespective of throttle valve position.

V

Vacuum A negative pressure or a pressure less than atmospheric. Measured in millibars or inches of mercury.

Vacuum gauge A gauge used to measure the level of vacuum in the engine intake system.

Vacuum conversion table

in.Hg	mm.Hg	kPa	millibar
0.5	12.75	1.7	17
1.0	25.395	3.386	33.86
1.003	25.50	3.4	34
2.0	51.00	6.8	68
3.0	76.50	10.2	102
4.0	102.00	13.6	136
5.0	127.50	17.0	170
6.0	153.00	20.4	204
7.0	178.50	23.8	238
8.0	204.00	27.2	272
9.0	229.50	30.5	305
10.0	255.00	34.0	340
11.0	280.50	37.3	370
12.0	306.00	40.8	408
13.0	331.50	44.2	442

Vacuum conversion table (continued)

in.Hg	mm.Hg	kPa	millibar	
14.0	357.00	47.6	476	
15.0	382.50	51.0	510	
16.0	408.00	54.0	544	
17.0	433.50	57.8	578	) normal
18.0	459.00	61.2	612	) engine
19.0	484.50	64.6	646	) operating
20.0	510.00	68.0	680	) range
21.0	535.50	71.4	714	) at idle
22.0	561.00	74.8	748	
23.0	586.50	78.2	782	
24.0	612.00	81.6	816	
25.0	637.50	85.0	850	
26.0	663.00	88.4	884	
27.0	688.50	91.8	918	
28.0	714.00	95.2	952	
29.0	739.50	98.6	986	
29.53	750.00	100.0	1000	
30.0	765.00	102.0	1020	

Note: *in.Hg figures generally rounded to nearest whole number.*

VAF (Vane Air Flow sensor) Refers to a mechanical type of AFS.

VAG (Volkswagen Audi Group)

Valve timing The timing of valve opening and closing in relation to the piston and crankshaft position

Vanos Variable camshaft control fitted to BMW cars

VAT (Vane Air Temperature sensor - Ford term) Refers to the ATS mounted in the vane AFS.

Vb batt (+) Voltage supplied from the ECM - Toyota term

Vc Reference voltage at the vane AFS - Toyota term

Venturi A restriction in the carburettor throat which results in a speed up of air flow.

Vf (feedback voltage)

VIN (Vehicle Identification Number) A serial number to identify the vehicle, The number often contains coded letters to identify model & year.

VIS (Variable Induction System) A control system where the ECM controls the airflow through the inlet manifold, in order to improve torque and power at different engine speeds and loads. See ICOV.

Vm Vehicle manufacturer

Volt A unit of electrical pressure.

Voltage drop Voltage drop is voltage expended when a current flows through a resistance. The greater the resistance then the greater the voltage drop. The total voltage drop in any automotive circuit should be no more than 10%.

Voltage reserve The ignition system must provide sufficient voltage to bridge the rotor and sparkplug gaps under normal operating conditions. In addition, an adequate reserve of coil voltage must be maintained to meet the greater demands made by the ignition system during conditions such as hard acceleration or high engine rpms. If at some point during engine operation the coil reserve becomes lower than the voltage demanded by the ignition, misfiring and loss of power will be the result. A low voltage reserve can be caused by poor ignition components (i.e. plugs, HT leads etc) or poor primary ignition connections.

Voltmeter An instrument used to measure voltage in an electrical circuit.

VRS (Variable Reluctance Sensor - Ford term)

Vs (Variable signal from the AFS to the ECM -Toyota term)

VSS (Vehicle Speed Sensor.) A sensor to measure the road speed of the vehicle.

VSTP (Vacuum Solenoid Throttle Plate - Ford term)

VSV (Vacuum Switching Valve) term commonly used by Asian vehicle manufacturers to describe solenoid valves that control vacuum supply.

VTEC (Variable Valve Timing and Electronic Control - Honda Term)

W

WAC (Wide-open throttle A/C cut-off)

WCS (Wastegate Control Solenoid - Ford term) See TBCV

Watt A unit of electrical power. 746 watts are equal to one mechanical horsepower.

Wiggle test A test to determine electrical wiring and connector faults. With the engine running, a suspect connection is wiggled, gently tapped or gentle heat or a cooling effect is applied. If the engine misfires or otherwise misbehaves, that connection may be suspect.

Warning lamp A lamp located in the instrument panel that illuminates when a fault is detected in the SD system. In some systems the lamp can be initiated to 'flash' a coded indication of the fault. see 'Flash Codes'

WOT (Wide Open Throttle) Throttle position when fully open. Many EFi systems provide more fuel when this condition is met.

Zirconia Oxygen Sensor (OS) The most common form of OS. A Zirconia OS is a ceramic device placed in the exhaust manifold on the engine side of the catalytic converter. Essentially, the OS contains two porous platinum electrodes. The outer surface electrode is exposed to exhaust air and coated in porous ceramic. The inner surface electrode is exposed to ambient atmospheric air. The difference in oxygen at the two electrodes generates a voltage signal which is transmitted to the ECM. This voltage is inversely proportional to the amount of oxygen The quantity of oxygen remaining after combustion is an excellent indicator of a deficit or surplus of air (rich or weak mixture). The Oxygen Sensor closed loop voltage is quite low and switches between 100 mV (weak) to 1.0 volt (rich).

The signal actually takes the form of a switch and switches from weak to rich at the rate of approximately 1 Hz. A digital voltmeter connected to the signal wire, would display a mean voltage of approximately 0.45 volts.

Warnings: Precautions to be taken with electronics

1 The electronic ignition high tension (HT) system generates a high secondary voltage. Care must be taken so that vulnerable parts of the body, such as hands or arms, do not contact HT components. Shock or injury may be caused by allowing the HT to pass to earth through the human body. Do NOT work on electronic vehicle systems if you have a heart condition or any form of heart pacemaker. Pacemaker operation can also be disrupted by radiated RFI.

2 The ECM and other electronic components can easily be damaged by an open HT circuit. When HT is faced with an impossible gap to jump, it will look for an alternative path. This path may be via the ECM and sensitive components such as transistors may be damaged. In addition, spurious electrical signals from the HT circuit or from other sources of RFI (i.e. the alternator) may disrupt ECM operation.

3 **VERY IMPORTANT**: Avoid severe damage to the ECM, or Amplifier by switching the ignition OFF before disconnecting the multi-plug to these components. It is generally safe to disconnect the multi-plug to other sensors, actuators and components with the ignition switched on, or even with the engine running.

4 Many modern radios are coded as a security measure and the radio will lose its coding and its pre-selected stations when the battery is disconnected. The code should be obtained from the vehicle owner before disconnecting the battery for renewal or to make other repairs.

5 When taking voltage readings at a multi-plug or terminal block, the use of meter leads with thin probes is strongly recommended. However, it is useful to attach a paper clip or split pin to the terminal and attach the voltmeter to the clip. Be very careful not to short out these clips. A number of systems employ gold plated pins at the ECM multi-plug. Particular care should be taken that this gold plating is not removed by insensitive probing. DO NOT push round tester probes into square or oblong terminal connectors. This leads to terminal deformation and poor connections. The use a BOB is particularly recommended to avoid all such problems.

6 DO NOT use an analogue voltmeter, or a digital voltmeter with an electrical impedance of less than 10 megohms, to take voltage readings at an ECM or AFS with the ECM in circuit. (Unless the manufacturer of the equipment warranties that no damage will ensue).

7 To prevent damage to a DMM or to the vehicle electronic system, the appropriate measuring range should be selected before the instrument probes are connected to the vehicle.

8 During resistance tests with an ohmmeter, always ensure that the ignition is OFF and that the circuit is isolated from a voltage supply. Resistance tests should NOT be made at the ECM pins. Damage could be caused to sensitive components, and in any case results would be meaningless.

9 When removing battery cables, good electrical procedure dictates that the earth (negative) cable is disconnected before the live (positive) cable. This will prevent spurious voltage spikes that might cause damage to electronic components.

10 Use protected jumper cables when jump starting a vehicle equipped with an ECM. If unprotected cables are used, and the vehicle earth cables are in poor condition, a voltage spike may destroy the ECM.

11 When a battery is discharged, by far the best course of action is to recharge the battery (or renew if faulty), before attempting to start the vehicle. The ECM is put at risk from defective components such as battery, starter, battery cables and earth cables.

12 Do not use a boost charger or allow a voltage higher than 16.0 volt when attempting to start an engine. The battery leads should be disconnected before a boost charger is used to quick charge the battery.

13 All fuel injection systems operate at high pressure. Keep a fire extinguisher handy and observe all safety precautions. It is good practice to de-pressurise the system before loosening fuel banjos or fuel hoses.

14 A number of diagnostic procedures - such as engine cranking and power balance - may result in unburnt fuel passing into the exhaust and this is potentially harmful to catalyst equipped vehicles. Each test must be completed quickly and back to back tests must not be attempted if damage to the catalytic converter is to be avoided.

Do not therefore, make repeated cranking or power balance tests with catalyst equipped vehicles. Always run the engine at a fast idle for at least 30 seconds between such tests to clear the exhaust of the fuel residue. Where the engine is a non-runner, the catalyst may need to be disconnected to allow cranking to continue. If this advice is not followed the petrol in the catalyst may explode once the temperature in the exhaust reaches a certain temperature.

15 Catalyst damage can be caused when the catalyst temperature exceeds 900° C. When unburnt fuel passes into the catalyst, as the result of any engine malfunction or misfire, the catalyst temperature could easily pass the 900° C mark causing the catalyst to melt. Apart from catalyst destruction, the melted catalyst will usually cause an exhaust blockage with loss of engine power.

16 Disconnect all ECM 's when welding repairs are to be made upon a vehicle.

17 The ECM must not be exposed to a temperature exceeding 80° C. If the vehicle is to be placed in a vehicle spray booth, the ECM must be disconnected and removed from the car to a place of safety.

18 Compression test: Where possible, disable both ignition and injection systems before attempting a compression test.. The above advice about avoiding catalyst damage should also be heeded.

19 The following precautions must be taken with vehicles that utilise Hall Effect electronic ignition.

  a *Do not connect a suppresser or condenser to coil terminal 1.*
  b *If the vehicle is to be towed and the the electronic ignition is suspect, the HES connection to the distributor and to the amplifier should be disconnected.*
  c *During engine cranking tests - compression test or otherwise - remove the HES connection to the distributor.*

20 Do not run the fuel pump (by-pass the relay), when the fuel tank is empty, the pump or pumps will overheat and may be damaged.

21 Some modern vehicles are now equipped with SRS (Supplemental Restraint System) which is an airbag assembly installed in the steering column or passenger compartment.

Extreme caution must be exercised when repairing components situated close to the wiring or components of the SRS. In some vehicles, the SRS wiring runs under the dash and related SRS components are situated in the steering wheel, in and around the under dash area and adjacent to some components used in the vehicle EMS. Any damage to the SRS wiring must be repaired by renewing the whole harness. Improper removal or disturbance of SRS components or wiring could lead to SRS failure or accidental deployment.

Failure to observe these precautions can lead to unexpected deployment of the SRS and severe personal injury. In addition, the SRS must be repaired and serviced according to the procedures laid down by the manufacturer. Any impairment of the SRS could lead to its failure to deploy in an emergency and leave the vehicle occupants unprotected.

22 The turbocharger generates very high temperatures. In the interests of safety, the turbo should be allowed to cool before adjustments or checks are attempted.

Master component key

A1	Ignition control unit		B81	Hall Sensor (Cylinder Identification)
A10	Ignition amplifier Module		B85	Cylinder Identification sensor (Inductive)
A20	Knock Control Module		B90	Camshaft Position Sensor (inductive)
A21	Knock Filter Module		B91	Camshaft Sensor (Hall effect)
A30	Fuel injection control unit		B92	Camshaft Sensor (frequency based)
A35	Injector power amplifier		B95	Suspension G-Force sensor
A40	Engine management Control Module (ECM)		B100	Vehicle Speed Sensor (VSS)
A50	Idle Speed control unit		B101	Vehicle Speed Signal (VSS)
A60	Fuel Pump Run on control unit		C1	Suppresser
A61	Fuel Pump Supply Module		E1	Ignition Distributor
A62	ECM Supply Module		E6	Spark plugs
A70	EGR amplifier module		E30	Throttle Body
A80	Induction Changeover Module		E31	Throttle Control Assembly (TCA)
A90	Instrument Interface Module		E111	Cooling fan
A100	Vehicle Speed Sensor amplifier		E112	Auxiliary fan
A110	Trip computer		E115	Heater blower
A111	Radiator Fan Module		E151	Starter interlock
A115	Instrument cluster		E160	Headlights
A118	Lamp control module		E161	Headlight switch
A120	Check Control Module		E163	Windscreen wipers
A130	Central timer control unit		E165	Heated Rear Window
A140	Central Locking control unit with motor		E166	Fog light
A141	Central Locking control unit		E180	Variable damping control
A150	Seat control unit		E200	A/C component
A170	Convenience system control unit		E300	Automatic Transmission
A171	Traveller assistance system control unit		E600	Anti Theft
B1	Hall Sensor (ignition)		F1-F50	Fuse number and rating
B10	Crank Angle Sensor (CAS)		F3	Fuse (general)
B11	TDC Sensor		G1	Battery
B12	RPM Sensor		G50	Alternator
B15	Crank Angle Sensor (CAS), frequency based		H40	Self Diagnosis (SD) Warning Lamp
B17	Optical Crank Angle Sensor (OCAS)		H41	Engine check light
B18	Optical Cylinder Identification Sensor (OCID)		H50	Service warning lamp
B20	Knock Sensor (KS)		H52	Oil pressure warning lamp
B21	Knock Sensor (KS), digital		K1	Ignition relay
B26	Octane coding plug		K30	Main relay
B27	Vehicle coding		K35	Fuel Pump Relay
B31	Airflow Sensor (AFS) Flap type		K40	Reverse polarity protection relay
B32	Mass Air Flow (MAF) Sensor		K41	Overload Relay
B33	Air flow sensor (Karmen Vortex)		K50	Preheating relay
B40	Air Temperature Sensor in Air Flow Sensor		K55	Oil pressure relay
B41	Air Temperature Sensor (ATS)		K60	Coolant pump relay
B42	Turbo Charge Air Temperature Sensor (TCATS)		K65	Anti-percolation relay
B43	Ambient Air Temperature Sensor (AATS)		K70	Secondary Air Pump relay
B50	Coolant Temperature Sensor (CTS)		K71	Oxygen sensor relay
B51	Coolant Temperature Sensor (dual resistor)		K80	Induction Changeover Valve Relay
B55	EGR Temperature Sensor		K85	Camshaft control valve relay
B58	Fuel Temperature Sensor (FTS)		K90	Cold Start relay
B59	Oil Temperature Sensor (OTS)		K110	Engine cooling fan relay
B60	MAP Sensor (analogue)		K150	Starter inhibitor relay
B61	MAP Sensor (digital)		K151	Starter Relay
B62	Barometric Pressure Sensor (BPS)		M30	Fuel Pump
B63	MAP Sensor in ECM		M31	Fuel Transfer Pump
B68	Electronic Pressure Transducer (EPT)		M40	Stepper Motor (ISSM)
B69	Differential pressure transducer		M60	Coolant pump
B70	Unheated Oxygen Sensor (OS) (zirconia)		M70	ECM Cooling Fan
B71	Heated Oxygen Sensor (OS) (zirconia)		M75	Secondary Air Pump
B72	Oxygen Sensor (titanium)		M110	Radiator Cooling fan
B73	Post cat Heated Oxygen Sensor (Zirconia)		M150	Starter Motor
B80	Hall Sensor (Idle control)		MT	Manual Transmission

P1	Tachometer		V41	Idle speed control diode
P111	Fuel Gauge		X01	Self Diagnosis connector, 1-pin
P120	Temperature Control Gauge		X02	Self Diagnosis connector, 2-pin
R	Ignition switch supply, accessory position		X10	Self Diagnosis connector, 10-pin
R1	Shunt resistor		X16	Self Diagnosis connector, 16-pin
R30	Throttle Position Sensor (TPS)		X20	Self Diagnosis connector, 20-pin
R31	Throttle Position Sensor (TPS), dual		X50	Service Connector
R35	Throttle Valve Position Sensor (TVPS)		X51	Fuel pump check connector
R40	CO Pot		X52	Coding Connector
R41	Equaliser connector		X53	Engine speed check connector
R42	Oil level sensor		X54	Idle speed test connector
R45	Timing adjust sensor		X55	Oxygen sensor test connector
R50	Intake Manifold heater		X120	Miscellaneous Connector
R60	Injector Series Resistor		X130	Instrument Panel Connector
R65	Fuel Pump Resistor		Y1	Ignition timing valve
R70	Linear EGR Position Sensor		Y30	Fuel injector (Multi point injection)
R90	Crankcase breather heating element		Y31	Fuel injector (Single point injection)
S1	Ignition switch		Y32	Cold Start Valve (CSV)
S31	Throttle Switch (TS)		Y33	Hot Start Valve
S32	Idle Switch		Y40	Auxiliary Air Valve (AAV)
S33	Full Load Position Switch		Y41	Idle Speed Control Valve (ISCV), 2-wire
S34	Accelerator Pedal Switch		Y42	Idle Speed Control Valve (ISCV), 3-wire
S35	Fuel pump cut-off switch		Y50	Purge Valve (CFSV)
S40	Thermo Time Switch (TTS)		Y51	Cut off Solenoid Valve (CFCOSV)
S50	Power Steering Pressure Switch (PSPS)		Y60	Camshaft Control Valve
S51	Coolant temperature switch		Y69	Differential pressure regulator
S55	Pressure Switch		Y70	EGR solenoid valve
S58	Fuel temperature switch (FS)		Y75	Secondary Air Injection Solenoid Valve
S59	Oil Temperature Switch (OTS)		Y76	Secondary Air Suction Control Solenoid
S60	Fuel Pump Run on Pressure Switch		Y77	Secondary Air pump magnetic clutch
S61	Fuel control switch		Y78	Pulse Air Solenoid Valve (PASV)
S70	Manifold Heater Switch		Y80	Induction Changeover Valve (ICOV)
S80	Inertia Switch (IS)		Y81	By-pass air solenoid
S85	Camshaft control oil pressure switch		Y83	Vacuum control box
S90	Clutch Switch, MT		Y84	Resonator solenoid valve
S91	Neutral Switch, MT		Y85	Camshaft control solenoid valve
S96	Turbo-Boost Pressure Switch		Y90	Fuel Pressure Solenoid Valve
S110	Radiator Fan Switch		Y95	Vacuum Control Valve
S115	Gearbox Switch		Y96	Turbo Boost Control Valve (TBCV)
S120	Temperature Control Switch		15	Ignition switch supply
S124	Dual Temperature Switch		30	Battery supply
S130	Stop Lamps Switch		31	Earth connection
S150	Hydraulic Pressure Switch		50	Starter circuit
S300	Park/Neutral switch		85	Relay Winding
S316	1st gear identification switch		86	Relay Winding
S317	reverse gear recognition		87	Relay Output
T1	Ignition coil		87a	First Relay Output
T2	Distributorless ignition coil (wasted spark)		87b	Second Relay Output
T3	Distributorless ignition coil (single sparkplug)		87c	Third Relay Output
V15	Ignition supply diode			

Conversion factors

Length (distance)

Inches (in)	x 25.4	= Millimetres (mm)	x 0.0394	=	Inches (in)
Feet (ft)	x 0.305	= Metres (m)	x 3.281	=	Feet (ft)
Miles	x 1.609	= Kilometres (km)	x 0.621	=	Miles

Volume (capacity)

Cubic inches (cu in; in³)	x 16.387	= Cubic centimetres (cc; cm³)	x 0.061	=	Cubic inches (cu in; in³)
Imperial pints (Imp pt)	x 0.568	= Litres (l)	x 1.76	=	Imperial pints (Imp pt)
Imperial quarts (Imp qt)	x 1.137	= Litres (l)	x 0.88	=	Imperial quarts (Imp qt)
Imperial quarts (Imp qt)	x 1.201	= US quarts (US qt)	x 0.833	=	Imperial quarts (Imp qt)
US quarts (US qt)	x 0.946	= Litres (l)	x 1.057	=	US quarts (US qt)
Imperial gallons (Imp gal)	x 4.546	= Litres (l)	x 0.22	=	Imperial gallons (Imp gal)
Imperial gallons (Imp gal)	x 1.201	= US gallons (US gal)	x 0.833	=	Imperial gallons (Imp gal)
US gallons (US gal)	x 3.785	= Litres (l)	x 0.264	=	US gallons (US gal)

Mass (weight)

Ounces (oz)	x 28.35	= Grams (g)	x 0.035	=	Ounces (oz)
Pounds (lb)	x 0.454	= Kilograms (kg)	x 2.205	=	Pounds (lb)

Force

Ounces-force (ozf; oz)	x 0.278	= Newtons (N)	x 3.6	=	Ounces-force (ozf; oz)
Pounds-force (lbf; lb)	x 4.448	= Newtons (N)	x 0.225	=	Pounds-force (lbf; lb)
Newtons (N)	x 0.1	= Kilograms-force (kgf; kg)	x 9.81	=	Newtons (N)

Pressure

Pounds-force per square inch (psi; lbf/in²; lb/in²)	x 0.070	= Kilograms-force per square centimetre (kgf/cm²; kg/cm²)	x 14.223	=	Pounds-force per square inch (psi; lbf/in²; lb/in²)
Pounds-force per square inch (psi; lbf/in²; lb/in²)	x 0.068	= Atmospheres (atm)	x 14.696	=	Pounds-force per square inch (psi; lbf/in²; lb/in²)
Pounds-force per square inch (psi; lbf/in²; lb/in²)	x 0.069	= Bars	x 14.5	=	Pounds-force per square inch (psi; lbf/in²; lb/in²)
Pounds-force per square inch (psi; lbf/in²; lb/in²)	x 6.895	= Kilopascals (kPa)	x 0.145	=	Pounds-force per square inch (psi; lbf/in²; lb/in²)
Kilopascals (kPa)	x 0.01	= Kilograms-force per square centimetre (kgf/cm²; kg/cm²)	x 98.1	=	Kilopascals (kPa)
Millibar (mbar)	x 100	= Pascals (Pa)	x 0.01	=	Millibar (mbar)
Millibar (mbar)	x 0.0145	= Pounds-force per square inch (psi; lbf/in²; lb/in²)	x 68.947	=	Millibar (mbar)
Millibar (mbar)	x 0.75	= Millimetres of mercury (mmHg)	x 1.333	=	Millibar (mbar)
Millibar (mbar)	x 0.401	= Inches of water (inH₂O)	x 2.491	=	Millibar (mbar)
Millimetres of mercury (mmHg)	x 0.535	= Inches of water (inH₂O)	x 1.868	=	Millimetres of mercury (mmHg)
Inches of water (inH₂O)	x 0.036	= Pounds-force per square inch (psi; lbf/in²; lb/in²)	x 27.68	=	Inches of water (inH₂O)

Torque (moment of force)

Pounds-force inches (lbf in; lb in)	x 1.152	= Kilograms-force centimetre (kgf cm; kg cm)	x 0.868	=	Pounds-force inches (lbf in; lb in)
Pounds-force inches (lbf in; lb in)	x 0.113	= Newton metres (Nm)	x 8.85	=	Pounds-force inches (lbf in; lb in)
Pounds-force inches (lbf in; lb in)	x 0.083	= Pounds-force feet (lbf ft; lb ft)	x 12	=	Pounds-force inches (lbf in; lb in)
Pounds-force feet (lbf ft; lb ft)	x 0.138	= Kilograms-force metres (kgf m; kg m)	x 7.233	=	Pounds-force feet (lbf ft; lb ft)
Pounds-force feet (lbf ft; lb ft)	x 1.356	= Newton metres (Nm)	x 0.738	=	Pounds-force feet (lbf ft; lb ft)
Newton metres (Nm)	x 0.102	= Kilograms-force metres (kgf m; kg m)	x 9.804	=	Newton metres (Nm)

Power

Horsepower (hp)	x 745.7	= Watts (W)	x 0.0013	=	Horsepower (hp)

Velocity (speed)

Miles per hour (miles/hr; mph)	x 1.609	= Kilometres per hour (km/hr; kph)	x 0.621	=	Miles per hour (miles/hr; mph)

Fuel consumption*

Miles per gallon, Imperial (mpg)	x 0.354	= Kilometres per litre (km/l)	x 2.825	=	Miles per gallon, Imperial (mpg)
Miles per gallon, US (mpg)	x 0.425	= Kilometres per litre (km/l)	x 2.352	=	Miles per gallon, US (mpg)

Temperature

Degrees Fahrenheit = (°C x 1.8) + 32

Degrees Celsius (Degrees Centigrade; °C) = (°F - 32) x 0.56

It is common practice to convert from miles per gallon (mpg) to litres/100 kilometres (l/100km), where mpg x l/100 km = 282